A GUIDE TO THE
2012 IRC®
WOOD WALL BRACING PROVISIONS

INTERNATIONAL
CODE COUNCIL®

APA

A Guide to the 2012 IRC Wood Wall Bracing Provisions

ISBN: 978-1-60983-300-8
Copyright © 2012

By

International Code Council Inc.
500 New Jersey Avenue, NW, 6th Floor
Washington, DC 20001

And

APA – The Engineered Wood Association
7011 South 19th Street
Tacoma, Washington 98466

First printing: September 2012

Printed in the United States of America

TABLE OF CONTENTS

PREFACE

A Guide to the 2012 IRC Wood Wall Bracing Provisions is jointly published by the International Code Council® (ICC) and *APA – The Engineered Wood Association* with the shared goal of promoting the accurate understanding and correct application of the International Residential Code® (IRC) for safer buildings and communities.

More specifically, this (the third) edition of the guide was developed to help building designers, builders, building officials and others using the code in the application of the lateral bracing requirements of the 2012 International Residential Code® (IRC). While bracing is just one of many important factors to consider when designing, performing plan review, building, or inspecting a structure, it is a common source of confusion and misapplication. The authors of this publication, a team of wall bracing experts from APA, worked closely with the ICC, the ICC Ad Hoc Wall Bracing Committee and industry representatives to identify and explain the key elements of bracing and to demystify the prescriptive bracing provisions of the IRC.

While some content in this 2012 edition of the guide has been carried over from the 2006 and 2009 editions, the format of the book has changed significantly. Previous editions were divided into chapters by subject, which was adequate but not optimal for the reader who wanted to quickly search for discussion on a specific code section. To better accommodate this type of use, the 2012 guide has been reorganized into four chapters:

- **CHAPTER 1** provides background and theoretical information on the subject of wall bracing. While familiarity with the reasoning behind the wall bracing provisions will benefit all users in the application of the bracing requirements, this chapter will be of particular interest to the reader who is seeking a greater understanding of related theory and engineering principles.

- **CHAPTER 2** reviews the 2012 IRC provisions that are related to bracing, but are located outside of the Sections R602.10-R602.12 bracing provisions. While some of these other provisions are referenced in IRC Sections R602.10-R602.12 and others are not, they have all been compiled in this chapter in order to permit the stand-alone use of this guide. (In other words, when using this book, a copy of the 2012 IRC won't be necessary for referencing these additional provisions.) Even the experienced user of the bracing provisions may be surprised to learn how these provisions are tied to other sections of the code!

- **CHAPTER 3** is the heart of the *Guide to the 2012 IRC Wood Wall Bracing Provisions*. The ICC was kind enough to allow the authors of this book to completely reproduce all of IRC Sections R602.10-R602.12 bracing provisions in this chapter. After each excerpted section of the code, we provide an explanation of that section. This discussion is often accompanied by illustrations, tables and/or examples; essentially, whatever is needed to help better clarify the section. For quicker reference, the IRC Section addressed on any given page is annotated at the top of that page. For example, if you are looking for discussion on IRC Section R602.10.6.5.1 *Length of bracing*, simply thumb through pages until you locate "R602.10.6.5.1" printed on the top-outside corner (in this case, on page 171).

- **CHAPTER 4** features numerous whole-house design scenarios that offer application examples of various bracing methods used together in modern house plans. For consistency with the previous edition of the guide, the 2012 examples are similar to those provided in 2009, with a few revised scenarios and solutions. For example, one scenario is "solved" using the new IRC Section R602.12 *Simplified wall bracing* provisions. Other scenarios have been altered to allow for more examples based on Wind Exposure C.

Beyond these four chapters, this guide reviews additional bracing concepts that can be helpful when dealing with more complex applications. Drag struts/collectors, bracing for T- and L-shaped buildings (also known as the multiple-rectangle method) and interpolation are addressed in appendices following **CHAPTER 4**. For quick reference, a two-page summary of all of the addressed bracing methods is provided in the **2012 IRC BRACING METHODS OVERVIEW** at the very end of this book.

Immediately following this preface is an instructional page titled **HOW TO USE THIS GUIDE**. This page provides guidance on how and where to locate specific code section discussions, examples and the additional information provided within this guide.

Note that this guide is based on the content of the third printing of the 2012 IRC.

The authors of this publication have over 50 combined years of bracing experience:

EDWARD KEITH, P.E., the Senior Engineer for APA's Technical Services Division, co-authored the 2006 and 2009 editions of *A Guide to the IRC Wood Wall Bracing Provisions*. Keith graduated from Stanford University with an MS in Structural Engineering and has more than 28 years experience in wood engineering, product development and building code development. He has served on numerous national committees, including the SBCCI Standards for Hurricane Resistant Residential Construction (SSTD-10) and Seismic Resistant Construction (SSTD-13), as well as the ICC Ad Hoc Wall Bracing Committee. Keith is registered in the states of Florida and Washington.

KARYN BEEBE, P.E., LEED AP, is an APA Engineered Wood Specialist serving the Southwest. A licensed Professional Engineer in the state of California, Beebe graduated from Purdue University with a BS in Civil Engineering and an emphasis in Structures. Her duties include consulting with designers and end-users on the efficient specification, selection and use of engineered wood products in construction. She is an active member of the Structural Engineers Association and the U.S. Green Building Council, and serves as Secretary for the San Diego Area Chapter of the ICC. Prior to joining APA, Beebe worked as a structural engineer and also worked in plan review for the San Diego building department.

MERRITT KLINE is the lead Product Support Specialist for the APA Engineered Wood Product Support Help Desk. His responsibilities include providing recommendations for the proper selection and application of engineered wood products in residential and commercial construction. Kline has over 16 years of experience helping builders, designers and code officials to interpret and comply with building code provisions.

ROGER ROATCH is a Senior Engineered Wood Specialist for APA and is based in Gig Harbor, Washington. Roatch has managed the Western Region of the APA Field Services Division and currently serves the Pacific Northwest region on behalf of APA. His areas of specialty include post-frame construction, building science, jobsite forensics and IRC wall bracing. He is an ICC wall bracing seminar instructor and has presented on the topic throughout the Pacific Northwest. Prior to joining APA, Roatch was a commercial construction superintendent and residential framer. He holds a BA degree in Marketing.

ICC staff members who contributed to this publication include **SANDRA HYDE, P.E.,** Staff Engineer, and **JOHN HENRY, P.E.,** Principal Staff Engineer. Their contribution ran the gambit from technical to philosophical with a lot of encouragement and invaluable support. With a short production schedule for this edition, and in spite of a reduced staff and accelerated code cycle, their input was invaluable to the process and the quality of this guide.

The ICC Technical Services Department also deserves recognition for providing technical reviews of the content and working behind the scenes to keep this publication on track. Special thanks to **LARRY FRANKS, P.E.,** for providing the numerous insights and interpretations needed to complete this guide.

The authors would have been lost without the efforts of APA's Market Communications team, which developed the figures, edited the text, designed the pages and coordinated production of this guide. **KELLY DEVLIN,** Writer & Web Specialist, served as lead editor and project coordinator for both the 2012 and 2009 editions of the guide. **RICK SAMPHAO,** Graphic Designer, was the book's lead designer. Additional support was provided by **MARY TRODDEN,** Typographer, and **MARILYN THOMPSON,** Market Communications Director.

And last, but certainly not the least, ICC and APA would like to express our gratitude to those from other industry organizations who provided their invaluable time and expertise to thoroughly reviewing and improving this publication. Our thanks go out to **GARY EHRLICH, P.E.,** Program Manager, Structural Codes and Standards, National Association of Home Builders, and **DREXEL HERMANN, P.E.,** Structural Frame Engineer, Weyerhaeuser Company.

HOW TO USE THIS GUIDE

When reading *A Guide to the 2012 IRC Wood Wall Bracing Provisions*, it will be helpful to keep the following in mind:

- Excerpts from the International Residential Code® (IRC) are printed in orange text.

- Inline references to chapters, figures and tables that appear in this guide are printed in **BOLD, ITALICIZED CAPS** to distinguish them from references to the IRC. For example, **FIGURE 3.2** is a reference to the second figure in **CHAPTER 3** of this guide. **TABLE 2.4** refers to the fourth table in **CHAPTER 2**.

- If you have a question about a specific section in the IRC Sections R602.10-R602.12 bracing provisions, go directly to **CHAPTER 3** (beginning on page 65) and look for that section number printed on the top-outside corner of the page.

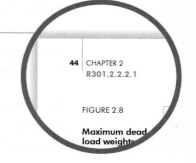

- To learn about an IRC provision related to bracing but outside of the IRC Sections R602.10-R602.12 bracing provisions, refer to **CHAPTER 2** (beginning on page 29) and look for that section number printed on the top-outside corner of the page.

- To learn more about the history, theoretical information and engineering principles behind the IRC bracing provisions, refer to **CHAPTER 1**.

- To see examples of how to use the bracing length and related adjustment tables to determine the length of bracing, go to the **CHAPTER 3** examples (pages 103-124).

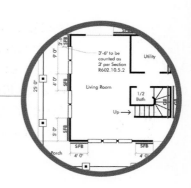

- To review whole-house design scenarios with application examples of various bracing methods used together in modern house plans, go to **CHAPTER 4** (beginning on page 221).

- To view a two-page summary of the IRC bracing methods, refer to the **2012 IRC BRACING METHODS OVERVIEW** table on page 264.

1

WALL BRACING: WHY IT'S NEEDED AND HOW IT WORKS

All buildings, regardless of size or location, must be designed to safely resist the structural loads anticipated during their lifetime. These loads can be divided into two categories: *vertical loads* and *lateral loads*. Wood-frame construction makes it easy for building professionals to construct strong, attractive and durable structures that resist these loads, meet building code requirements and assure good performance.

Vertical loads

Vertical loads act in the "up" or "down" direction. In most cases the "down" loads are caused by gravity. These loads are the obvious ones: the weight of the building itself (dead load), the weight of everything and everybody in the building (live load), and environmental loads, such as those from snow, wind or earthquake. The "up" loads act in an upward direction. An example of an "up" load is wind uplift.

These loads are easy to understand and typical construction practice has evolved into an efficient system that does a good job of accommodating them. Generally speaking, builders in high wind areas are as comfortable installing uplift straps as they are placing headers on cripple studs.

CHAPTER 1

Summary

Because downward loads are always present (due to gravity), any deficiencies in the vertical load path are almost immediately apparent due to structural instability. For example, a beam with support at only one end will fall down during construction.

Lateral loads

The real challenge lies not with the vertical loads, but rather with the "sideways" loads, or, as they are referred to in the design community, *lateral loads*. Lateral loads act in a direction parallel to the ground. Most often the result of wind or seismic (earthquake) forces, lateral loads can cause structures to bend and sway, collapse, or even – in cases where the structure is not well attached to the foundation – roll over.

A wood beam carrying an excessive vertical load may creak, groan, split or deflect over time, warning that repair may be necessary to prevent failure. Because the wind and seismic forces that result in lateral loads are sudden and infrequent, there are no such warning indicators of an impending failure.

In every region of the country, lateral load resistance – an essential part of which is wall bracing – has to be planned during design and built into the structure during construction. While this is especially important in regions susceptible to strong wind and seismic forces, the provisions or requirements of the International Residential Code (IRC) make lateral load resistance an important consideration in every part of the country. The IRC prescriptively requires specific building elements to resist lateral forces for all structures within its scope.

When designing a residence to meet the seismic or wind bracing requirements of the code, it is important to understand how lateral loads act on wood framing systems and how construction detailing and fasteners affect the ultimate lateral performance of the structure. Builders, designers and building officials can use the IRC wood wall bracing requirements to ensure strength, quality and safety in residential structures. Certainly, a better understanding of these requirements will ensure fewer mistakes in design and plan review, as well as in construction.

Wind forces

During a wind event, wind pushes against one wall while pulling on the opposite wall, as demonstrated in *FIGURE 1.1*. Because the two walls receiving wind pressures – the receiving walls – push and pull the structure in the same direction as the wind, the walls on the sides of the structure – the bracing walls – must restrain the structure from moving. When the wind is in the perpendicular direction, the walls change roles: walls that previously restrained the structure now receive the wind pressures, and walls that previously received the wind pressures now must restrain the structure. Thus, all walls must be strong enough to resist the wind forces that push against the structure, regardless of whether they must act as a receiving wall or a restraining wall.

FIGURE 1.1

Wind forces acting on a structure

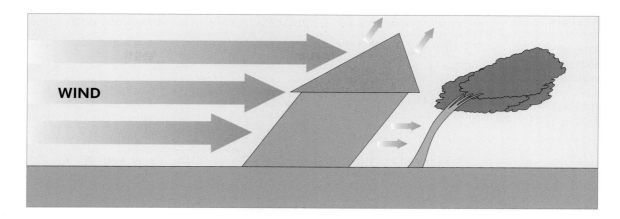

WIND

The 2012 IRC wall bracing provisions for wind apply only to residential structures located in areas where the basic wind speed is <u>less than</u> 110 miles per hour. Basic wind speeds are obtained from IRC Figure R301.2(4)A (**FIGURE 1.2**). However note that some regions of the U.S. that are subject to very high winds, as identified in IRC Figure R301.2(4)B (**FIGURE 1.3**), require the use of alternate engineering-based standards or engineered design and are not eligible for prescriptive bracing. If a specific location is defined by IRC Figure R301.2(4)B as a "wind design required" region, or the wind design speed is 110 mph or greater, the IRC wind design provisions do not apply and alternate standards or the IBC must be used. An area designated as a "special wind region" requires the designer to check with the local building official to determine the design wind speed for that location. IRC Section R301.2.1 and **CHAPTER 2** cover these requirements in detail.

FIGURE 1.2

Map of basic wind speeds

Adapted from IRC Figure R301.2(4)A

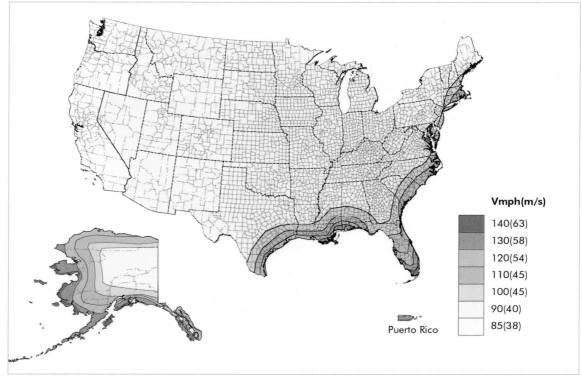

Puerto Rico

Vmph(m/s)

140(63)
130(58)
120(54)
110(45)
100(45)
90(40)
85(38)

FIGURE 1.3

Map of regions that require wind design

Adapted from IRC Figure R301.2(4)B

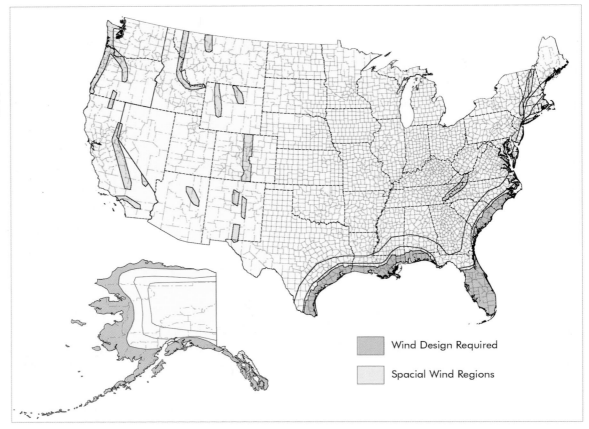

Wind Design Required

Spacial Wind Regions

In addition to the basic wind speed, the IRC requires identification of the building site's wind exposure category. As explained in IRC Section R301.2.1.4 and **CHAPTER 2** of this guide, wind exposure category is determined by evaluation of the site characteristics that affect the building's exposure to wind from any direction. The evaluation considers variations in topography, vegetation and nearby structures. Historically, the four wind exposure categories were: A, B, C and D; for engineered structures, however, the design community has merged A and B into a single exposure under Exposure B. While the IRC still lists Exposure Category A in the definition section (IRC Section 202), it is not used elsewhere in the code.

The wind bracing requirements of IRC Table R602.10.3(1) (**TABLE 3.3**) are based on Exposure Category B. For Exposure Categories C and D, bracing requirements increase up to 70 percent in accordance with the adjustment factors found in IRC Table R602.10.3(2) (**TABLE 3.4**).

The wind exposure category is also used to determine the IRC Section R301.2.1 design load performance requirements for components and cladding. The proper selection of wall sheathing products and the correct amount of products is essential to ensure the exterior wall assembly has the capacity to resist component and cladding wind pressure and suction forces when acting as the receiving wall. For example, IRC Table R602.3(3) addresses the proper selection and installation of wood structural panel sheathing based on the design wind speed and exposure category. See **CHAPTER 2**.

Seismic forces

Seismic forces are generated by ground motions during an earthquake event, as shown in **FIGURE 1.4**. The ground motion causes the structure's mass to accelerate back and forth, up and down. This acceleration causes forces to develop within the structure in locations where the structure's mass is concentrated (Newton's Second Law: Force = Mass x Acceleration). Essentially, the seismic ground motion moves the foundation (*acceleration*), while inertia (*mass of the structure*) attempts to resist this motion. Instead of mass, building codes use seismic weight to determine seismic forces. The seismic weight multiplied by an acceleration expressed as a fraction of the earth's gravity produces the seismic force. Because seismic forces are directly proportional to the weight (mass) of the structure, IRC Section R301.2.2.2.1 (see **CHAPTER 2**) imposes limits on the weights of materials used to construct the building. The seismic weight of the structure is generally concentrated at the floors and roof of the structure.

FIGURE 1.4

Earthquake forces acting on a structure

Vertical (upward) forces not shown for clarity

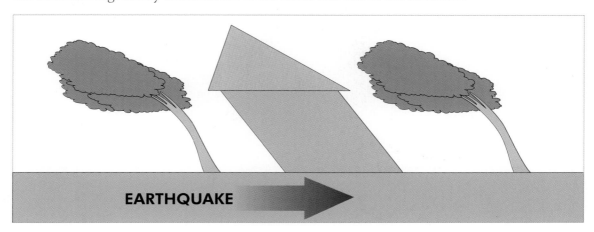

EARTHQUAKE

Similar to the wind maps discussed previously, the IRC provides an earthquake map (IRC Figure R301.2(2)) that displays the various Seismic Design Categories for regions of the country. The portion of the map showing the eastern half of the continental United States is excerpted in **FIGURE 1.5** of this guide.

FIGURE 1.5

Portion of Seismic Design Categories – Site Class D map

Adapted from IRC Figure R301.2(2)

Eastern U.S. shown (all of U.S. not shown for clarity)

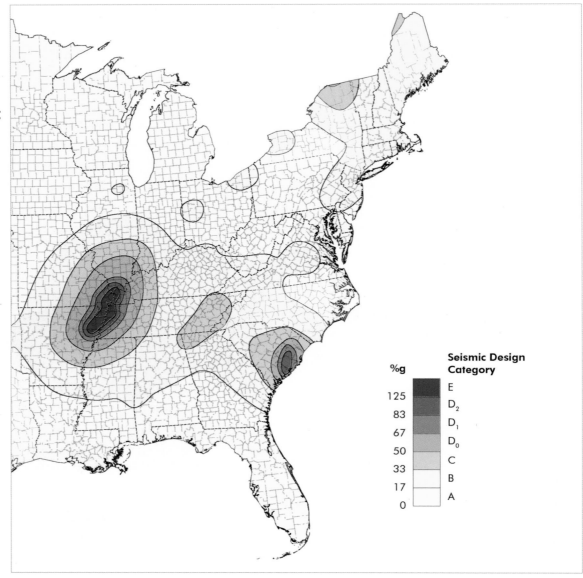

%g	Seismic Design Category
125	E
83	D_2
67	D_1
50	D_0
33	C
17	B
0	A

The use of Seismic Design Categories is a simplified means of determining the potential hazard of an earthquake in a region. For residential structures, these categories range from Seismic Design Category (SDC) A to E, with A being the lowest hazard and D_2 the highest covered by the IRC.

For SDC E, the IRC contains provisions for reclassification of structures from SDC E to D_2 (see IRC Section R301.2.2.1.2, excerpted in **CHAPTER 2**) under certain circumstances.

For SDC E structures that cannot be reclassified, the prescriptive structural requirements of the IRC cannot be used and the International Building Code (IBC) or other referenced standards must be used to engineer the structure.

The wind and seismic maps in IRC Figures R301.2(4) and R301.2(2) respectively (copied and excerpted in **FIGURES 1.2** and **1.5**) are used to determine the bracing requirements for a given structure in a particular location. In those regions of the country where the lateral loads for the design-level event (wind or seismic) are lower, minimal bracing is required for residential-type structures. Other areas are considered high wind regions, seismic regions, or both. In these regions, additional wall bracing is required to accommodate the potentially larger lateral loads.

Determining wind and seismic requirements

Your local building officials have already determined the wind or seismic design criteria (and other design criteria, including snow load, frost depth, termite danger, flood hazard, etc.) for your location. When a local jurisdiction adopts the IRC, they identify the information required in IRC Table R301.2(1) *Climatic and Geographic Design Criteria* (**TABLE 2.1**). Contact your local building official and ask for a copy of this information. Note that some building departments post this information on their website. See **CHAPTER 2** for further information.

Important terminology

When discussing the lateral load path, it is helpful to be familiar with commonly used terminology, such as diaphragms, braced wall panels and shear walls. Section R202 of the IRC defines these terms as follows:

Braced wall line: A straight line through the building plan that represents the location of the lateral resistance provided by the wall bracing.

Braced wall panel: A full-height section of wall constructed to resist in-plane shear loads through interaction of framing members, sheathing material and anchors. The panel's length meets the requirements of its particular bracing method, and contributes toward the total amount of bracing required along its braced wall line in accordance with Section R602.10.1.

Diaphragm: A horizontal or nearly horizontal system acting to transmit lateral forces to the vertical resisting elements. When the term "diaphragm" is used, it includes horizontal bracing systems.

Shear wall: A general term for walls that are designed and constructed to resist racking from seismic and wind by use of masonry, concrete, cold-formed steel or wood framing in accordance with Chapter 6 of this code and the associated limitations in Section R301.2 of this code.

(Editorial note: this term is most often used in engineered design in accordance with the IBC or other appropriate referenced standards.)

In the IRC, diaphragms are simply the roof and floor systems. Due to the prescriptive nature of the IRC, the diaphragm is "defined" by the minimum thicknesses of roof and floor sheathing (as provided in IRC Table R503.2.1.1(1)) along with the minimum nailing required by IRC Table R602.3(1), Items 32–34. Roof and floor diaphragms built to these specifications are deemed to provide sufficient capacity for the loads and exposures covered by the IRC for residential-type structures.

Shear walls and braced wall panels each serve the same purpose: to transfer the shear (lateral loads) from the diaphragm above to the structure below while resisting racking from the lateral loads. In this guide, the term "shear wall" refers to an engineered wall segment designed in accordance with the IBC or referenced standards, and "braced wall" or "braced wall panel" refers to a wall segment constructed in accordance with the prescriptive bracing provisions of the IRC. Further discussion about the differences between shear walls and braced wall panels is presented later in this chapter.

What is the lateral load path?

It is very important to understand the concept of a lateral load path because it helps make sense of the IRC prescriptive wall bracing requirements. In short, the lateral load path is simply the path that the lateral or horizontal load takes as it passes through the structure, including components and connections, on its way to the supporting foundation and ultimately the ground. **FIGURE 1.6** shows the critical parts of the lateral load path. Vertical loads (gravity and uplift) follow a similar load path, moving through other structural components on their way to the foundation and ground.

The lateral load path for wind loads is simpler to visualize than the load path for seismic loads. **FIGURE 1.6** provides a basic example of the lateral load path resulting from wind loading of a wall. The load is shown acting on a windward receiving wall with its subsequent load path through the building. For simplicity, the suction pressure on the leeward receiving wall and wind pressures on the roof are not included in this illustration.

FIGURE 1.6

Critical parts and flow of the load path

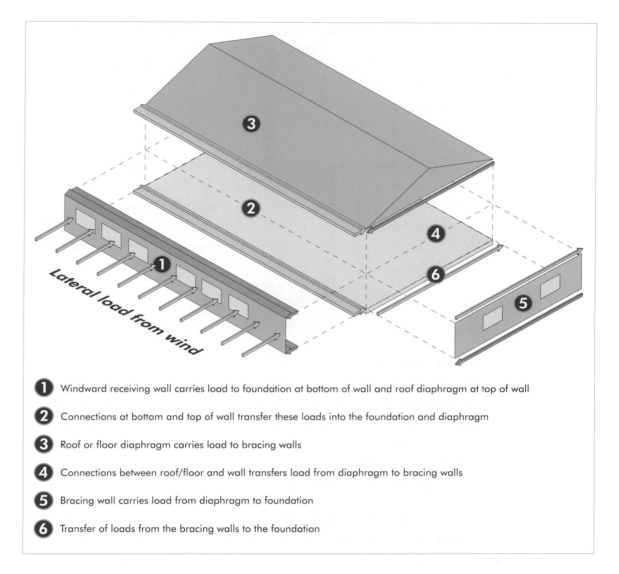

1. Windward receiving wall carries load to foundation at bottom of wall and roof diaphragm at top of wall

2. Connections at bottom and top of wall transfer these loads into the foundation and diaphragm

3. Roof or floor diaphragm carries load to bracing walls

4. Connections between roof/floor and wall transfers load from diaphragm to bracing walls

5. Bracing wall carries load from diaphragm to foundation

6. Transfer of loads from the bracing walls to the foundation

What is the vertical load path?

In the downward vertical load path, all structural members carrying gravity load (for example, rafters, trusses and joists) must bear on members below (for example, posts, cripple walls, beams and headers) designed to carry that load. Each of these members must bear on others until the load is transferred through the foundation and into the ground. The downward load path is fairly easy to understand. Just like a child's first set of building blocks, one block is stacked on another. Due to the force of gravity, vertical loads are always present and it is relatively easy to identify the load path, as shown in **FIGURE 1.7**.

FIGURE 1.7

Example of vertical load path

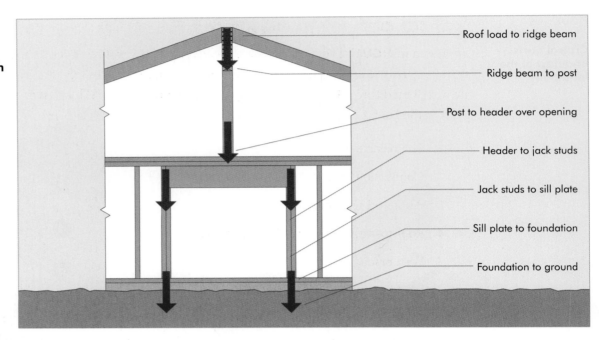

Roof load to ridge beam

Ridge beam to post

Post to header over opening

Header to jack studs

Jack studs to sill plate

Sill plate to foundation

Foundation to ground

The upward load path is the same as the downward load path except the load is acting in the "up" direction. Upward (wind uplift) loads must be resisted by uplift straps and/or structural wall sheathing, connectors and anchors that keep the structure intact and attached to the foundation.

While the objective of the lateral load path (to get the applied loads into the ground) is exactly the same as the vertical load path, the actual path it takes is not always obvious. Another key difference is that connections are even more important in the lateral load path. Unlike the downward vertical load path, in which gravity causes many members to bear on each other, there is nothing holding the different components together in the upward vertical or lateral load paths unless the builder makes a connection using nails, straps or framing anchors. The location and requirement for these connections is not always obvious.

Also, unlike downward vertical loads, upward vertical loads and lateral loads are intermittent as high winds and/or earthquakes are relatively uncommon occurrences. When these intermittent load events do occur, the lateral and upward load paths must be in place with each element and connection properly sized and constructed to resist these transient loads. Buildings missing connections in these critical load paths are subject to failure.

Critical parts of the lateral load path

As shown in **FIGURE 1.6**, there are six critical parts in the load path for a simple rectangular structure. This section identifies these six parts and explains how the wind and/or seismic loads are distributed through a simple rectangular structure and into the foundation. The critical parts of the lateral load path are:

1. The receiving wall

2. Connections at top and bottom of receiving wall

3. Floor and roof diaphragms

4. Roof-to-wall/wall-to-wall connections

5. Wall bracing

6. Wall bracing-to-foundation connections

The numbered areas in **FIGURE 1.6** do not necessarily relate to the load path sequence (which are slightly different for wind and seismic) but are used to define each part, and correlate the following photos and discussion to the theoretical load path concept. Each part of the load path is critical. If any one element in the load path fails, the structure typically fails. Like a chain, the lateral load path is only as strong as the weakest link. While this discussion focuses on a simple rectangular structure, the principles also apply to multi-story structures and T- and L-shaped structures (discussed in **APPENDIX B**).

1. The receiving wall

The receiving walls for wind are perpendicular to the direction of the lateral load. These walls receive or catch the wind like the sail of a sailboat. The walls themselves must be capable of resisting the loads – for example, both positive (pressure) and negative (suction) wind loads – in order to transfer them to the next link in the load path.

Note that while the receiving wall is under positive pressure, the opposite wall and perpendicular walls are subjected to suction pressures. These suction pressures can pull off poorly attached wall cladding, siding, windows and doors. This loss of nonstructural components is especially critical during high wind events, as it is often a failure of the structure's weatherproofing system. High wind events are often accompanied by rain, and while ensuing water damage may not cause a failure of the structural system, it can lead to the total destruction of the contents of the house.

Some examples of wind related failures at the receiving wall due to its inability to resist the applied loads are shown in **FIGURES 1.8** through **1.10**.

FIGURE 1.8

Wall covering is an essential part of the first step of the load path for wind. The wall studs can be seen behind the failed wall covering system. The failure could have been due to various reasons. Approved wall coverings installed per code would most likely have been able to withstand the pressure of the wind. (Photo taken after windstorm in Evansville, Indiana.)

FIGURE 1.9

Not all wall coverings are by themselves capable of resisting code-required wind pressures (see IRC Table R301.2(2)). This house was subjected to an 85 mph wind. Failure could have been due to multiple issues, including improper installation or flying object damage. (Photo taken after windstorm in Evansville, Indiana.)

FIGURE 1.10

A partial failure of the wall covering system. Note also the house in the background, to the right, which had a similar failure. (Photo taken after Hurricane Katrina in Gulfport, Mississippi, three-to-four miles inland, where wind speeds were within the scope of IRC.)

Unlike wind, an earthquake acts on the entire structure and not just the receiving walls. The receiving walls, in the case of a seismic event, are not exposed to pressure, but contribute to the seismic weight that is spread throughout the structure.

Assuming the receiving walls themselves can withstand the force of the lateral load, the receiving walls transfer this load to the next component in the load path.

2. Connections at top and bottom of receiving wall

The receiving walls must be properly attached at the base and at the top to adequately transfer the forces into the foundation (base attachment via anchor bolts per IRC Section R403.1.6 or attachment to floor framing per IRC Table R602.3(1), Items 15 and 16) and into the roof diaphragm (attachment per IRC Table R602.3(1), Items 1–3 and 5). The proper connection between structural elements of the load path is just as important as the proper selection and detailing of the elements themselves and <u>cannot be over-emphasized</u>. Great attention to connection detail is especially important in areas of high wind or moderate-to-high seismic force.

3. Floor and roof diaphragm

The floor and roof sheathing and framing form the diaphragms which transfer loads from the receiving wall to the bracing walls. Floor and roof diaphragm failures are rare. When a roof system failure does occur, it is typically due to inadequate attachment of the roof sheathing. This often occurs in roof areas vulnerable to high wind pressure, such as gable ends and roof overhangs. A roof sheathing failure is shown in **FIGURE 1.11**.

FIGURE 1.11

The loss of sheathing compromises the strength of the roof diaphragm. It is likely that the complexity of the connection between the roof sheathing and the step-down trusses has resulted in poor resistance to negative pressure. (Photo taken after a tornado in Fayetteville, North Carolina.)

During a seismic event, the roof and floor diaphragms represent a concentration of the mass (seismic weight) of the building. As a result, the seismic forces originate (at least in part) at the roof and floor.

4. Roof-to-wall/wall-to-wall connections

A proper connection from the roof to the walls below and/or walls to the walls below (in the case of multi-story structures) is critical to the load path and is a common failure point. **FIGURES 1.12** through **1.15** demonstrate this failure mode. As the walls support the roof for both vertical and lateral loads, such a failure can lead to a partial or total building collapse, as illustrated in the figures.

For roof-to-wall connections, it is important to realize that the roof diaphragm actually begins and ends at the exterior wall lines and the connection between the roof and wall is critical to the formation of an effective load path (see sidebar.) Connections between the walls and floor are specified in IRC Table R602.3(1), Items 15 and 16. These attach-ment requirements are minimum connections and are deemed to be sufficient to transfer the wind and seismic loads covered by the scope of the IRC. Note that in the more severe wind and seismic regions addressed by the IRC, if the minimum connection is used, it becomes critical that every fastener be properly sized and placed. Note also that the often overlooked Footnotes f and g of IRC Table R602.3(1) require additional attachment for roof sheathing in areas with wind speeds of 100 mph or greater. The additional nailing provides enhanced diaphragm performance and prevents sheathing from pulling off in high wind events.

ROOF SHEATHING EDGE NAILING

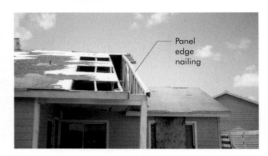

Panel edge nailing

An important design consideration often overlooked in diaphragm connec-tions is that the roof diaphragm actually ends at the supporting wall line and not at the end of the overhang. At the wall line, the panel "edge" nailing (6 inches on center) as specified in IRC Table R602.3(1), Item 32, should be used to attach the roof sheathing.

FIGURE 1.12

The walls that made up the gable end of the building were found essentially intact on the ground in front of the structure (**FIGURE 1.13**). This was a panelized building and the wall panels were not attached sufficiently to the floor and roof to resist the wind loads. (Photo taken after a tornado in Fayetteville, North Carolina.)

FIGURE 1.13

Damage likely initiated from the failure of garage doors. Subsequent pressurization of the garage portion of the home and insufficient attachment caused the gable end wall and rear of the garage to be pushed out. As a result, these portions of the wall could no longer provide bracing or vertical support for the rest of the structure. (Photo taken after a tornado in Fayetteville, North Carolina.)

FIGURE 1.14

This figure shows insufficient attachment of the end walls of the structure. It also shows failures in the wall covering products used to weatherproof the structure, as well as failure of the connection of the braced wall panel to the structure (at the far end of the wall). (Photo taken after a tornado in Evansville, Indiana.)

FIGURE 1.15

This building failed due to insufficient attachment of numerous structural elements, including receiving wall-to-roof, roof-to-wall, and wall-to-wall. The entire roof of this structure was lifted off in one piece and struck the house across the street. (Photo taken after Hurricane Iniki.)

For multi-story structures in high wind areas, builders may be accustomed to using strap-type anchors between floors. These greatly increase the structure's ability to stay together. While most often required for wind uplift, these straps also provide reinforcement to the lateral load path, if for no other reason than to prevent uplift forces from damaging the connections that also form part of the lateral load path.

5. Wall bracing

From a lateral load perspective, the walls support the roof and floor diaphragms through the use of bracing panels. The type, amount, and number of bracing panels are, of course, dependent on the magnitude of the lateral load. Stronger resistance (greater numbers or lengths of bracing panels) and reduced braced wall line spacing (through the use of interior braced wall lines) may be required in areas of high wind and/or seismic activity.

Failure of a braced wall line is evidenced by racking of the wall line. Racking occurs when a rectangular wall deforms to a parallelogram shape, in which the top and the bottom of the wall remain horizontal but the sides are no longer vertical. The purpose of wall bracing is to prevent such failures. Examples of racking in various degrees are shown in **FIGURE 1.16**.

FIGURE 1.16

Failures in wall bracing as indicated by wall racking

(File photos, both wind and seismic events.)

6. Wall-to-foundation connections

Just as the receiving walls must be attached to the foundation in order to resist the loads imposed, the bracing walls must be attached to the foundation. These connections are critical. Examples of inadequate connections between the walls and foundation are demonstrated in **FIGURES 1.17** and **1.18**.

FIGURE 1.17

Insufficient (or non-existent) anchorage of the walls to the foundation caused the entire structure to slide approximately 6 feet off the foundation. (Photo taken after a tornado in Fayetteville, North Carolina.)

FIGURE 1.18

A closer look at the foundation shows negligible connection of the sill plate to the foundation. The framer attempted to use nails to make this connection; however the nails are mostly bent at the tip and did not significantly penetrate the masonry foundation walls. (Photo taken after a tornado in Fayetteville, North Carolina.)

During several recent high-wind events a number of total building failures were traced back to the attachment of exterior walls to the foundation with nails, both concrete nails and conventional nails. The nails had failed to penetrate the concrete surface or just fractured the concrete in the area of the fastener. Nails do not provide adequate resistance to wind or seismic loading, which code-required anchor bolts do provide.

The 2009 IRC contained a number of rewritten provisions that deal directly with the connection of braced wall lines to the structure above and below. These provisions, maintained in the 2012 IRC, are an attempt to address a number of gaps in the load path that had existed in previous IRC editions. These provisions can be found in IRC Section R602.10.8 and will be discussed in greater detail in **CHAPTER 3** of this guide.

The solution

The previous photos may suggest that damage is probable in wind or seismic events but this is not always the case. In all of these examples, the damage to the building could have been prevented or minimized if the structure had been designed or built in accordance with the prevailing building code. In nearly all of these cases, there were similar structures in very close proximity that sustained little or no damage because they were built to the requirements of the building codes that existed when they were constructed.

This guide explains in detail how to use the IRC to provide adequate wall bracing so that a house can be built to resist lateral loads. **FIGURES 1.19** and **1.20** show two examples of how properly built homes can survive even the most severe wind or seismic events.

FIGURE 1.19

After the 1964 Good Friday earthquake in Alaska, a house continuously sheathed with plywood siding retained its box-like structure, even after a significant portion of the ground below shifted more than 20 feet. Note that the walls are strong enough to cantilever the structure over the collapsed foundation. The house to the left also appears to have performed well without any noticeable damage. (Photo taken after the Great Alaska Earthquake.)

FIGURE 1.20

After Hurricane Andrew struck in 1992, a waterfront house in Florida stands in near perfect condition, even after being battered by significant winds and water. Such cases of survival demonstrate that a proper load path works. (Photo taken after Hurricane Andrew.)

What's the difference between a braced wall panel and shear wall?

Braced walls and shear walls each serve the same purpose in the lateral load path. Both provide racking resistance to lateral loads, but each comes from a distinctly different set of model building code provisions.

Wall bracing, the primary focus of this guide, comes from prescriptive building code. In the IRC, wall bracing is prescribed and required bracing lengths are provided in tables; few, if any, calculations are necessary. From the designer's and builder's perspective, there is no "engineering" required in conventional residential construction since construction requirements are prescribed in the code.

Shear walls, on the other hand, are used in portions of structures that do not meet the prescriptive limits and conventional construction parameters of the IRC. Shear walls are designed or "engineered" by a design professional and have specific design values depending on fastener spacing, fastener size, sheathing type and thickness, and framing species. Shear walls usually require manufactured hold downs to resist overturning. Shear walls must resist the loads that are calculated through engineering analysis and are generally associated with the design provisions of the IBC.

PRESCRIPTIVE VS. ENGINEERED

Prescriptive Construction

Limitations:

- 3 stories max
- Wind < 110 mph (not allowed in areas shown in IRC Figure R301.2(4)B)
- SDC A-D2
- Many others (see IRC Chapter 3)

Generally uses braced wall panels without hold downs to prevent walls from racking.

Engineered Design

Applications:

- Any size/shape within IBC limits
- Wind – no limit
- Seismic – no limit
- Governed by engineers' calculations

Generally uses shear walls with wood structural panels and pre-engineered hold downs (in addition to anchor bolts) to prevent walls from racking and overturning.

What is bracing and how does it work?

The framing elements of a typical stud wall are shown in **FIGURE 1.21**. When subjected to lateral loads, the stud wall without bracing has very little racking resistance because each of the joints act as a hinge (shown as a small circle in the figure). It takes very little lateral load to "rack" the wall, turning it into a parallelogram.

FIGURE 1.21

Bare stud wall has no lateral load resisting capacity

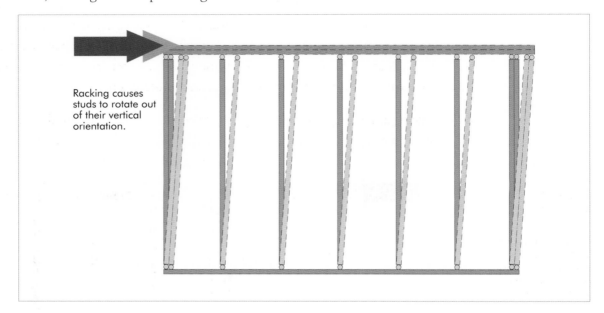

Racking causes studs to rotate out of their vertical orientation.

In prescriptive (also referred to as conventional) construction, there are two common ways to provide a stud wall with lateral load resistance. One method is to use a diagonal 1x4 let-in brace between 45 and 60 degrees to the horizontal, as shown in **FIGURE 1.22**. The other method is through the attachment of relatively rigid rectangular panels (**FIGURE 1.23**) to the stud wall, as shown in **FIGURE 1.24**. (There is a third method permitted – the use of diagonal wood boards along the entire wall surface – that is seldom used today and, therefore, is not addressed in this chapter.)

Let-in bracing

Let-in bracing, known in the 2012 IRC as Method LIB and shown in **FIGURE 1.22**, is the original method of bracing that was used before panel-type sheathing products were developed.

The effectiveness of let-in bracing depends on the craftsmanship of the framer when cutting the notches for the 1x4 brace, the nails that attach the brace to the top and bottom plates, and the condition and species of the brace. Since there are only two nails at each point where the 1x4 brace crosses the framing, the strength of this bracing method is limited. Up until the last 50 years or so, residential structures were relatively small and divided into many small rooms. For these types of houses, let-in bracing was (and still may be) an effective bracing method.

A number of manufacturers have developed proprietary metal straps designed to function like a 1x4 brace. These straps either require no modification of the studs or just a shallow saw kerf to inset the strap. Generally, the thin flat straps only resist tension and have to be used in pairs to make an "X" pattern, while the straps with an "L" or "T" cross section resist tension and compression and normally can be used singly, like 1x4 let-in bracing. These proprietary products are recognized for use in code-conforming construction in ICC Evaluation Service (ICC-ES) or other reports. Copies of these reports, which include use restrictions, are available at www.icc-es.org or other agencies' websites. It is important to review the details of all relevant reports, as well as the manufacturer's installation recommendations carefully. While some of these strap-type anchors are approved for use as bracing, others are meant only for temporary bracing during construction.

Let-in bracing and proprietary strap-type products have limited structural capacity. As such, the IRC and proprietary ICC-ES reports limit their use to areas of low wind and seismic loads.

FIGURE 1.22

Stud wall with let-in brace

The diagonal brace and two nails into the top and bottom plates and each stud it crosses prevent the wall from racking

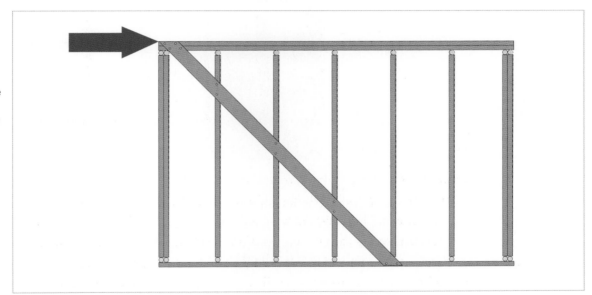

Panel-type bracing (and Portland cement lath and plaster)

Offering considerably more structural capacity than let-in bracing, and consequently of greater use, are panel-type products. While installation and fastening requirements vary greatly, all panel-type bracing methods work in the same manner and have the same capacity (the exception is Method GB (gypsum board), which requires double siding and additional length) for wind resistance. In regards to seismic resistance, strength varies from Method CS-WSP, which provides the greatest bracing capacity, to Method GB, which offers the lowest capacity.

FIGURE 1.23

Rectangular panel products

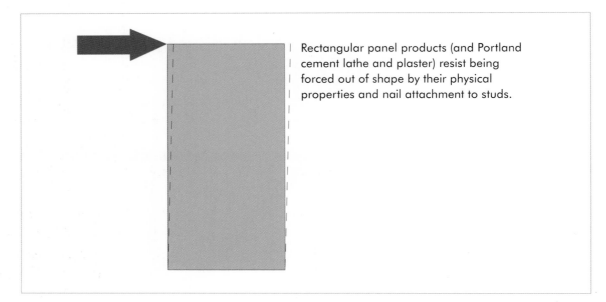

Rectangular panel products (and Portland cement lathe and plaster) resist being forced out of shape by their physical properties and nail attachment to studs.

- Fasteners are used to attach panel products to wall framing members. The spacing of the fasteners around the perimeter of the panel (typically called the edge) ranges from 3 to 7 inches on center depending on the bracing method used. The spacing of the fasteners in the middle of the panel (commonly called the "field") typically ranges from 6 to 12 inches depending on the bracing method selected. It is these fasteners that transfer the panel's resistance to racking into the structure to which they are fastened.

- When panel products are properly attached to a stud wall, such as the one shown in **FIGURE 1.21**, they provide racking resistance to the whole wall, as shown in **FIGURE 1.24**.

- Portland cement lath and plaster is considered panel bracing because, although it is formed in place, it performs in a similar manner and capacity as the panel bracing methods.

- Bracing Method GB (gypsum board) is similar to the other panel-type bracing methods except that its capacity is about half as strong as other panel products when applied to one side of the wall for wind loads.

FIGURE 1.24

Stud wall with panel bracing

Perimeter nailing prevents the wall from racking. (Intermediate nailing not shown for clarity.)

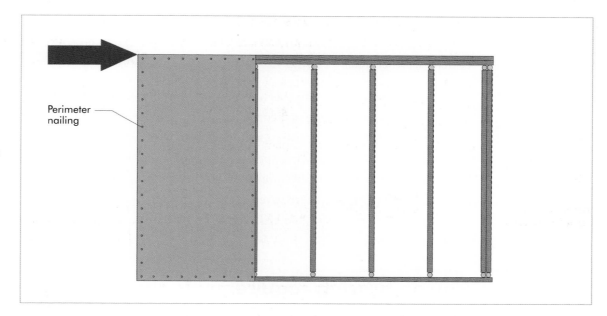

Perimeter nailing

The ability of a panel to resist loads depends on the physical properties of the panel, primarily its strength and rigidity. The strength of the panel is imparted to the wall by the fasteners installed at its perimeter to connect it to the wall framing. The number, size and placement of the nails (or other fasteners), along with the structural capacity of the framing and physical properties of the panel (such as fastener bearing strength, tear resistance and fastener pull-through resistance), affect the attachment capacity. Variations in bracing panel mechanical properties and prescribed attachments account for the different installation requirements and capacities for the various panel type bracing methods. These differences are discussed in more detail in **CHAPTER 3**.

History of wall bracing

Wall bracing requirements are not new to the codes. In fact, several of the current bracing methods, including let-in bracing, diagonal wood boards and Portland cement plaster, reflect conventional construction practices that were common over 50 years ago.

To keep pace with changing construction materials and home design, model building code bracing provisions have gradually evolved from the simple 1920's era "... thoroughly and effectively angle braced ..." requirement.

With the introduction of the International Residential Code in 2000, a decade of significant progress and improvement to wall bracing commenced. Several new bracing provisions and methods, such as minimum bracing percentage, maximum braced wall line spacing, continuous sheathing, portal frames and separate bracing requirements for wind and seismic loads, were added to the code. These advances have ensured that prescriptive wall bracing continues to deliver safe and durable lateral load resistance in today's increasingly complex residential structures.

A number of clarifications have been incorporated into the 2012 IRC to make the bracing section more understandable and consistent. Also new are the simplified wall bracing provisions, an alternative to the conventional bracing provisions that may be used in lower seismic areas (SDC A-C) with basic wind speeds of 90 mph and lower and Wind Exposure Category A or B. As its name implies, the simplified bracing method is considerably easier to use but does not provide as many alternatives to the designer. In addition to wind and seismic restrictions that apply to the simplified bracing method, there are also limitations imposed on the structure's geometry.

Why do bracing requirements change?

The simple answer is that we don't build houses the way we used to!

In the 1960s, when more prescriptive bracing provisions began appearing in model building codes, houses were much smaller (seldom over two stories) and had a greater number of interior walls and fewer windows. See **FIGURE 1.25**.

FIGURE 1.25

A typical single-family residence built in the 1960s and earlier.

Houses today are on average twice as large as those built in the 1960s. Popular features include walk-out basements or third stories, two-story entrance foyers, great rooms, window walls, two- and three-car garages, complex roof lines and dramatic stairways that require large openings in the floor diaphragms. Any one of these features can have a negative impact on the structural performance of a building if not accounted for in the structural frame. **FIGURE 1.26** is an example of a modern house containing many of these features.

FIGURE 1.26

A typical single-family residence built today.

Another factor is the prevalence of new building materials, including nonstructural sheathing products. In the 1960s, the building industry had little concern about wall bracing because the majority of sheathing products available for use were structural to one degree or another. Today, there are a number of nonstructural sheathing products that are popular for energy conservation. Builders are compelled by market pressures to balance the structural and energy requirements of the building. As a result, builders often inadvertently minimize the structural sheathing in an effort to maximize the insulating materials. The trends toward energy efficiency, new construction methods and materials, and other changes in modern residential design are driving the seemingly endless changes to the prescriptive bracing requirements.

Many of the changes to wall bracing in the last two decades have been made in an attempt to permit narrower bracing segments, as space for multiple 4-foot bracing segments is not always available in today's home designs. Garage door openings are the classic example. Seldom do walls with garage door openings have the full 48 inches of bracing length necessary on either side of the opening, as required by the codes since the 1970s. Narrow wall bracing options now make it easier for home designers to meet prescriptive code requirements while enhancing the architectural appearance of the home.

TODAY'S COMPLEX HOUSE

For the reasons listed on the previous page, in addition to high gravity or lateral loads, many homes constructed in certain regions are engineered. For example, in Tacoma, Washington, 90 percent of all new houses constructed have an engineered load path. This is also true for new homes in parts of Florida, California, Oregon and other regions such as those where wind design is required as indicated by IRC Figure R301.2(4)B.

The one thing that has not changed, however, is the need to ensure that the new housing stock is safe. Safety concerns prompted the evolution of building codes in the 1950s and 1960s, and that evolution is expected to continue well into the future. Today's houses are very different from those built 50 years ago, and the houses of the future will likely differ significantly from today's home designs.

Loads and limits of the International Residential Code

As discussed earlier in this chapter, the IRC is a prescriptive code with seismic and wind limitations. In addition to these limitations, IRC Chapter 3 includes a number of geometric limitations on the size, shape, number of stories, and architectural features of the home or townhome. It is not feasible for a prescriptive code to cover every possible combination of wall layouts, cantilevers, large wall line offsets, three-sided structures, and split-level floor plans. These limitations are necessary to prevent the IRC from being applied to homes having configurations to which conventional building practices cannot safely apply. Structures or elements of structures that exceed these limitations must be designed in accordance with the International Building Code (IBC) or other referenced standards.

The scope of the IRC (what to do when details of the structure go beyond the IRC)

For residences outside of the geographic or geometric scope of the IRC, the designer may use the structural provisions of the International Building Code (IBC). Not only may the IBC be used to completely design residential structures, it also may be used to design any part or portion of the structure that is outside of the scope of the IRC. (Note that when beyond the limits of the IRC, the engineered provisions of the IBC may be used but the conventional provisions of Section 2308 are not allowed.) This means that the IRC and IBC can be used in combination to design a structure. This is clearly permitted by the following code sections:

> **R104.11 Alternative materials, design and methods of construction and equipment.** The provisions of this code are not intended to prevent the installation of any material or to prohibit any design or method of construction not specifically prescribed by this code, provided that any such alternative has been *approved*. An alternative material, design or method of construction shall be *approved* where the *building official* finds that the proposed design is satisfactory and complies with the intent of the provisions of this code, and that the material, method or work offered is, for the purpose intended, at least the equivalent of that prescribed in this code. Compliance with the specific performance-based provisions of the International Codes in lieu of specific requirements of this code shall also be permitted as an alternate.

Note: IRC Section R104.11 is also the enabling language typically used to approve alternative products via evaluation reports, such as those found at www.icc-es.org.

R301.1.3 Engineering Design. When a building of otherwise conventional construction contains structural elements exceeding the limits of Section R301 or otherwise not conforming to this code, these elements shall be designed in accordance with accepted engineering practice. The extent of such design need only demonstrate compliance of nonconventional elements with other applicable provisions and shall be compatible with the performance of the conventional framed system. Engineering design in accordance with the *International Building Code* is permitted in all buildings and structures, and parts thereof, included in the scope of this code.

Note: from IRC Section R301.1.3, it is clear that only the element or elements that fall outside the scope of the IRC must be *designed*. It is reasonable to expect that portions of the structure that provide necessary support for these elements must also be checked to ensure compatibility. In addition to using the IBC to design parts or portions of the structure, IRC Section R301.1.1 permits the use of the following as an alternative to the provisions of the IRC for wood construction:

- AF&PA *Wood Frame Construction Manual* (WFCM)
- ICC-400 *Standard on the Design and Construction of Log Structures*

In IRC Section R301.2.1.1 (**TABLE 2.2**), the code requires that when a wood-framed home is built in a region where wind design is required (IRC Figure R301.2(4)B) or where basic wind speed equals or exceeds 110 miles per hour, the design of wood construction for wind loads should be based on one or more of the following documents:

1. AF&PA *Wood Frame Construction Manual* (WFCM)
2. ICC *Standard for Residential Construction in High Wind Regions* (ICC-600)
3. ASCE *Minimum Design Loads for Buildings and Other Structures* (ASCE-7)
4. *International Building Code*

Section R301.2.1.1 also requires that elements of design not addressed by the above documents must be in accordance with the provisions of the IRC. This requirement is provided for clarification because the referenced documents only address the structural frame and other related elements of the building; the IRC is to be used for all of the remaining aspects of the project.

IRC Table R301.2(2) gives the component and cladding pressure requirements that must be met by applicable exterior components. In the table, pressure values are given for basic wind speeds in 5-10 mph increments, based on wind speed (V_{ASD}), roof slope and effective wind area for the various zones of the structure (as defined in IRC Figure R301.2(7)). The zones are the building locations to which the pressure values are applied. Zones 1, 2 and 3 apply to roofs. Zones 4 and 5 apply to walls. The footnote to IRC Figure R301.2(7) specifies a 4-foot dimension for the width of the end zones ("a") at the corners and edges of the structure. For component and cladding loads (IRC Table R301.2(2)), buildings having roof slopes exceeding the maximum slopes (45 degrees or 12/12 slope) must be engineered using the IBC, per IRC Section R301.1.1.

The term *effective wind area,* used in IRC Table R301.2(2), is defined in Footnote a of the table.

a. The effective wind area shall be equal to the span length multiplied by an effective width. This width shall be permitted to be not less than one-third the span length. For cladding fasteners, the effective wind area shall not be greater than the area that is tributary to an individual fastener.

EXAMPLE: *What is the effective wind area for a piece of 4-foot by 8-foot wall sheathing applied vertically on an 8-foot-tall wall?* **The effective wind area is calculated by multiplying the height by the width. Since the wall studs vertically span 8 feet (effective height), the effective width is one-third the vertical span of the stud, which is 8 feet ÷ 3 = 2.67 feet. The effective wind area need not be less than the vertical stud span (effective height) times the effective width, which is 8 feet x 2.67 feet = 21.3 square feet. Thus, using an approximate effective wind area of 20 square feet would be reasonable for use in IRC Table R301.2(2) with respect to panel design.**

Note however that if fastener selection were the goal, the tributary area of the critical fastener would be less than the 20 square feet required for the panel design. For intermediate fasteners at 12 inches on center with studs spaced 16 inches on center, the tributary area of a critical fastener would be (12/12 x 16/12 =) 1.33 square feet.

IRC Table R301.2(2) shows that wall pressures for components and cladding range from +14.6 (pressure) to -19.5 pounds per square foot (suction) for 90 mph basic wind speed in Wind Exposure Category B, Zone 5. The pressure from this table is then modified by a height and exposure factor from IRC Table R301.2(3) to determine the design pressure. The exposure categories range from A to D and are defined in IRC Section R301.2.1.4 (discussed later in this chapter). The exterior wall cladding components (wall coverings, curtain walls, roof coverings, exterior windows, skylights, doors) must have sufficient capacity to withstand these wind pressures.

Component pressure capacities can be obtained from the product manufacturers, evaluation reports or appropriate trade associations. It cannot be assumed that a product meets the code pressure requirements just because the product is commonly used. Some exterior components may require additional fastening or closer support spacing to meet the requirements of this section. IRC Table R602.3(3), for example, requires larger nails and restricts stud spacing for wood structural panel sheathing for certain wind speeds and exposure categories within the scope of the IRC.

The example below shows how to determine the component and cladding wall pressures.

EXAMPLE: *What is the "worst case" wind pressure for the wall sheathing panel in the previous wind area calculation example?*

The panel is in a single-story home (mean roof height less than 30 feet) and located in a 90 mph wind zone, Exposure Category B. The worst case for a wall panel is placement at the corner of the building. This is Zone 5 (see IRC Figure R301.2(7)). From IRC Table R301.2(2) (Wall, Zone 5, 20 square feet, 90 miles per hour), values of +13.9 psf (pounds per square foot) and −18.2 psf are shown. The height and exposure adjustment from IRC Table R301.2(3) is 1.0. The positive (+) value is for wind load acting from the outside toward the inside of the house (pushing the panel toward the wall studs). The negative (−) value is the wind load pulling the panel away from the studs, creating suction.

ANSWER: **The "worst case" wind suction pressure is 18.2 psf. The exterior components of the structure (wall sheathing/wall system) must be selected to withstand this wind pressure per IRC Section R301.2.1.**

Notice that there are two wind pressure values given in the example above. This is because, as the orientation of the wind changes with respect to the structure, the wind can cause either suction (− numbers) or positive pressures (+ numbers) on the structure. For example, a wind blowing on the north side of a structure causes a positive pressure on the north side and simultaneously causes negative pressure, or suction, on the south side. As wind may blow from any direction, both pressures must be considered when sizing and selecting an exterior wall element.

Siding, sheathing and siding/sheathing combinations must be strong and stiff enough to resist positive wind pressures. They must also be sufficiently attached to prevent fastener pull out of the framing or pull through of the fastener head to avoid the result of negative wind pressures pulling cladding materials off of the framing. If a sheathing system, made up of a number of components that must work together to resist the external wind forces, is used, it is essential to select components and attachment schedules such that the loss of one component due to strength, stiffness or attachment deficiency does not precipitate the overload/failure of the remaining components.

R301.2.1.1 Wind limitations and wind design required. The wind provisions of this code shall not apply to the design of buildings where wind design is required in accordance with Figure R301.2(4)B or where the basic wind speed from Figure R301.2(4)A equals or exceeds 110 miles per hour (49 m/s).

If a specific location is defined by IRC Figure R301.2(4)B as a "wind design required" region, or the wind design speed is 110 mph or greater, the IRC wind design provisions do not apply and alternate standards or the IBC must be used, as shown in *TABLE 2.2*.

TABLE 2.2

Applicable design standards

IRC Section R301.2.1.1

Basic Wind Speed	Applicable Document
Less than 110 mph	IRC
110 mph or more "Wind Design Required" locations as seen in IRC Figure R301.2(4)B[a]	1. AF&PA Wood Frame Construction Manual (WFCM); or 2. Standard for Residential Construction In High Wind Regions (ICC-600)[b] ; or 3. ASCE Minimum Design Loads for Buildings and Other Structures (ASCE-7); or 4. International Building Code

a. Including Puerto Rico, Guam, Virgin Islands, American Samoa and Special Wind Regions in Hawaii.
b. ICC-600 provides both engineered and prescriptive solutions for residential structures in wind speed areas outside the scope of the IRC. In many cases, it provides prescriptive solutions for problems that formerly required design.

R301.2.1.4 Exposure category. For each wind direction considered, an exposure category that adequately reflects the characteristics of ground surface irregularities shall be determined for the site at which the building or structure is to be constructed. For a site located in the transition zone between categories, the category resulting in the largest wind forces shall apply. Account shall be taken of variations in ground surface roughness that arise from natural topography and vegetation as well as from constructed features. For a site where multiple detached one- and two-family dwellings, *townhouses* or other structures are to be constructed as part of a subdivision, master-planned community, or otherwise designated as a developed area by the authority having jurisdiction, the exposure category for an individual structure shall be based upon the site conditions that will exist at the time when all adjacent structures on the site have been constructed, provided their construction is expected to begin within one year of the start of construction for the structure for which the exposure category is determined. For any given wind direction, the exposure in which a specific building or other structure is sited shall be assessed as being one of the following categories:

Exposure category takes into account the shielding effects on wind load from other buildings, natural topography and vegetation. Adjacent buildings can deflect wind, thus reducing the pressure on the building. Tall vegetation, such as trees and terrain with numerous, closely spaced obstructions the size of single-family houses or larger can also reduce the effect of wind. Topographical features, such as flat and open areas, are associated with higher exposure categories because there are no obstructions to reduce the effects of the wind. The code defines four wind exposure categories, ranging from Exposure A (the lowest wind pressures) to Exposure D (the highest wind pressures). Exposure Category B (IRC R301.2.1.4, Item 2) is the assumed wind exposure category unless otherwise directed by IRC Table R301.2(1) in your jurisdiction's adopted code.

1. Exposure A. Large city centers with at least 50 percent of the buildings having a height in excess of 70 feet (21 336 mm). Use of this exposure category shall be limited to those areas for which terrain representative of Exposure A prevails in the upwind direction for a distance of at least 0.5 mile (0.8 km) or 10 times the height of the building or other structure, whichever is greater. Possible channeling effects or increased velocity pressures due to the building or structure being located in the wake of adjacent buildings shall be taken into account.

FIGURE 2.3

**Exposure
Category A**

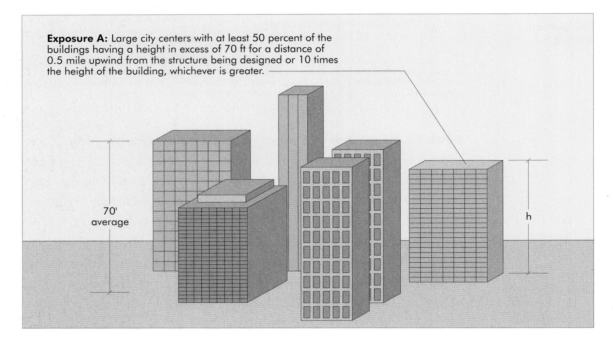

Exposure A: Large city centers with at least 50 percent of the buildings having a height in excess of 70 ft for a distance of 0.5 mile upwind from the structure being designed or 10 times the height of the building, whichever is greater.

70'
average

h

2. Exposure B. Urban and suburban areas, wooded areas, or other terrain with numerous closely spaced obstructions having the size of single family dwellings or larger. Exposure B shall be assumed unless the site meets the definition of another type exposure.

FIGURE 2.4

**Exposure
Category B**

Shall be assumed
unless the site
meets the definition
of another type
exposure

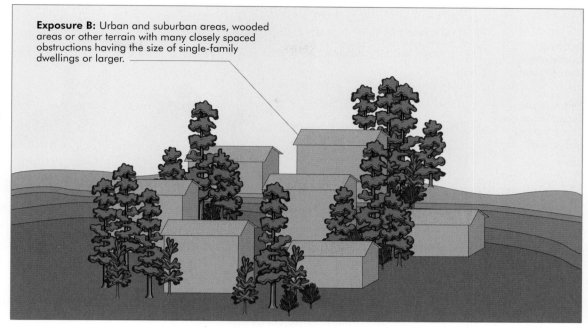

Exposure B: Urban and suburban areas, wooded
areas or other terrain with many closely spaced
obstructions having the size of single-family
dwellings or larger.

3. Exposure C. Open terrain with scattered obstructions, including surface undulations or
other irregularities, having heights generally less than 30 feet (9144 mm) extending more
than 1,500 feet (457 m) from the building site in any quadrant. This exposure shall also
apply to any building located within Exposure B type terrain where the building is directly
adjacent to open areas of Exposure C type terrain in any quadrant for a distance of more
than 600 feet (183 m). This category includes flat, open country and grasslands.

FIGURE 2.5

**Exposure
Category C**

This category
includes flat open
country and
grasslands

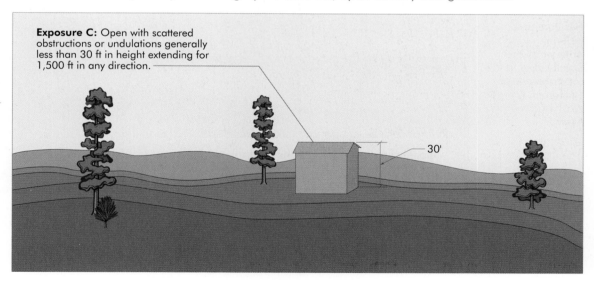

Exposure C: Open with scattered
obstructions or undulations generally
less than 30 ft in height extending for
1,500 ft in any direction.

30'

FIGURE 2.6

Exposure Category C (Continued)

This category includes flat open country and grasslands

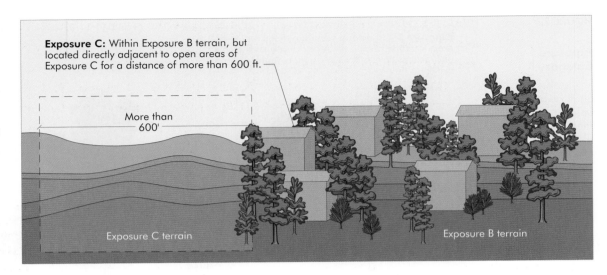

Exposure C: Within Exposure B terrain, but located directly adjacent to open areas of Exposure C for a distance of more than 600 ft.

More than 600'

Exposure C terrain

Exposure B terrain

4. Exposure D. Flat, unobstructed areas exposed to wind flowing over open water for a distance of at least 1 mile (1.61 km). Shorelines in Exposure D include inland waterways, the Great Lakes, and coastal areas of California, Oregon, Washington and Alaska. This exposure shall apply only to those buildings and other structures exposed to the wind coming from over the water. Exposure D extends inland from the shoreline a distance of 1500 feet (457 m) or 10 times the height of the building or structure, whichever is greater.

FIGURE 2.7

Exposure Category D

This category includes inland waterways, the Great Lakes, and coastal areas of California, Oregon, Washington and Alaska

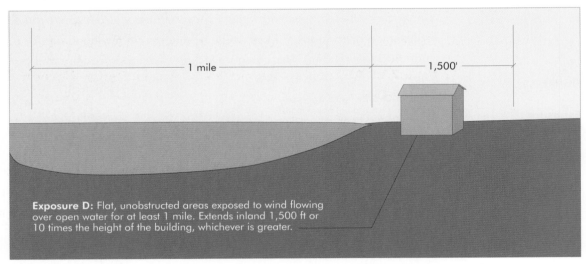

1 mile

1,500'

Exposure D: Flat, unobstructed areas exposed to wind flowing over open water for at least 1 mile. Extends inland 1,500 ft or 10 times the height of the building, whichever is greater.

R301.2.2 Seismic provisions. The seismic provisions of this code shall apply as follows:

1. Townhouses in Seismic Design Categories C, D_0, D_1 and D_2.

2. Detached one- and two-family dwellings in Seismic Design Categories D_0, D_1 and D_2.

IRC Section R301.2.2 is rewritten for the 2012 edition to clearly exempt detached one- and two-family dwellings in Seismic Design Categories (SDC) A, B, C and townhouses in SDC A and B. This change was specifically added to clarify the intent of the older provisions of the building code.

TABLE 2.3, adapted from IRC Section R301.2.2, illustrates the importance of distinguishing between dwellings and townhouses. Note that dwellings located in SDC A, B and C are exempt from all of the seismic requirements of the IRC. This means that these dwellings are not required to comply with the seismic provisions of IRC Section R301.2.2 or its subsections, or those in IRC Chapters 4, 5, 6 and 7. This exception significantly reduces the construction requirements for any dwelling built in SDC A or B, and for one- and two-family dwellings built in SDC A, B and C. However, dwellings in SDC D_0, D_1 and D_2, as well as townhouses in SDC C, must comply with the seismic requirements of IRC Section R301.2.2.

TABLE 2.3

Scope of seismic provisions

Adapted from IRC Section R301.2.2

Seismic Design Categories	Seismic Requirements	
	One- and Two-Family Dwellings	Townhouses
A – B	Exempt	Exempt
C	Exempt	No Exemption
D_0 – D_2	No Exemption	No Exemption

IRC Section R202 provides the definitions of dwelling unit, dwelling and townhouse. These definitions are provided on pages 30-32.

R301.2.2.1 Determination of seismic design category. Buildings shall be assigned a seismic design category in accordance with Figure R301.2(2).

IRC Figure R301.2(2) is reproduced in part in **FIGURE 1.5** of this guide.

R301.2.2.1.2 Alternative determination of Seismic Design Category E. Buildings located in Seismic Design Category E in accordance with Figure R301.2(2) are permitted to be reclassified as being in Seismic Design Category D_2 provided one of the following is done:

1. A more detailed evaluation of the seismic design category is made in accordance with the provisions and maps of the *International Building Code*. Buildings located in Seismic Design Category E per Table R301.2.2.1.1, but located in Seismic Design Category D per the *International Building Code*, may be designed using the Seismic Design Category D_2 requirements of this code.

2. Buildings located in Seismic Design Category E that conform to the following additional restrictions are permitted to be constructed in accordance with the provisions for Seismic Design Category D_2 of this code:

    2.1. All exterior shear wall lines or *braced wall panels* are in one plane vertically from the foundation to the uppermost story.

    2.2. Floors shall not cantilever past the exterior walls.

    2.3. The building is within all of the requirements of Section R301.2.2.2.5 for being considered as regular.

While the IRC does not provide wall bracing guidance for buildings in SDC E, IRC Section R301.2.2.1.2 provides two methods for downgrading the SDC of the structure to Seismic Design Category D_2. These two methods are:

1. The re-evaluation of the building site via the International Building Code (IBC) and

2. The addition of a number of additional provisions to those for SDC D_2 that enable the building to be constructed in accordance with the IRC as a structure located in an SDC D_2 locale.

Neither method is a "guaranteed downgrade". In fact, few buildings will actually be eligible unless specifically designed to be compliant with this section.

R301.2.2.2 Seismic Design Category C. Structures assigned to Seismic Design Category C shall conform to the requirements of this section.

The limitations provided in this section apply to townhouses in SDC C. This section details the scoping limitations aimed at restricting architectural features that may make a structure unsuitable for the prescriptive methodology used in the IRC. As noted previously, detached one- and two-family dwellings in SDC C are exempt from the seismic requirements of the code, so these provisions only apply to townhouses. These limitations are also applied to buildings in SDC D_0, D_1 and D_2 per IRC Section R301.2.2.3

R301.2.2.2.1 Weights of materials. Average dead loads shall not exceed 15 pounds per square foot (720 Pa) for the combined roof and ceiling assemblies (on a horizontal projection) or 10 pounds per square foot (480 Pa) for floor assemblies, except as further limited by Section R301.2.2. Dead loads for walls above *grade* shall not exceed:

1. Fifteen pounds per square foot (720 Pa) for exterior light-frame wood walls.

2. Fourteen pounds per square foot (670 Pa) for exterior light-frame cold-formed steel walls.

3. Ten pounds per square foot (480 Pa) for interior light-frame wood walls.

4. Five pounds per square foot (240 Pa) for interior light-frame cold-formed steel walls.

5. Eighty pounds per square foot (3830 Pa) for 8-inch-thick (203 mm) masonry walls.

6. Eighty-five pounds per square foot (4070 Pa) for 6-inch-thick (152 mm) concrete walls.

7. Ten pounds per square foot (480 Pa) for SIP walls.

Exceptions:

1. Roof and ceiling dead loads not exceeding 25 pounds per square foot (1190 Pa) shall be permitted provided the wall bracing amounts in Chapter 6 are increased in accordance with Table R301.2.2.2.1.

The seismic loads on a building are related to building weight (mass). The greater the building weight, the greater the seismic load (Force = Mass x Acceleration). During ground motion/acceleration, the structural parts of a building must resist the lateral forces to prevent collapse. Therefore, the IRC sets limits on the weights of floors, walls, ceiling and roofs. *TABLE 2.4* lists the maximum building weights defined by this section for wood frame construction. This section does permit the increase of some building weights, provided the amount of wall bracing is increased. Increasing the amount of wall bracing makes the building stronger, stiffer and more capable of resisting the greater seismic loads that result from the greater building mass. See *FIGURE 2.8*.

TABLE 2.4

Bracing adjustment factors based on weights of construction materials

Adapted from IRC Table R301.2.2.2.1

	Dead Loads and Wall Bracing Adjustment Factors			
Component	Story Location	Maximum Dead Load Permitted for Standard Wall Bracing (psf)	Maximum Dead Load Permitted with Wall Bracing Adjustment (psf)	Bracing Panel Amount Adjustment Factor[a]
Floor		10	N/A	N/A
Roof/Ceiling Dead Load For Wall Supporting the Roof Only		15[b]	25[b]	1.2
Roof/Ceiling Dead Load For Wall Supporting the Roof Plus One or Two Stories		15[b]	25[b]	1.1

a. This factor is to be applied to the required bracing amount (length) of the wall line. See IRC Table R602.10.1.3(3).
b. The allowable load given for roofs is the weight of the roof based on the horizontal projection of the roof.
   This is the total weight of the roof and ceiling divided by the area of the roof in plan view.

FIGURE 2.8

Maximum dead load weights

IRC Section R301.2.2.2.1

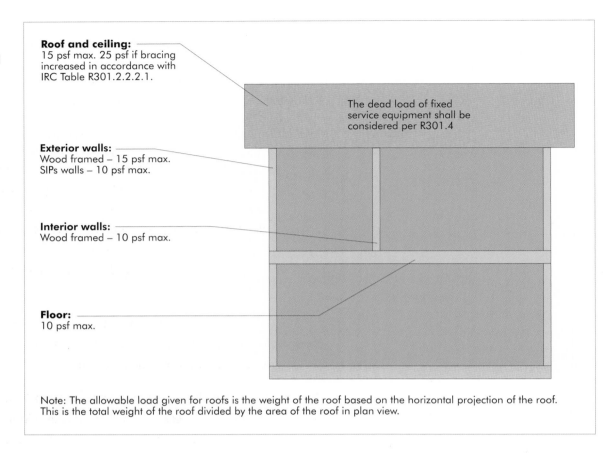

Roof and ceiling:
15 psf max. 25 psf if bracing increased in accordance with IRC Table R301.2.2.2.1.

The dead load of fixed service equipment shall be considered per R301.4

Exterior walls:
Wood framed – 15 psf max.
SIPs walls – 10 psf max.

Interior walls:
Wood framed – 10 psf max.

Floor:
10 psf max.

Note: The allowable load given for roofs is the weight of the roof based on the horizontal projection of the roof. This is the total weight of the roof divided by the area of the roof in plan view.

EXAMPLE: Consider a braced wall that has only a roof above it. The roof is heavy tile with a total dead load of 20 psf measured on the horizontal projection. Since 20 psf exceeds the 15 psf limit, but is less than 25 psf, the amount of bracing required per IRC Table R602.10.1.3(3) must be increased by a factor of 1.2. While not specifically provided for in the code provisions, interpolation between 1.0 and 1.2 is justifiable from an engineering perspective.

Note that the adjustment in accordance with IRC Table R301.2.2.2.1 is a duplicate of the provision contained in IRC Table R602.10.3(4) roof/ceiling dead load (fifth row). These are the same requirement and are not to be used together. The adjustment is meant to be used only once in determining the bracing for a specific application.

EXAMPLE: A home designer draws up a set of plans for a two-story townhouse. After working through the bracing section of the IRC, the designer determines that the structure, based on the seismic bracing requirements, requires each exterior wall on the first story to have 18 feet of bracing and the second story to have 10 feet of bracing. The designer assumes that, like most townhouses in the area, the structure will have a typical lightweight wood roof (roof/ceiling dead load of 15 psf or less); however, the owner later asks the designer to consider a slate roof. This roofing material adds 6 psf to the weight to the horizontal projection of the roof. *How does this impact the amount of bracing needed for the first and second stories?*

With a slate roof, the weight of the roof/ceiling becomes 21 (15+6) psf. From *TABLE 2.4*, 21 psf is less than the maximum dead load permitted (25 psf). This means that a bracing length adjustment factor of 1.1 is required for the first story and 1.2 for the second story.

> *FIRST STORY*   18 feet x 1.1 = 19.8 feet of bracing required
>
> *SECOND STORY* 10 feet x 1.2 = 12 feet of bracing required

Note that the provisions of IRC Table R301.2.2.2.1 (*TABLE 2.4*) appear on the surface to be counterintuitive. According to the table, the impact of increased roof seismic weight appears greater for a single story than for a two-story structure. From an engineering perspective, this is correct. When there is just a roof over a single-story structure, any increase in the seismic weight of the roof will have approximately the same increase in the required bracing on the walls of the first story. For example, a 50 percent increase in roof seismic weight causes the loads on the braced wall below to be increased by approximately the same amount.

However, when there is a full story above the first story walls, any increase in the seismic weight on the roof of a given percentage when combined with the seismic weight of the second floor results in a smaller percentage increase to the walls on the first floor.

What the table indicates is that with a roof-ceiling dead load increase from 15 to 25 pounds per square foot, the walls supporting the roof experience a 20 percent increase in load on the braced wall lines. For the walls supporting the roof and second floor, this is only a 10 percent increase.

> 2. Light-frame walls with stone or masonry veneer shall be permitted in accordance with the provisions of Sections R702.1 and R703.

The IRC provides specific bracing provisions for one- and two-family dwellings in SDC D_0, D_1 and D_2 with stone or masonry veneer exceeding the first story wall height and attached in accordance with IRC Section R703.7. These provisions are found in IRC Section R602.10.6.5. Provisions for stone or masonry veneer exceeding the first story wall height and townhouses can be found in IRC Table R602.10.3(4) (*TABLE 3.6*).

Stone and masonry construction is outside the scope of this guide. Stone and masonry veneer, which is within the scope of this book, is different from stone and masonry construction.

> **R301.2.2.2.5 Irregular buildings.** The seismic provisions of this code shall not be used for irregular structures located in Seismic Design Categories C, D_0, D_1 and D_2. Irregular portions of structures shall be designed in accordance with accepted engineering practice to the extent the irregular features affect the performance of the remaining structural system. When the forces associated with the irregularity are resisted by a structural system designed in accordance with accepted engineering practice, design of the remainder of the building shall be permitted using the provisions of this code. A building or portion of a building shall be considered to be irregular when one or more of the following conditions occur:

This section of the code defines building shapes that are irregular. It is important to note that this section applies only to structures located in SDC C-D$_2$, excluding one- and two-family dwellings in SDC C. The IRC seismic provisions assume that a building has a relatively uniform shape. If the building deviates to far from the assumed uniform shape, the building or portion of the building is considered irregular. IRC Section R301.2.2.2.5 defines these irregularities and places limits on them for purposes of inclusion within the seismic bracing provisions of the IRC.

The problem with irregular buildings is that the irregular shape of the structure can cause an unusual load path. Such structures are difficult to design and almost impossible to effectively specify using the prescriptive provisions of the IRC. In order to permit some degree of building irregularity that the prescriptive provisions can safely accommodate, this section was developed. Those structures, or portions thereof, that are outside of these limitations are irregular shaped buildings and must be designed using the IBC to ensure that the building has adequate capacity and a load path to resist seismic forces. Buildings having a regular shape can be constructed by following the prescriptive provisions of the IRC.

Many contemporary home designs may be considered irregular by one of the seven conditions of this section. These provisions, however, include some exceptions that may permit an otherwise irregular home to be constructed by the IRC.

1. When exterior shear wall lines or *braced wall panels* are not in one plane vertically from the foundation to the uppermost *story* in which they are required.

   Exception: For wood light-frame construction, floors with cantilevers or setbacks not exceeding four times the nominal depth of the wood floor joists are permitted to support *braced wall panels* that are out of plane with *braced wall panels* below provided that:

   1. Floor joists are nominal 2 inches by 10 inches (51 mm by 254 mm) or larger and spaced not more than 16 inches (406 mm) on center.

   2. The ratio of the back span to the cantilever is at least 2 to 1.

   3. Floor joists at ends of *braced wall panels* are doubled.

   4. For wood-frame construction, a continuous rim joist is connected to ends of all cantilever joists. When spliced, the rim joists shall be spliced using a galvanized metal tie not less than 0.058 inch (1.5 mm) (16 gage) and 1-1/2 inches (38 mm) wide fastened with six 16d nails on each side of the splice or a block of the same size as the rim joist of sufficient length to fit securely between the joist space at which the splice occurs fastened with eight 16d nails on each side of the splice; and

   5. Gravity loads carried at the end of cantilevered joists are limited to uniform wall and roof loads and the reactions from headers having a span of 8 feet (2438 mm) or less.

The first irregularity provision prohibits braced wall panels that are not vertically aligned in one plane.

Following this irregularity provision, an exception is listed for buildings constructed using wood light-frame construction, as shown in ***FIGURE 2.9***. This exception is not applicable to other types of construction, such as masonry or concrete. According to the exception, braced wall panels do not have to be in one plane vertically if:

Setbacks or cantilevers do not exceed four times the nominal depth of the wood floor joists and ALL of the following conditions are met:

1. Floor joists are nominal 2x10 or larger and spaced not more than 16 inches on center. (Note that some engineered I-joist products are manufactured at 9-1/2-inch depths. These can be considered within the scope of this condition.)

2. The ratio of the backspan to cantilever is at least 2:1.

3. Floor joists at the ends of braced wall panels are doubled.

4. A continuous rim joist is connected to the ends of all cantilevered joists.

5. Gravity loads at the end of the cantilever are limited to uniform wall and roof loads and any headers in the wall must have a span of 8 feet or less.

FIGURE 2.9

Irregularity #1: Braced wall panels with vertical irregularities

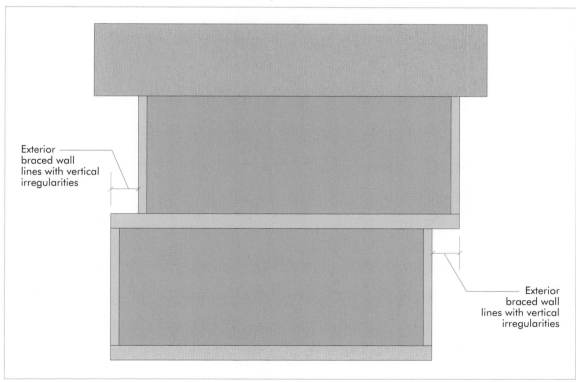

Exterior braced wall lines with vertical irregularities

Exterior braced wall lines with vertical irregularities

2. When a section of floor or roof is not laterally supported by shear walls or *braced wall lines* on all edges.

> **Exception:** Portions of floors that do not support shear walls or *braced wall panels* above, or roofs, shall be permitted to extend no more than 6 feet (1829 mm) beyond a shear wall or *braced wall line*.

According to the second provision, a building is considered irregular when a braced wall line is not beneath (or supporting) a portion of a roof or floor. If this section of the floor or roof is not in turn supporting any braced wall panels located above, it is permitted to extend out not more than 6 feet. The exception to the irregularity is shown in **FIGURE 2.10**.

FIGURE 2.10

Exception to Irregularity #2: Portions of floor or roof not supported are permitted to extend up to 6 feet

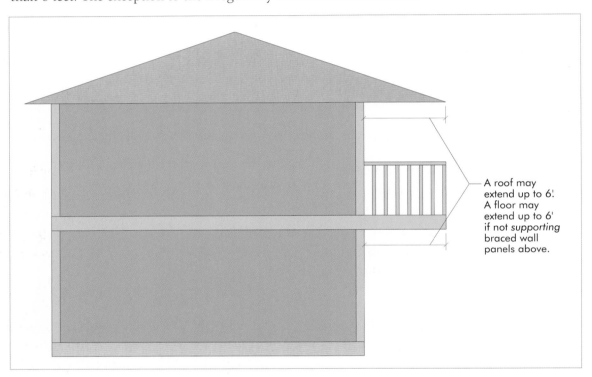

A roof may extend up to 6'. A floor may extend up to 6' if not *supporting* braced wall panels above.

This second irregularity provision is different than the first, in that the first irregularity provision relates to braced wall lines being supported by floor framing. In the exception to the second irregularity provision, a roof or floor can be unsupported by a braced wall line for a maximum of 6 feet.

3. When the end of a *braced wall panel* occurs over an opening in the wall below and ends at a horizontal distance greater than 1 foot (305 mm) from the edge of the opening. This provision is applicable to shear walls and *braced wall panels* offset in plane and to *braced wall panels* offset out of plane as permitted by the exception to Item 1 above.

Exception: For wood light-frame wall construction, one end of a *braced wall panel* shall be permitted to extend more than 1 foot (305 mm) over an opening not more than 8 feet (2438 mm) wide in the wall below provided that the opening includes a header in accordance with the following:

1. The building width, loading condition and framing member species limitations of Table R502.5(1) shall apply; and

2. Not less than one 2 × 12 or two 2 × 10 for an opening not more than 4 feet (1219 mm) wide; or

3. Not less than two 2 × 12 or three 2 × 10 for an opening not more than 6 feet (1829 mm) wide; or

4. Not less than three 2 × 12 or four 2 × 10 for an opening not more than 8 feet (2438 mm) wide; and

5. The entire length of the *braced wall panel* does not occur over an opening in the wall below.

The third irregularity provision in this section places limitations on the location of the end of braced wall panels relative to openings in the braced wall line below. In general, a braced wall panel is only permitted to extend 1 foot over an opening in a lower wall line, as shown in **FIGURE 2.11**. For wood light-frame construction, a braced wall panel is permitted to extend more than 1 foot over the opening below, provided the entire braced wall panel is not located over the opening, and the exceptions are met.

For wood light-frame wall construction, a number of limits apply to the exception for the third irregularity. Provided that the building width, loading conditions and framing member species meet the requirements of IRC Table R502.5(1), and the entire length of the braced wall panel does not occur over the opening, the header sizes shown in **TABLE 2.5** may be used to exempt the third irregularity.

FIGURE 2.11

**Irregularity #3:
Braced wall panel
over openings**

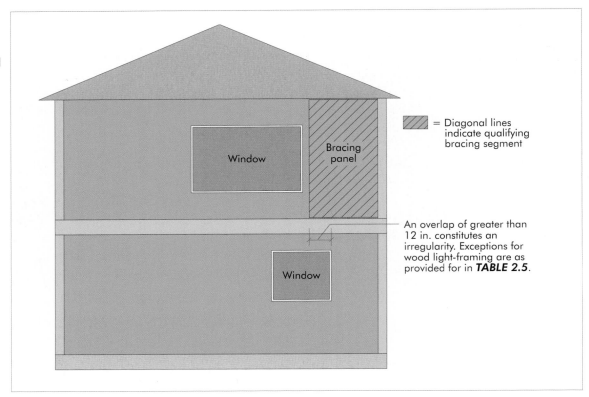

= Diagonal lines indicate qualifying bracing segment

Window

Bracing panel

Window

An overlap of greater than 12 in. constitutes an irregularity. Exceptions for wood light-framing are as provided for in *TABLE 2.5*.

TABLE 2.5

**Header
requirements
to exempt
Irregularity #3**

Maximum Window Opening Width Below Bracing	Minimum Header Requirements
4 ft	1 – 2x12
	2 – 2x10
6 ft	2 – 2x12
	3 – 2x10
8 ft	3 – 2x12
	4 – 2x10

4. When an opening in a floor or roof exceeds the lesser of 12 feet (3658 mm) or 50 percent of the least floor or roof dimension.

The fourth irregularity limits the size of the floor opening between stories or an opening in the roof. This limitation applies to all types of construction. The purpose of this restriction is to limit the size of a hole in the floor or roof diaphragm. An example of an opening between floors would be a stairway or room with a height that extends through the story above. A skylight would be considered a roof opening. The size of floor and roof openings is limited to the lesser of 12 feet or 50 percent of the least floor or roof dimension as shown in *FIGURE 2.12*.

FIGURE 2.12

Irregularity #4: Excessive hole in roof or floor sheathing

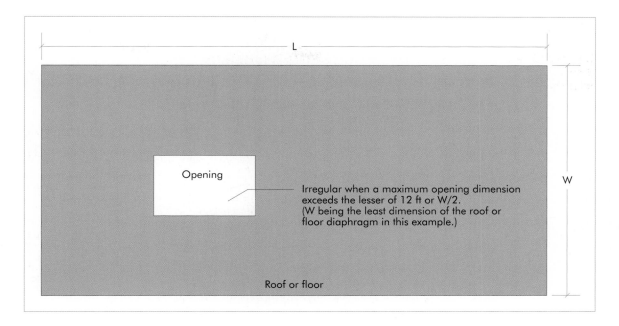

Opening

Irregular when a maximum opening dimension exceeds the lesser of 12 ft or W/2. (W being the least dimension of the roof or floor diaphragm in this example.)

Roof or floor

5. When portions of a floor level are vertically offset.

Exceptions:

1. Framing supported directly by continuous foundations at the perimeter of the building.

2. For wood light-frame construction, floors shall be permitted to be vertically offset when the floor framing is lapped or tied together as required by Section R502.6.1.

For the fifth irregularity provision, a building is considered irregular when a floor has a vertical offset as shown in *FIGURE 2.13*. For wood light-framed construction, the building is considered regular if the floor framing is lapped or tied together per IRC Section R502.6.1. For all construction types (wood, steel, etc.), vertical offsets in a floor level shall not be considered irregular if the perimeter framing of the floor is supported directly on a continuous foundation at the building perimeter.

IRC Section R502.6.1 states that joist framing must be lapped a minimum of 3 inches and face-nailed together with three 10d nails. As an alternate, a wood or metal splice with equal strength is permitted. These measures address the problems associated with floor-offset irregularities.

FIGURE 2.13

**Irregularity #5:
Offset in floor
framing**

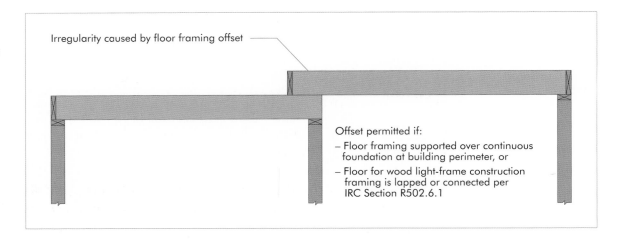

6. When shear walls and *braced wall lines* do not occur in two perpendicular directions.

The sixth irregularity provision simply states that if braced wall lines are not perpendicular to each other, the building must be considered irregular. **FIGURE 2.14** illustrates such an irregularity. There is no exception to mitigate this type of irregularity.

Note that an angled wall as described in IRC Section R602.10.1.4 (**FIGURE 3.4**) is not such an irregularity, but rather an architectural feature found on a basically rectangular structure. This section permits the bracing that may be found on the angled portion to be counted towards the minimum length required for one wall. The angled corner is limited to 8 feet in length, thus minimizing its impact on the structural regularity of the building.

FIGURE 2.14

**Irregularity #6:
Braced wall lines
not at right angles
to each other**

7. When stories above *grade* plane partially or completely braced by wood wall framing in accordance with Section R602 or steel wall framing in accordance with Section R603 include masonry or concrete construction.

> **Exception:** Fireplaces, chimneys and masonry veneer as permitted by this code.

> When this irregularity applies, the entire *story* shall be designed in accordance with accepted engineering practice.

(Editorial note: for clarity, we have moved this statement regarding the application of the irregularity to a new sentence, separated from the exception that precedes it. This statement applies to the seventh irregularity itself and not the exception. In the code, the exception and this statement are connected due to a typographical error.)

The seventh irregularity provision states that wood- and steel-framed buildings braced in accordance with IRC Chapter 6 are irregular when they include above grade plane masonry or concrete construction. Fireplaces, chimneys and masonry veneer are permitted, provided they are constructed in accordance with other provisions of the IRC. Note that when this irregularity exists, the entire story shall be designed, not just the portion causing the irregularity.

R301.3 Story height. The wind and seismic provisions of this code shall apply to buildings with story heights not exceeding the following:

1. For wood wall framing, the laterally unsupported bearing wall stud height permitted by Table R602.3(5) plus a height of floor framing not to exceed 16 inches (406 mm).

> **Exception:** For wood-framed wall buildings with bracing in accordance with Tables R602.10.3(1) and R602.10.3(3), the wall stud clear height used to determine the maximum permitted *story height* may be increased to 12 feet (3658 mm) without requiring an engineered design for the building wind and seismic force-resisting systems provided that the length of bracing required by Table R602.10.3(1) is increased by multiplying by a factor of 1.10 and the length of bracing required by Table R602.10.3(3) is increased by multiplying by a factor of 1.20. Wall studs are still subject to the requirements of this section.

Individual walls or wall studs shall be permitted to exceed these limits as permitted by Chapter 6 provisions, provided the *story heights* are not exceeded. Floor framing height shall be permitted to exceed these limits provided the *story height* does not exceed 11 feet 7 inches (3531 mm.) An engineered design shall be provided for the wall or wall framing members when they exceed the limits of Chapter 6. Where the *story height* limits of this section are exceeded, the design of the building, or the noncompliant portions thereof, to resist wind and seismic loads shall be in accordance with the *International Building Code*.

TABLE 2.6

Maximum story height for wood-frame construction permitted in the IRC

Stud Height	Floor Framing Depth	Maximum Story Height[a]
10 feet	Varies	11 feet 7 inches
12 feet[b]	Varies	13 feet 7 inches

a. Laterally unsupported bearing wall heights.
b. Wall stud clear height shall be permitted to be increased to 12 ft provided the length of bracing required by IRC Table R602.10.3(1) is increased by multiplying by a factor of 1.10, and the length of bracing required by IRC Table R602.10.3(3) is increased by multiplying by a factor of 1.20 in accordance with IRC Section R301.3, Item 1, Exception.

FIGURE 2.15

Story height measurement for wood, structural insulated panels, and cold-formed steel framing

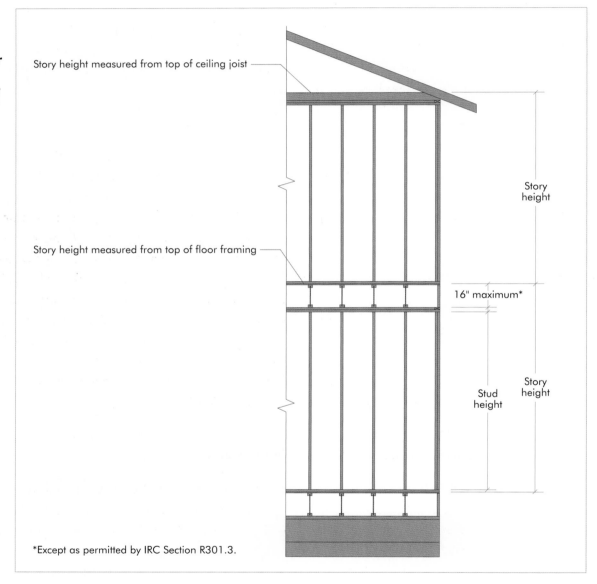

Story height measured from top of ceiling joist

Story height

Story height measured from top of floor framing

16" maximum*

Story height

Stud height

Story height

*Except as permitted by IRC Section R301.3.

There is a slight but significant change to the language in IRC Section R301.3. Former editions of the IRC began this section with the following statement: "Buildings constructed in accordance with these provisions…" For the 2012 edition, the text has been changed to: "The wind and seismic provisions…" This change was made to clarify that the building height provisions are critical to the bracing portions (wind and seismic provisions) of the structure <u>only</u> and that the rest of the building can be built to the requirements of the IRC with only the lateral bracing of the building subjected to engineering. See IRC Section 301.1.3.

IRC Section R301.3 limits the floor framing depth to a maximum of 16 inches. However, a provision (new in the 2009 IRC) states that floor framing depths greater than 16 inches may be used as long as the overall story height (wall height + floor framing depth + floor sheathing thickness) does not exceed 11 feet 7 inches. This means that if 24-inch deep floor framing is used, the maximum stud/wall height would be 9 feet 7 inches (11 feet 7 inches - 24 inches = 9 feet 7 inches). The 2012 IRC permits the use of any depth of floor framing provided the combined height of the studs and floor framing does not exceed 11 feet 7 inches. This provision in IRC Section R301.3 is reproduced below:

> Floor framing height shall be permitted to exceed these limits provided story height does not exceed 11 feet 7 inches (3531 mm).

Note that the intention of this provision is to permit the floor framing to be greater than 16 inches in depth as long as the stud height is adjusted downward accordingly. This does not preclude the use of the provision in IRC Section R301.3, Item 1, Exception, that permits the increase of the nominal stud height from 10 feet to 12 feet if wall bracing is increased. Because the 11-feet 7-inch maximum story height is based on a 10-foot stud height (prescribed 10-foot nominal stud height + prescribed 1-foot 4-inch floor framing + presumed 3-inch allowance for floor sheathing and plates), if a 12-foot stud height is used based on IRC Section R301.3, Item 1, Exception, the story height is permitted to be increased to a maximum of 13-feet 7-inches (12-foot nominal stud height + 1-foot 4-inch floor framing + 3-inch allowance for floor sheathing and plates). Remember, the intent of this section is not to limit the stud height, it is to permit the increase in floor framing depth to over 16 inches as long as the stud height is reduced accordingly. See **TABLE 2.7** and **FIGURE 2.15**.

QUESTION: *Can a floor depth greater than 16 inches be used as long as I do not exceed <u>my</u> maximum story height of 136 inches (120 + 16)?*

ANSWER: Yes. From an engineering perspective, the load contributed by a wall 136 inches high is essentially the same regardless of how much of the 136 inches in overall height is stud length and how much is floor-framing depth. The provision added to IRC Section R301.3 permits just such an adjustment. The floor framing can be increased as long as the story height does not exceed 11 feet 7 inches (139 inches). Therefore, for this example, using a 24-inch-deep floor joist would be permissible as long as the stud length is 109 inches or less (136 inches – 24 inches = 112 inches wall height. For stud length, 112 inches – 3 inches for plates = 109 inches).

NOTE: The story height can be increased by an additional 2 feet if the bracing length is correspondingly increased per IRC Section R301.3, Exception 1 or IRC Tables R602.10.3(2) and (4). The same provision is listed in both places.

For wood framed-residences, the stud height for a laterally unsupported bearing wall is limited to 10 feet by IRC Table R602.3(5). Studs are laterally supported at the top and bottom by connections to diaphragms, such as a floor or roof. However, studs are not typically laterally supported along their height between the diaphragms, ceilings and/or foundations, and can deflect front-to-back and side-to-side. Section R301.3 of the 2012 IRC permits increasing laterally unsupported stud height to 12 feet, provided the length of bracing is increased by an adjustment factor to compensate for the increased lateral load (side-to-side) on the structure resulting from the taller stud walls.

The adjustment factor is 1.1 when using the wind bracing table (IRC Table R602.10.3(1), reproduced in **TABLE 3.3**) and is 1.2 when using the seismic bracing table (IRC Table R602.10.3(3), reproduced in **TABLE 3.5**). The different factors resulted from separating the previously single bracing table into separate tables for wind and seismic forces (different methodologies were used in developing the two separate tables, resulting in different adjustment factors). See **TABLE 2.7** for the bracing adjustment factors for wood-framed walls. Using linear interpolation to determine the bracing factor for stud heights between 10 and 12 feet is justifiable from an engineering perspective. The maximum story height equals the stud height (12 foot maximum) plus floor framing height (16 inches maximum plus floor sheathing and plate thickness).

TABLE 2.7

Bracing adjustments required for wood-framed walls greater than 10 feet

Bracing Criteria	Wall Height (Feet)	Bracing Increase Factor
Wind Bracing	10 or less	1.0
	>10 to 12	1.1
Seismic Bracing	10 or less	1.0
	>10 to 12	1.2

For 2012, a story-height provision was added to IRC Section R301.3 to clarify the use of either of the two stud height tables, IRC Tables R602.3(5) and R602.3.1, from Chapter 6. Although IRC Table R602.3(5) limits bearing wall studs to 10 feet in height, IRC Section R301.3, Exception 1 may be applied to allow 12-foot stud height using the table. When stud height is greater than 12 feet, IRC Table R602.3.1 may be used if the limitations in the footnotes are met. These limitations restrict front-to-back movement of the stud wall due to wind loads pressing against the wall, similar to the sail on a ship.

Examples of taller stud height include balloon-framed gable end walls and two-story entrance foyer walls. As long as the adjacent story heights do not exceed the permitted limits, wall elements are permitted to meet the more liberal allowable lengths as provided for in IRC Table R602.3.1. When studs do not meet the requirements of either IRC Table R602.3(5) or Table R602.3.1, engineering is necessary to check stud movement front-to-back. As long as the wall bracing requirements are met, engineering is not necessary to check stud movement side-to-side.

Structures built to the provisions of the IRC may have sections of walls that exceed the prescribed wall heights of IRC Section R301.3, as long as the wall sections occur between qualified bracing units (20-foot spacing measured between adjacent edges) or at gable ends.

R302

R302.6 Dwelling/garage fire separation. The garage shall be separated as required by Table R302.6. Openings in garage walls shall comply with Section R302.5. This provision does not apply to garage walls that are perpendicular to the adjacent *dwelling unit* wall.

This section of the IRC is referenced in IRC Section R602.10.4.3, which exempts specified bracing methods from the requirement for gypsum wall board interior finish because the methods were developed to meet the structural/bracing requirements of the IRC without an interior gypsum board finish. These exemptions are appropriate, provided the dwelling/garage fire separation provision does not otherwise require the interior gypsum finish. The garage fire separation provisions, which require gypsum wall board between the garage and living spaces of the structure, take precedence over IRC Section R602.10.4.3 when applicable.

R403

R403.1 General. All exterior walls shall be supported on continuous solid or fully grouted masonry or concrete footings, crushed stone footings, wood foundations, or other *approved* structural systems which shall be of sufficient design to accommodate all loads according to Section R301 and to transmit the resulting loads to the soil within the limitations as determined from the character of the soil. Footings shall be supported on undisturbed natural soils or engineered fill. Concrete footings shall be designed and constructed in accordance with the provisions of Section R403 or in accordance with ACI 332.

IRC Section R403.1 is referenced in IRC Section R602.10.9, requiring masonry stem walls longer than 48 inches to be designed in accordance with IRC Section R403.1. This section requires all exterior walls (braced wall lines) to be supported...

...on continuous solid or fully grouted masonry or concrete footings, crushed stone footings, wood foundations, or other approved structural systems...

R403.1.2 Continuous footing in Seismic Design Categories D_0, D_1 and D_2. The *braced wall panels* at exterior walls of buildings located in Seismic Design Categories D_0, D_1 and D_2 shall be supported by continuous footings. All required interior *braced wall panels* in buildings with plan dimensions greater than 50 feet (15 240 mm) shall also be supported by continuous footings.

Subsequent to IRC Section R403.1, IRC Section R403.1.2 includes additional provisions for continuous footings in high seismic areas (Seismic Design Categories D_0, D_1 and D_2). In addition to the requirement for continuous foundations for braced wall panels on all exterior walls is an additional requirement for braced walls on the interior of the structure. When the building has a plan dimension greater than 50 feet, all interior braced wall panels must also be supported by continuous footings.

R403.1.4.2 Seismic conditions. In Seismic Design Categories D_0, D_1 and D_2, interior footings supporting bearing or bracing walls and cast monolithically with a slab on grade shall extend to a depth of not less than 12 inches (305 mm) below the top of the slab.

While not referenced in the IRC Sections R602.10-R602.12 bracing provisions, the above requirement for the use of a thickened, monolithically-cast slab at least 12-inches-thick under an interior braced wall line is a code requirement.

R403.1.6 Foundation anchorage. Sill plates and walls supported directly on continuous foundations shall be anchored to the foundation in accordance with this section.

Wood sole plates at all exterior walls on monolithic slabs, wood sole plates of *braced wall panels* at building interiors on monolithic slabs and all wood sill plates shall be anchored to the foundation with anchor bolts spaced a maximum of 6 feet (1829 mm) on center. Bolts shall be at least 1/2 inch (12.7 mm) in diameter and shall extend a minimum of 7 inches (178 mm) into concrete or grouted cells of concrete masonry units. A nut and washer shall be tightened on each anchor bolt. There shall be a minimum of two bolts per plate section with one bolt located not more than 12 inches (305 mm) or less than seven bolt diameters from each end of the plate section. Interior bearing wall sole plates on monolithic slab foundation that are not part of a *braced wall panel* shall be positively anchored with *approved* fasteners. Sill plates and sole plates shall be protected against decay and termites where required by Sections R317 and R318. Cold-formed steel framing systems shall be fastened to wood sill plates or anchored directly to the foundation as required in Section R505.3.1 or R603.3.1.

Exceptions:

1. Foundation anchorage, spaced as required to provide equivalent anchorage to 1/2-inch-diameter (12.7 mm) anchor bolts.

2. Walls 24 inches (610 mm) total length or shorter connecting offset *braced wall panels* shall be anchored to the foundation with a minimum of one anchor bolt located in the center third of the plate section and shall be attached to adjacent *braced wall panels* at corners as shown in item 8 of Table R602.3(1).

3. Connection of walls 12 inches (305 mm) total length or shorter connecting offset *braced wall panels* to the foundation without anchor bolts shall be permitted. The wall shall be attached to adjacent *braced wall panels* at corners as shown in item 8 of Table R602.3(1).

This section is referenced in IRC Sections R602.10.8, R602.11 and R602.11.2. All references require the wall anchorage for braced wall panels to be in accordance with IRC Section R403.1.6. The provisions of this section are for both interior and exterior braced wall lines and are self-explanatory. The reference to Item 8 of IRC Table R602.3(1) ensures that the connection of intersecting corners meets the new nailing requirement of 16d (3-1/2" x 0.135") at 12 inches on center.

R403.1.6.1 Foundation anchorage in Seismic Design Categories C, D_0, D_1 and D_2.

In addition to the requirements of Section R403.1.6, the following requirements shall apply to wood light-frame structures in Seismic Design Categories D_0, D_1 and D_2 and wood light-frame townhouses in Seismic Design Category C.

1. Plate washers conforming to Section R602.11.1 shall be provided for all anchor bolts over the full length of required *braced wall lines* except where *approved* anchor straps are used. Properly sized cut washers shall be permitted for anchor bolts in wall lines not containing *braced wall panels*.

2. Interior braced wall plates shall have anchor bolts spaced at not more than 6 feet (1829 mm) on center and located within 12 inches (305 mm) of the ends of each plate section when supported on a continuous foundation.

3. Interior bearing wall sole plates shall have anchor bolts spaced at not more than 6 feet (1829 mm) on center and located within 12 inches (305 mm) of the ends of each plate section when supported on a continuous foundation.

4. The maximum anchor bolt spacing shall be 4 feet (1219 mm) for buildings over two stories in height.

5. Stepped cripple walls shall conform to Section R602.11.2.

6. Where continuous wood foundations in accordance with Section R404.2 are used, the force transfer shall have a capacity equal to or greater than the connections required by Section R602.11.1 or the *braced wall panel* shall be connected to the wood foundations in accordance with the *braced wall panel*-to-floor fastening requirements of Table R602.3(1).

In addition to the foundation anchorage provisions of IRC Section R403.1.6 (referenced in IRC Sections R602.10.8, R602.11 and R602.11.2) are the Seismic Design Category specific requirements for SDCs C (townhouses only), D_0, D_1 and D_2. These provisions address exterior braced wall lines as well as braced wall lines on the interior of the structure.

R404

R404.1.9.3 Masonry piers supporting braced wall panels. Masonry piers supporting *braced wall panels* shall be designed in accordance with accepted engineering practice.

While not referenced in the IRC Sections R602.10-R602.12 bracing provisions, this section permits a house braced in accordance with IRC Section R602.10 to be supported on a pier-and-beam (or "raised floor") system consisting of isolated masonry piers supporting wood framing, provided the isolated masonry piers and their foundations are engineered. This section is also the default requirement when the prescriptive provisions of IRC Section R602.10.9 (masonry stem walls not longer than 48 inches) cannot be met.

R502

R502.2.1 Framing at *braced wall lines*. A load path for lateral forces shall be provided between floor framing and *braced wall panels* located above or below a floor, as specified in Section R602.10.8.

IRC Section R502.2.1, which is located within the floor framing provisions of the IRC, addresses the framing requirements above and under braced wall lines necessary to meet the load path requirements of the code. This section directs the user to the bracing provisions of IRC Section R602.10.8 *Braced wall panel connections*.

R502.3.3 Floor cantilevers. Floor cantilever spans shall not exceed the nominal depth of the wood floor joist. Floor cantilevers constructed in accordance with Table R502.3.3(1) shall be permitted when supporting a light-frame bearing wall and roof only. Floor cantilevers supporting an exterior balcony are permitted to be constructed in accordance with Table R502.3.3(2).

This section is referenced in IRC Section R602.10.9, Item 1 as the only cantilever that may be used to support a braced wall panel. Note that in moderate to high seismic areas, SDC C and greater, the irregularity requirements in IRC Section R301.2.2.2.5, Items 1 and 2 limit the use of cantilevers.

R602

R602.3.5 *Braced wall panel* uplift load path. *Braced wall panels* located at exterior walls that support roof rafters or trusses (including stories below top *story*) shall have the framing members connected in accordance with one of the following:

1. Fastening in accordance with Table R602.3(1) where:

   1.1. The basic wind speed does not exceed 90 mph (40 m/s), the wind exposure category is B, the roof pitch is 5:12 or greater, and the roof span is 32 feet (9754 mm) or less, or

1.2. The net uplift value at the top of a wall does not exceed 100 plf. The net uplift value shall be determined in accordance with Section R802.11 and shall be permitted to be reduced by 60 plf (86 N/mm) for each full wall above.

2. Where the net uplift value at the top of a wall exceeds 100 plf (146 N/mm), installing *approved* uplift framing connectors to provide a continuous load path from the top of the wall to the foundation or to a point where the uplift force is 100 plf (146 N/mm) or less. The net uplift value shall be as determined in Item 1.2 above.

3. Wall sheathing and fasteners designed in accordance with accepted engineering practice to resist combined uplift and shear forces.

The uplift load path requirements of IRC Section R602.3.5 are referenced in IRC Section R602.10.2.1 as the attachment requirements necessary for panels to be considered as bracing.

R602.9 Cripple Walls. Foundation cripple walls shall be framed of studs not smaller than the studding above. When exceeding 4 feet (1219 mm) in height, such walls shall be framed of studs having the size required for an additional *story.*

Cripple walls with a stud height less than 14 inches (356 mm) shall be continuously sheathed on one side with wood structural panels fastened to both the top and bottom plates in accordance with Table R602.3(1) or the cripple walls shall be constructed of solid blocking.

All cripple walls shall be supported on continuous foundations.

This section is referenced in IRC Section R602.10.11 and provides some information that is not included in the bracing provisions: the important requirement that cripple walls less than 14 inches high be fully sheathed with wood structural panels on one side, fastened in accordance with IRC Table R602.3(1), Item 32 or solidly blocked. Also not included in the bracing provisions are the stud height requirements that require the cripple wall to be designated as a story.

R613

R613.5.3 Wall bracing. SIP walls shall be braced in accordance with Section R602.10. SIP walls shall be considered continuous wood structural panel sheathing for purposes of computing required bracing. SIP walls shall meet the requirements of Section R602.10.4.2 except that SIPs corners shall be fabricated as shown in Figure R613.9. When SIP walls are used for wall bracing, the SIP bottom plate shall be attached to wood framing below in accordance with Table R602.3(1).

The above provision recognizes the SIP (Structural Insulated Panel) panels specified in IRC Section R613 as meeting the bracing requirements for Method CS-WSP.

R703

R703.7 Stone and masonry veneer, general. Stone and masonry veneer shall be installed in accordance with this chapter, Table R703.4 and Figure R703.7. These veneers installed over a backing of wood or cold-formed steel shall be limited to the first *story* above-grade plane and shall not exceed 5 inches (127 mm) in thickness. See Section R602.10 for wall bracing requirements for masonry veneer for wood-framed construction ...

This provision is referenced in IRC Sections R602.10.3 and R603.10.6.5 and provides the other-than-bracing installation and attachment requirements for stone or masonry veneer.

R802

R802.8 Lateral support. Roof framing members and ceiling joists having a depth-to-thickness ratio exceeding 5 to 1 based on nominal dimensions shall be provided with lateral support at points of bearing to prevent rotation. For roof rafters with ceiling joists attached per Table R602.3(1), the depth-to-thickness ratio for the total assembly shall be determined using the combined thickness of the rafter plus the attached ceiling joist.

> **Exception:** Roof trusses shall be braced in accordance with Section R802.10.3.

IRC Section R802.8 is referenced in IRC Section R602.10.8.2 as a requirement for rafter and ceiling joist bracing. It is important to note that the bracing discussed in IRC Section 802.8 is not wall bracing; rather, it is lateral bracing made up of relatively small cross-section lumber members used to stabilize the rafters and ceiling joists during and after erection.

R802.10.3 Bracing. Trusses shall be braced to prevent rotation and provide lateral stability in accordance with the requirements specified in the *construction documents* for the building and on the individual truss design drawings. In the absence of specific bracing requirements, trusses shall be braced in accordance with accepted industry practice such as the *SBCA Building Components Safety Information (BCSI) Guide to Good Practice for Handling, Installation & Bracing of Metal Plate Connected Wood Trusses.*

IRC Section R802.10.3 is referenced in IRC Section R602.10.8.2 as a requirement for trusses installed over the top of braced wall panels. It is important to note that the bracing discussed in IRC Section 802.10.3 is not wall bracing; rather, it is truss bracing that is made up of relatively small cross-section lumber members used to stabilize the truss members during and after erection.

R802.11 Roof tie-down.

R802.11.1 Uplift resistance. Roof assemblies shall have uplift resistance in accordance with Sections R802.11.1.2 and R802.11.1.3.

Where the uplift force does not exceed 200 pounds, rafters and trusses spaced not more than 24 inches (610 mm) on center shall be permitted to be attached to their supporting wall assemblies in accordance with Table R602.3(1).

Where the basic wind speed does not exceed 90 mph, the wind exposure category is B, the roof pitch is 5:12 or greater, and the roof span is 32 feet (9754 mm) or less, rafters and trusses spaced not more than 24 inches (610 mm) on center shall be permitted to be attached to their supporting wall assemblies in accordance with Table R602.3(1).

R802.11.1.2 Truss uplift resistance. Trusses shall be attached to supporting wall assemblies by connections capable of resisting uplift forces as specified on the truss design drawings. Uplift forces shall be permitted to be determined as specified by Table R802.11, if applicable, or as determined by accepted engineering practice.

R802.11.1.3 Rafter uplift resistance. Individual rafters shall be attached to supporting wall assemblies by connections capable of resisting uplift forces as determined by Table R802.11 or as determined by accepted engineering practice. Connections for beams used in a roof system shall be designed in accordance with accepted engineering practice.

IRC Section R602.10.2.1 contains a requirement for wall panels to be considered as braced wall panels only when uplift loads are resisted in accordance with IRC Section R602.3.5. IRC Section R602.3.5 provides for roof uplift connectors to be attached to braced wall panels, where roof uplift loads exceed the capacity of standard nailed connections as provided in IRC Table R602.3(1). Taken together, it may appear that uplift loads only have to be resisted at braced wall panels. As braced wall panels can be spaced 20 feet apart, it begs the question about those uplift loads that fall between braced wall panels. The "answer" is in IRC Section R802.11, provided above. While not referenced in the bracing provisions, this information is essential to understanding this very important load path. It is clear from the above provisions that all vertical loads from roof framing must be carried down to their "supporting wall assemblies." The load path for all forces must be complete from the applied load into grade below.

R806.1 Ventilation required. Enclosed *attics* and enclosed rafter spaces formed where ceilings are applied directly to the underside of roof rafters shall have cross ventilation for each separate space by ventilation openings protected against the entrance of rain or snow. Ventilation openings shall have a least dimension of 1/16 inch (1.6 mm) minimum and 1/4 inch (6.4 mm) maximum. Ventilation openings having a least dimension larger than 1/4 inch (6.4 mm) shall be provided with corrosion-resistant wire cloth screening, hardware cloth, or similar material with openings having a least dimension of 1/16 inch (1.6 mm) minimum and 1/4 inch (6.4 mm) maximum...

This section is referenced in IRC Section R602.10.8.2 as a reminder that with all of the blocking and requisite lateral support at the ends of trusses and rafter systems, ventilation is also a requirement. The final solution for the blocking scheme selected shall include provisions for ventilation as well as the structural requirements for blocking.

3 2012 IRC BRACING PROVISIONS

This chapter of A *Guide to the 2012 IRC Wood Wall Bracing Provisions* reproduces the 2012 IRC bracing sections (IRC Chapter 6, Sections R602.10-R602.12) in full. Each excerpted section of the code is followed by discussion and, in many cases, illustrations, tables or examples to help better clarify the code. For quick reference, the IRC Section addressed on a given page is printed on the top-outside corner of that page.

There are numerous references in IRC Sections R602.10-R602.12 bracing provisions to other locations in the Residential Building Code. In addition, many important bracing-related provisions are scattered throughout the code, outside of this bracing section, and are easily missed by the designer when their attention is focused on IRC Chapter 6. To permit the stand-alone use of this guide, these sections have been compiled in **CHAPTER 2** of this guide.

Note the inline format used to reference chapters, figures and tables that appear in this guide, as opposed to specific references to IRC sections, figures and tables: those that appear in this guide appear in all caps and are bold and italicized. For example, **FIGURE 3.2** is a reference to the second figure in this chapter. **TABLE 2.4** is a reference to the fourth table in **CHAPTER 2**.

CHAPTER 3

Summary

Also note that IRC code excerpts are printed in orange text, and key bracing-related terms, such as *braced wall panel* and *braced wall line*, are italicized, just as they are in the text of the IRC. The code-specific definitions for these italicized terms are provided in **CHAPTER 2**, beginning on page 29 of this guide.

While this chapter and the discussion of the 2012 IRC bracing provisions is the heart of this guide, bracing background information and an explanation of a number of significant related subjects is provided in **CHAPTER 1**, including bracing theory, wind and seismic loads, shear walls and diaphragms, bracing history and more. The authors of this guide believe that the better the code is understood, the more likely it is to be correctly applied and enforced, and we encourage the reader to review the first chapter for a more thorough understanding of the concept of bracing and why it is required.

See **APPENDIX D** for a table that compares the location of wall bracing information in the 2006, 2009 and 2012 editions of the IRC.

R602.10 Wall bracing

R602.10 Wall Bracing. Buildings shall be braced in accordance with this section or, when applicable, Section R602.12. Where a building, or portion thereof, does not comply with one or more of the bracing requirements in this section, those portions shall be designed and constructed in accordance with Section R301.1.

When addressing wall bracing, the IRC uses the terms *braced wall panel, braced wall panel spacing, braced wall line* and *braced wall line spacing*. These terms are defined in Section R202 of the 2012 IRC and are reproduced in **CHAPTER 2** of this guide. It is important to understand what each of these terms means in the context of the code in order to properly apply the IRC bracing requirements. **FIGURE 3.1** shows how these terms relate to an actual structure.

FIGURE 3.1

Braced wall panels, braced wall panel spacing, braced wall lines and braced wall line spacing

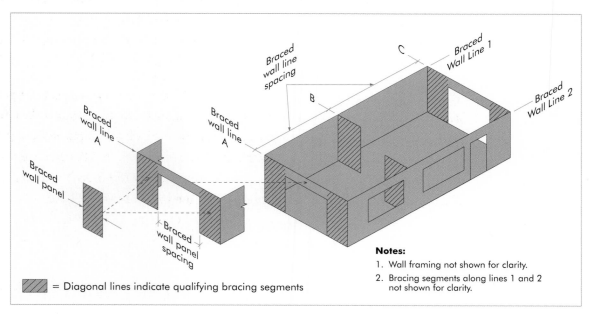

Notes:
1. Wall framing not shown for clarity.
2. Bracing segments along lines 1 and 2 not shown for clarity.

= Diagonal lines indicate qualifying bracing segments

R602.10.1 Braced wall lines

R602.10.1 *Braced wall lines.* For the purpose of determining the amount and location of bracing required in each story level of a building, *braced wall lines* shall be designated as straight lines in the building plan placed in accordance with this section.

FIGURE 3.1 shows two braced wall lines (1 and 2) in the longitudinal direction and three braced wall lines (A, B and C) in the transverse direction. Each wall line is made up of a number of braced wall panels. Not every braced wall line, interior or exterior, has to be continuous, as shown in braced wall line B. Furthermore, the code permits offsets of up to 4 feet (IRC Section R602.10.1.2). If sections of a wall line are offset by 4 feet or less, they may be assumed to act in combination to resist lateral loads. The resulting braced wall line, if it doesn't happen to fall over an actual wall line, is often called an effective (or imaginary) braced wall line. If the sections are farther than 4 feet from the braced wall line, they must be considered as separate braced wall lines.

Braced wall lines are not always exterior walls, as braced wall line B in **FIGURE 3.1** illustrates. A braced wall line in the interior of the structure may be required – depending on the size of the house, the wind speed, or Seismic Design Category (SDC) – to supplement the braced wall lines on the exterior walls. Braced wall lines located in the interior of a structure have requirements similar to exterior wall lines in terms of bracing length, panel location, wall line offsets and attachments. The foundation requirements and other attachment requirements are covered in IRC Section R403.1 (**CHAPTER 2** of this guide) and IRC Sections R602.10.8-R602.10.11 (discussed later in this chapter).

As in the 2009 IRC, a major challenge in working with braced wall lines occurs when a building is not a simple rectangle. In such cases, it can be difficult to determine the beginning and end points of braced wall lines, which can make measuring the braced wall line length problematic.

R602.10.1.1 Length of a *braced wall line.* The length of a *braced wall line* shall be the distance between its ends. The end of a *braced wall line* shall be the intersection with a perpendicular *braced wall line*, an angled *braced wall line* as permitted in Section R602.10.1.4 or an exterior wall as shown in Figure R602.10.1.1.

While this description of braced wall line length may seem simplistic, its significance becomes apparent as house plans deviate from simple rectangles. With permitted braced wall line offsets, enclosed porches, wall bump-outs, etc., it can be difficult for all parties to agree on where the beginning and end points for a given braced wall line are. This can become increasingly confusing when incorporating the new effective (imaginary) braced wall lines, as permitted in IRC Figure R602.10.1.1. These provisions are illustrated in **FIGURE 3.2**.

R602.10.1.2 Offsets along a *braced wall line*. All exterior walls parallel to a *braced wall line* shall be offset not more than 4 feet (1219 mm) from the designated *braced wall line* location as shown Figure R602.10.1.1. Interior walls used as bracing shall be offset not more than 4 feet (1219 mm) from a *braced wall line* through the interior of the building as shown in Figure R602.10.1.1.

FIGURE 3.2

Offsets along a braced wall line and effective (imaginary) braced wall lines (BWL)

IRC Figure R602.10.1.1

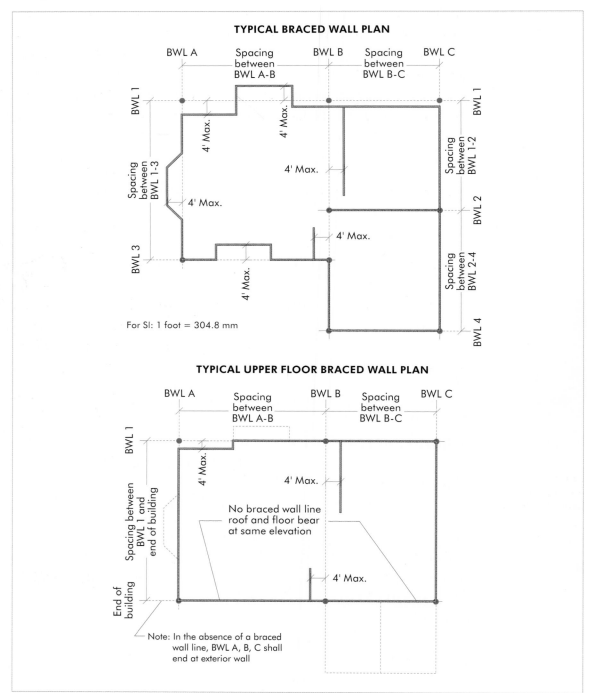

FIGURE R602.10.1.1
BRACED WALL LINES

Effective (imaginary) braced wall lines

The concept of the effective – or "imaginary" – braced wall line is based on the principle that while braced wall panels are located no more than 4 feet from a designated braced wall line, it is not necessary to have a bracing panel on the designated braced wall line. The designated braced wall line does not have to coincide with an actual wall line at all. A line of lateral resistance is known to exist between panels grouped together in close proximity, as shown on the left side of **FIGURE 3.3**. The location of the designated effective wall line is used for measuring the braced wall line spacing required for use of IRC Tables R602.10.3(1) **(TABLE 3.3)** and R602.10.3(3) **(TABLE 3.5)**. In addition, the lengths of the braced wall panels on the various wall line sections added together must be equal to or greater than the length of bracing required by IRC Tables R602.10.3(1) and R602.10.3(3), after adjustment by Tables R602.10.3(2) **(TABLE 3.4)** and R602.10.3(4) **(TABLE 3.6)**, respectively.

Note that the provisions for effective braced wall lines are not limited to exterior walls. In the 2012 IRC, there are few differences between the requirements for interior and exterior braced wall lines.

When the concept was debated by the ICC Ad Hoc Wall Bracing Committee, there was concern that this method would be used to reduce the distance between braced wall lines by arbitrarily moving the effective braced wall line inward from one or both exterior wall lines up to 4 feet. This is not the intent of the provision. The provision was placed in the code to permit a closely spaced grouping of wall segments to be counted as a single braced wall line to accommodate popular architectural variations in exterior wall lines. It is not appropriate to use effective braced wall lines solely as a tool to reduce the distance between braced wall lines.

The IRC Section R602.10.1.2 offset rules discussed previously apply to the effective braced wall line location. See **FIGURE 3.3**.

FIGURE 3.3

Effective (imaginary) braced wall line

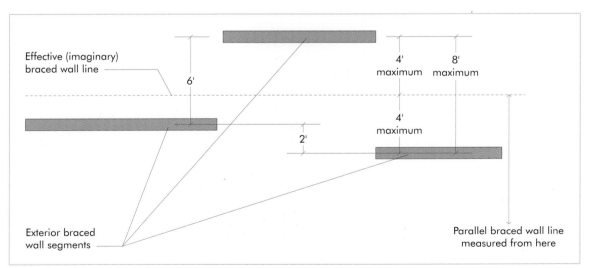

Effective (imaginary) braced wall line

6'

4' maximum   8' maximum

4' maximum

2'

Exterior braced wall segments

Parallel braced wall line measured from here

R602.10.1.3 Spacing of *braced wall lines*. The spacing between parallel *braced wall lines* shall be in accordance with Table R602.10.1.3. Intermediate *braced wall lines* through the interior of the building shall be permitted.

As shown in **FIGURE 3.1**, braced wall line spacing is the distance between parallel braced wall lines. New to the 2012 IRC, the braced wall line maximum spacing requirements are summarized in IRC Table R603.10.1.3, reproduced in **TABLE 3.1**. The length required for wind bracing is based on the braced wall line spacing and fixed at a maximum of 60 feet, but spacing for seismic bracing is fixed at 25 foot intervals with adjustments permitted.

TABLE 3.1

Braced wall line spacing for various conditions

IRC Table R602.10.1.3

TABLE R602.10.1.3
BRACED WALL LINE SPACING

Application	Condition	Building Type	Braced Wall Line Spacing Criteria	
			Maximum Spacing	Exception to Maximum Spacing
Wind bracing	85 mph to < 110 mph	Detached, townhouse	60 feet	None
Seismic bracing	SDC A – C	Detached	Use wind bracing	
	SDC A – B	Townhouse	Use wind bracing	
	SDC C	Townhouse	35 feet	Up to 50 feet when length of required bracing per Table R602.10.3(3) is adjusted in accordance with Table R602.10.3(4).
	SDC D_0, D_1, D_2	Detached, townhouses, one- and two-story only	25 feet	Up to 35 feet to allow for a single room not to exceed 900 square feet. Spacing of all other braced wall lines shall not exceed 25 feet.
	SDC D_0, D_1, D_2	Detached, townhouse	25 feet	Up to 35 feet when length of required bracing per Table R602.10.3(3) is adjusted in accordance with Table R602.10.3(4).

For SI: 1 foot = 304.8 mm, 1 square foot = 0.0929 m², 1 mile per hour = 0.447 m/s.

The 2012 IRC eliminates the need for a fixed braced wall line spacing limitation in areas of the country where the amount of bracing required for wind exceeds the amount of bracing required for seismic. The wind bracing table (IRC Table R602.10.3(1)) provides the required amount of bracing as a function of braced wall line spacing. The table recognizes braced wall line spacings up to 60 feet.

The seismic bracing table (IRC Table R602.10.3(3)) is presented in a slightly different format. Braced wall line spacing is limited to 25 feet (increasable to 35 feet). The table provides the length of bracing required based on the length of the braced wall line. This is reasonable, as the force on the structure is proportional to the mass (length) of the building in the direction of the seismic force.

Note that the seismic bracing adjustments for SDC D_0, D_1 and D_2 include two conditions under which the distance between braced wall lines can be increased above 25 feet:

- The first condition is for detached one- and two-family dwellings and townhouses for one- and two-story applications only. This provision permits the distance between braced wall lines to be increased to 35 feet in each unit to accommodate a single 900 square foot room, providing all other parallel braced wall lines spacings are limited to a maximum of 25 feet.

- The second is for detached one- and two-family dwellings and townhouses for up to three-story applications and permits an increase in braced wall line spacing up to 35 feet, provided the required length of the seismic braced panels in the braced wall lines are increased in accordance with IRC Table R602.10.3(4) (**TABLE 3.6**). Note that the braced wall lines impacted by this increase are the braced wall lines between which the increased braced wall line spacing is measured.

R602.10.1.4 Angled walls. Any portion of a wall along a *braced wall line* shall be permitted to angle out of plane for a maximum diagonal length of 8 feet (2438 mm). Where the angled wall occurs at a corner, the length of the *braced wall line* shall be measured from the projected corner as shown in Figure R602.10.1.4. Where the diagonal length is greater than 8 feet (2438 mm), it shall be considered a separate *braced wall line* and shall be braced in accordance with Section R602.10.1.

FIGURE 3.4

Angled walls in braced wall lines

IRC Figure R602.10.1.4

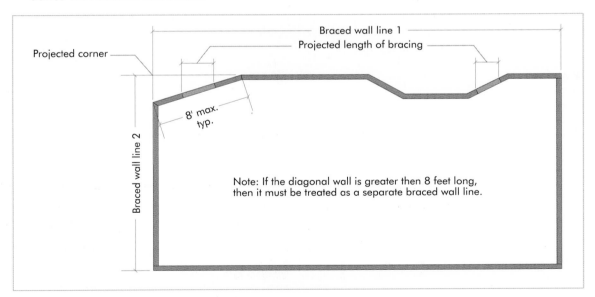

**FIGURE R602.10.1.4
ANGLED WALLS**

The section, previously called angled corners, has been renamed angled walls and modified to focus on wall length and the angle of the wall from the braced wall line being examined. As in the 2009 IRC, angled wall lines may be counted as part of a braced wall line when

8 feet (2438 mm) long or less. In the 2012 edition, the projected length of the braced wall line should be added to the total wall line length. **TABLE 3.2** provides the projected braced wall line length to add to the braced wall line length for 4, 6 and 8-foot (1219, 1829, and 2438 mm) long angled wall lines. If an angled wall line is longer than 8 feet (2438 mm), it should be considered a separate braced wall line. See IRC Figure R602.10.1.4 (**FIGURE 3.4**) for the projected angled wall length.

TABLE 3.2

Projected braced wall line (BWL) length contributed by the angled wall

Angle from BWL (degrees)	Projected BWL Length from Angled Wall Line (ft)		
	4	6	8
15	3.9	5.8	7.8
30	3.5	5.2	7.0
45	2.9	4.3	5.7

Note that the provision does not permit "double dipping"; you cannot count the bracing on an angled corner towards the total bracing length required for both braced wall lines connected to the corner.

What if the angled corner contains the entryway of the house and there is not sufficient space for bracing panels? The length of the angled entryway still counts towards the length of the wall line, and the 10 foot rule (IRC Section R602.10.2.2) also applies. As the length of the angled corner shown in **FIGURE 3.5** is less than or equal to 10 feet bracing panels are not required in the angled section, provided that the other requirements of IRC Section R602.10.1.4 are met.

FIGURE 3.5

Insufficient room in angled portion of wall to permit bracing

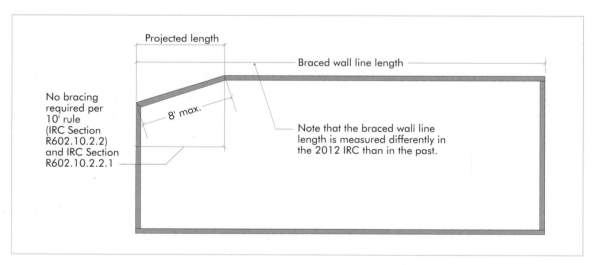

What happens if the angled wall segment is greater than 8 feet? Whenever the angled section of the wall is greater than 8 feet, the angled corner provision of IRC Section R602.10.1.4 no longer applies and the angled section is considered its own wall line that must be braced accordingly, as shown in **FIGURE 3.6**. A reasonable solution is to run a perpendicular line from the center of the angled wall until it intersects a parallel braced wall line and use that distance as the braced wall line spacing. Note that the required amount of bracing for the angled corner must be added to the total required amount of bracing for the parallel wall intersected by the perpendicular line.

FIGURE 3.6

Angled portion of wall greater than 8 feet

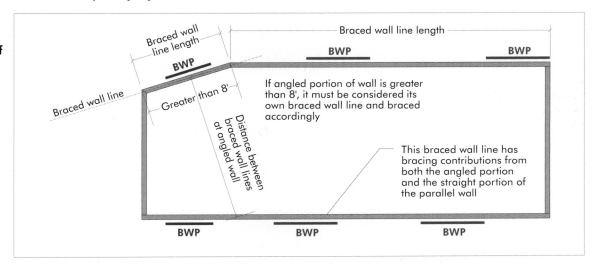

R602.10.2 Braced wall panels

R602.10.2 Braced wall panels. *Braced wall panels shall be full-height sections of wall that shall have no vertical or horizontal offsets. Braced wall panels shall be constructed and placed along a braced wall line in accordance with this section and the bracing methods specified in Section R602.10.4.*

Put simply, the term "braced wall panel" describes a code-qualified bracing element. The origin of the name "panel" most likely lies in the fact that most of the recognized methods of bracing use panel-type products; however, the term is somewhat of a misnomer. "Panel" can actually be used to describe a wall "section," "segment," or "unit." Even let-in bracing is often referred to as a bracing panel. As such, the terms braced wall panel, braced wall section, braced wall segment and bracing unit are often used interchangeably.

Each braced wall panel must extend the full height of the wall – from the bottom plate to the top of the double top plates of the wall. A "panel" may be constructed from more than one piece of sheathing. For example, a 6-foot long braced wall panel may be constructed by joining a 4-foot long panel with a 2-foot long panel. Any combination of full-width panels and narrow-width panels necessary to make up the length of the "panel" is usually acceptable.

Braced wall panels have a height and a length dimension. The permitted height of a braced wall panel ranges from 8 to 10 feet. For some bracing methods, the panel height is limited to 10 feet. The length dimension is measured parallel to the length of the wall. For example, the length of a 4x8 oriented strand board (OSB) bracing panel placed with the 8-foot dimension in the up-and-down direction is 4 feet. Knowing the length of a braced wall panel is important because the various bracing methods have different required minimum lengths. Also, the combined length of individual braced wall panels must total or exceed a required minimum length for a specific braced wall line. Note that a braced wall panel can include blocked horizontal joints. For example a 12-foot-high braced wall panel can be made up of an 8-foot-high piece with a 4-foot-high piece over it, as long as the adjoining panel edges occur over and are attached to common framing or blocking.

What is the required minimum length of a braced wall panel? It varies from 16 inches (Method PFH (portal frame with hold downs) or Method CS-PF (continuously sheathed portal frame)) in an 8-foot wall to 10 feet (Method LIB (let-in bracing)) at a 45 degree slope in a 10-foot high wall. The length depends on the bracing method used and the height of the wall. In addition to a number of specific narrow-width braced wall panels, in the 2012 IRC, traditional 4-foot braced wall panels are permitted to be used in lengths of less than 4 feet, provided certain reductions are taken into account when computing the amount of bracing necessary for the specific braced wall line in question. (See IRC Table R602.10.5.2, reproduced in **TABLE 3.29**.)

> **R602.10.2.1 Braced wall panel uplift load path.** The bracing lengths in Table R602.10.3(1) apply only when uplift loads are resisted in accordance with Section R602.3.5.

While the wording of this section is awkward, the bracing requirements of IRC Section R602.10.3 are always required. Not providing uplift continuity cannot be used as an excuse to ignore the wind bracing requirements. The intent of this section is to require uplift continuity at all bracing panel locations as a minimum. IRC Section R802.11 provides the generic roof tie-down requirements for all exterior wall locations. Note that the majority of information referenced in IRC Section R602.3.5 is not new to the 2012 IRC; it was formerly located in the actual bracing provisions (2009 IRC Section R602.10.1.2.1). However, for 2012 these provisions have been moved to the general design and construction section and modified to permit uplift connectors to be used to reduce net uplift to 100 plf or less. This provision is based on the assumption that the uplift connectors are used in addition to the normal nailed connection (IRC Table R602.3(1), Item 5).

A common question is how to interpret this provision for interior braced wall lines? The provisions of IRC Section R802.10 provide uplift capacity for trusses and roof rafters. Traditionally, both of these roof systems are attached to exterior wall lines, typically where braced wall lines occur. The provision is meant to ensure a proper load path at these locations. As these systems normally do not bear on interior braced wall lines, their uplift requirement at that point is zero. As such, these connections meet the letter of IRC Section R602.10.2.1 provisions in most cases. In the case of center-supported trusses or half trusses, the truss attachment documents will require attachment at these interior wall locations. If the interior walls are braced, they too meet the requirements of this section.

IRC Section R602.3.5 is reproduced in **CHAPTER 2** of this guide.

> **R602.10.2.2 Locations of braced wall panels.** A braced wall panel shall begin within 10 feet (3810 mm) from each end of a braced wall line as determined in Section R602.10.1.1. The distance between adjacent edges of braced wall panels along a braced wall line shall be no greater than 20 feet (6096 mm) as shown in Figure R602.10.2.2.

In the 2009 IRC the maximum end-distance to the first intermittent braced wall panel was 12.5 feet (8 feet for high seismic). In addition, this was the total end-distance that could be used for both ends of a single braced wall line. For example, if the first braced wall panel at one end was displaced from that end by 12.5 feet, the first braced wall panel at the opposite end could not be displaced from the corner. However, the total end-distance could be split between the two ends. If the first braced wall panel at one end was displaced 6 feet, the first braced wall panel at the opposite end could be displaced up to 6-1/2 feet.

The problem that the total end-distance provision in the 2009 IRC intended to correct was the potential negative impact of using the maximum end-distance provision at both ends of a single braced wall line for the express purpose of reducing the required amount of bracing in a braced wall line.

The addition of Section R602.10.2.3 in the 2012 IRC expanded the provisions for the minimum number of braced wall panels in a given braced wall line and made the total end-distance provisions that appeared in the 2009 IRC unnecessary. This is discussed in more detail in the IRC Section R602.10.2.3 discussion.

IRC Section R602.10.2.2 also reduces the 12.5 foot maximum end-distance to 10 feet. As the previous 12.5 foot limit was essentially arbitrary, changing it to 10 feet is slightly more conservative but easier to use and enforce.

The other change seen in IRC Section R602.10.2.2 for 2012 is the provision for spacing between braced wall panels in a braced wall line. Formerly, the requirement was a maximum separation of 25 feet measured between the centers of the braced wall panels. The problem with this requirement was that, while it worked well for braced wall panels exactly 48 inches long , it actually required more and more bracing as the segments increased in length. As can be seen in **FIGURE 3.7**, if two adjacent segments were each 25-feet long, then no distance between was permitted.

FIGURE 3.7

Distance between braced wall panels – long segment lengths (pre-2012 IRC)

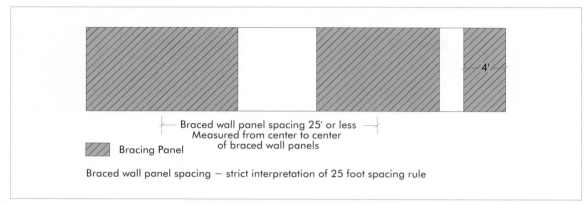

The intent of the code has always been to provide braced wall panels at multiple locations along the braced wall line to provide for a better lateral load path – to better distribute the diaphragm forces into the ground via the braced wall panels. The 25-foot "rule" was developed with discrete 4-foot-long braced wall panels in mind. See **FIGURE 3.8**.

FIGURE 3.8

Distance between braced wall panels - minimum segment lengths (pre-2012 IRC)

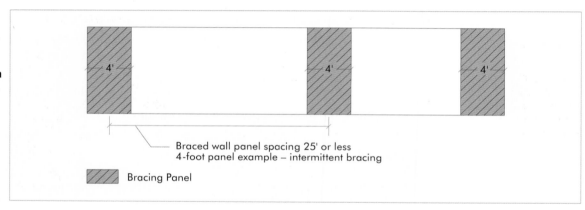

FIGURE 3.9

2012 IRC Distance between braced wall panels - any segment length

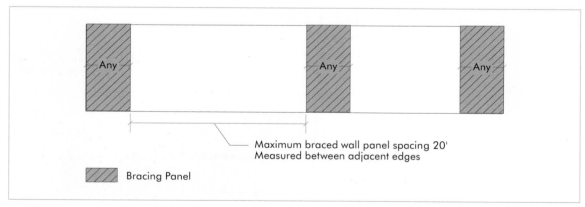

Given the intent, you can see that the resulting "clear" distance between braced wall panels is 21 feet (25 feet - 4 feet / 2 - 4 feet / 2 = 21 feet). In the 2012 IRC, 21 feet was rounded down to 20 feet and the intent of the old provisions was more clearly stated as "The distance between adjacent edges of *braced wall panels...*" See **FIGURE 3.9**.

This new "definition" of spacing between braced wall panels simplifies working with narrow wall and portal frame bracing methods. The "adjacent panel edge" is not dependent on the adjacent braced wall panel or portal frame length. It also facilitates code enforcement as edge-to-edge is very easy to measure.

R602.10.2.2.1 Location of *braced wall panels* in Seismic Design Categories D_0, D_1 and D_2. *Braced wall panels* shall be located at each end of a *braced wall line*.

Exception: *Braced wall panels* constructed of Methods WSP or BV-WSP and continuous sheathing methods as specified in Section R602.10.4 shall be permitted to begin no more than 10 feet (3048 mm) from each end of a *braced wall line* provided each end complies with one of the following.

Modified in 2012, this provision permits the first braced wall panel to be displaced from the corner by 10 feet in SDC D_0, D_1 and D_2, as long as one of the three provisions listed are met at that corner. This makes the permissible displacement identical to that in low seismic areas, as long as the required construction details are provided. See **FIGURE 3.10**.

FIGURE 3.10

For SDC D_0, D_1 and D_2, three options exist for bracing away from corners

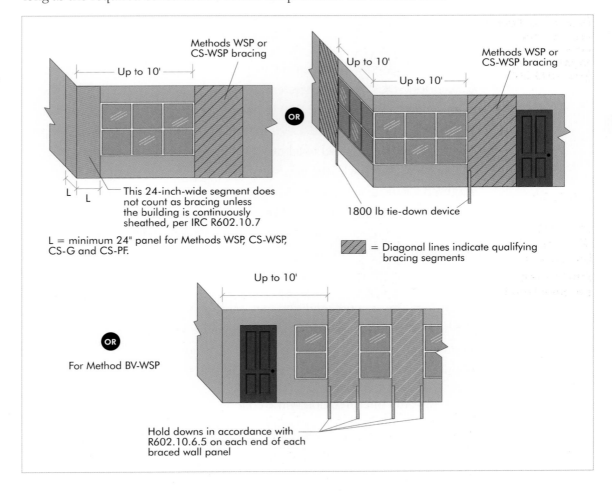

Methods WSP or CS-WSP bracing

Up to 10'

Methods WSP or CS-WSP bracing

Up to 10'

Up to 10'

OR

L   L   This 24-inch-wide segment does not count as bracing unless the building is continuously sheathed, per IRC R602.10.7

L = minimum 24" panel for Methods WSP, CS-WSP, CS-G and CS-PF.

1800 lb tie-down device

= Diagonal lines indicate qualifying bracing segments

Up to 10'

OR

For Method BV-WSP

Hold downs in accordance with R602.10.6.5 on each end of each braced wall panel

1. A minimum 24-inch-wide (610 mm) panel for Methods WSP, ~~BV-WSP~~, CS-WSP, CS-G, and CS-PF, ~~and 32-inch-wide (813 mm) panel for Method CS-SFB~~ is applied to each side of the building corner as shown in Condition 4 of Figure R602.10.7.

New for 2012 is a list of the approved bracing methods that may be used on one or both sides of the corner. Each of these methods will provide the requisite 24 inches of wood structural panel bracing. Two of these methods are portal frames. Previously, it was not clear that other methods besides Method WSP were permitted.

Note that we have taken the liberty to line out the option for "32-inch-wide (813 mm) panel for Method CS-SFB" and "BV-WSP", which were erroneously placed in this first condition. Method CS-SFB is restricted to SDCs less than D_0 by Footnote d to IRC Table R602.10.4. Method BV-WSP requires hold downs at each end of the panel. A 24-inch panel may not be substituted for the hold downs.

2. The end of each *braced wall panel* closest to the end of the *braced wall line* shall have an 1,800 lb (8 kN) hold-down device fastened to the stud at the edge of the *braced wall panel* closest to the corner and to the foundation or framing below as shown in Condition 5 of Figure R602.10.7.

Permitting a 10-foot displacement at the corner of the braced wall line in higher Seismic Design Categories (SDCs) requires greater foundation connection strength on the braced wall panels than can be provided by the 800 lb hold down permitted for wind and less-severe seismic loads. The IRC has required 1,800 lb for these applications since its inception. Note that when the first braced wall panel of a braced wall line is displaced from a corner, the adjacent wall at that corner also lacks the necessary end-restraint; therefore, an 1,800 lb hold down is also required for the adjacent wall. As mixing intermittent and continuous braced wall lines in a story is not permitted in higher SDCs (IRC Section R602.10.4.1, Item 2 only permits mixing of intermittent and continuous bracing in a story when in low to moderate SDCs and where the basic wind speed is 100 mph or less), if a single wall is continuously sheathed in that story, then all walls must be continuously sheathed in that story.

As written, this second condition may cause some confusion when interpreted for the use of Method BV-WSP panels (wood structural panels with stone or masonry veneer), which already require hold downs in accordance with IRC Section R602.10.6.5. The 1,800 lb hold-down requirement of this condition is not in addition to that already required.

Thus, the only interpretation of the code as written that makes sense for Method BV-WSP is that the 1,800 lb hold-down requirement is appropriate for all panel methods <u>except</u> for Method BV-WSP, which requires hold downs per IRC Table R602.10.6.5.

3. For Method BV-WSP, hold-down devices shall be provided in accordance with Table R602.10.6.5 at the ends of each *braced wall panel.*

This third condition recognizes that the hold downs that are required for Method BV-WSP in accordance with IRC Section R602.10.6.5 provide the requisite foundation connection strength for the braced wall panel displaced from the corner. This condition is redundant and should be incorporated into the second condition, which provides hold-down requirements for all of the panel-type bracing methods permitted for SDC D_0, D_1 and D_2.

> **R602.10.2.3 Minimum number of *braced wall panels.*** *Braced wall lines* with a length of 16 feet (4877 mm) or less shall have a minimum of two *braced wall panels* of any length or one *braced wall panel* equal to 48 inches (1219 mm) or more. *Braced wall lines* greater than 16 feet (4877 mm) shall have a minimum of two *braced wall panels.*

This 2012 provision is the IRC's latest attempt to define the minimum bracing required for a relatively short braced wall line to adequately resist applied loads. In the past, some designers arbitrarily used the permissible end-distances to minimize the number of required bracing panels. That was not the intent of the permissible end-distances.

There is also a concern that using the maximum permissible end-distance in relatively short braced wall lines could conceivably create an unsafe structural shell even if the minimum bracing amounts are met. Using the maximum permissible end-distances tends to isolate the bracing panels together in the middle of the walls, where current bracing theory holds that they are less effective. One bracing panel at each end of the wall performs better than two bracing panels side-by-side in the middle of the wall.

This was addressed in the 2009 IRC by setting the maximum <u>total</u> end-distance of a braced wall line (the total end-distance that could be used at both ends of a braced wall line) as 12.5 feet (8 feet for high seismic). For example, if the first braced wall panel at one end was displaced from that end by 12.5 feet, the first braced wall panel at the opposite end could not be displaced from the corner. However, the total end-distance could be split between the two ends. For example, if the first braced wall panel at one end was displaced 6 feet, the first braced wall panel at the opposite end could be displaced up to 6-1/2 feet.

For the 2012 IRC, this total end-distance provision was dropped in favor of IRC Section R602.10.2.3, as shown above. This provision requires a minimum of one braced wall panel 48 inches in length in braced wall lines 16-feet long or less. In lieu of the single 48-inch braced wall panel, two braced wall panels of any length may be used. This was added to permit the use of the narrow wall bracing methods (Methods PFH, PFG, CS-G, and CS-PF). The rationale was that many of these narrow braced wall lines are found on garage walls, for which portal frames and other narrow wall bracing methods were designed. Braced wall lines longer than 16 feet must have two braced wall panels. It is thought that once the wall exceeds 16 feet in length, the minimum length of bracing required and the two braced wall panel minimum requirement will together provide sufficient bracing. While it is possible that two narrow wall bracing methods could be used for this portion of the provision, it is likely that the required length of bracing would be greater than the portal bracing length available.

R602.10.3 Required length of bracing

R602.10.3 Required length of bracing. The required length of bracing along each *braced wall line* shall be determined as follows.

The 2012 IRC Section 301.2.2 (see **CHAPTER 2**) defines the applicability of the IRC bracing provisions. This section is provided to clarify when each table is used.

1. All buildings in Seismic Design Categories A and B shall use Table R602.10.3(1) and the applicable adjustment factors in Table R602.10.3(2).

The 2012 IRC Section R301.2.2 exempts all buildings covered by the IRC in SDC A and B from compliance with the seismic bracing provisions. As such these buildings only have to meet the wind bracing requirements.

2. Detached buildings in Seismic Design Category C shall use Table R602.10.3(1) and the applicable adjustment factors in Table R602.10.3(2).

The exemption from the seismic bracing provisions for detached buildings only is extended to SDC C by IRC Section R301.2.2. Again, only the wind bracing provisions apply to these structures.

3. Townhouses in Seismic Design Category C shall use the greater value determined from Table R602.10.3(1) or R602.10.3(3) and the applicable adjustment factors in Table R602.10.3(2) or R602.10.3(4) respectively.

As the exemption for townhouses is not applicable for SDC C and above, the bracing required for townhouses will be the greater value determined from the wind bracing provisions and the seismic bracing provisions.

4. All buildings in Seismic Design Categories D_0, D_1 and D_2 shall use the greater value determined from Table R602.10.3(1) or R602.10.3(3) and the applicable adjustment factors in Table R602.10.3(2) or R602.10.3(4) respectively.

The wall bracing length in SDC D_0-D_2 is the greater length determined from the wind and seismic bracing tables.

Only braced wall panels parallel to the braced wall line shall contribute toward the required length of bracing of that braced wall line. Braced wall panels along an angled wall meeting the minimum length requirements of Tables R602.10.5 and R602.10.5.2 shall be permitted to contribute its projected length toward the minimum required length of bracing for the braced wall line as shown in Figure R602.10.1.4. Any braced wall panel on an angled wall at the end of a braced wall line shall contribute its projected length for only one of the braced wall lines at the projected corner.

This provision was added to clarify that, in general, the only braced wall panels that contribute to the total length are those panels that are parallel to the braced wall line. The new text is necessary for clarification due to the angled wall provision. Note that short connecting walls between wall lines do not count towards the total bracing length along the braced wall line. When the continuous sheathing bracing methods are used, these short perpendicular walls often provide the required end fixity to the continuously sheathed walls, as required in IRC Section R602.10.7 and IRC Figure R602.10.7 *(FIGURES 3.49-3.53)*.

This provision also clarifies that there is one exception to the restriction against counting non-parallel walls as bracing length: the angled wall provisions of IRC Section R602.10.1.4. The angled wall contribution may only be added to one of the two braced wall lines intersected by that angled corner. (See *FIGURE 3.4*.)

> **Exception:** The length of wall bracing for dwellings in Seismic Design Categories D_0, D_1 and D_2 with stone or masonry veneer installed per Section R703.7 and exceeding the first-story height shall be in accordance with Section R602.10.6.5.

Note that this exception does not apply to just the preceding paragraph, but to the whole section. It is simply an "override" of the seismic bracing length requirements of IRC Tables R602.10.3(3) and (4) *(TABLES 3.5* and *3.6)* in high seismic zones, when stone or masonry <u>exceed the first floor in height</u>. Stone and masonry veneer that do not exceed single-story height are assumed to provide their own lateral-load resistance. Required bracing length is determined using IRC Tables R602.10.3(1) and R602.10.3(3) *(TABLES 3.3* and *3.5)*.

How much bracing is needed? The amount of wall bracing required in each braced wall line, as specified by the IRC, depends on the Seismic Design Category (SDC), wind speed, number of stories above the braced wall line and the method of bracing used.

The basic procedure for calculating bracing has not changed in the 2012 IRC. The user must still consult two separate bracing tables – one for wind loads and one for seismic loads – to compute the required amount of bracing. However, if the structure is located in a low seismic area, it may only be necessary to consult the wind bracing table because IRC Section R301.2.2 exempts detached one- and two-family dwellings in SDC A, B and C and townhouses in SDC A and B from the seismic provisions of the IRC.

A second Seismic Design Category table has been added to the 2012 IRC; however, this table is only applicable to wall bracing for one- and two-family dwellings with stone and masonry veneer (Method BV-WSP) in SDC D_0, D_1 and D_2, <u>when the stone or masonry veneer extends higher the first floor.</u> This information is not new to the 2012 IRC; the existing provisions were reformatted for clarity.

Why two tables? Prior to 2009, IRC bracing tables assumed a braced wall line spacing of 35 feet for wind speeds of 110 mph or less and SDC A, B and C, and a braced wall line spacing of 25 feet for SDC D_0, D_1 and D_2. Basing the bracing requirement on the width of the building (the braced wall line spacing) is appropriate for wind. As discussed in **CHAPTER 1**, wind pushes against a building in the same manner that it pushes against a sail on a boat. When wind acts on the building width, the length of the building (dimension parallel to the wind) is irrelevant to determining the bracing required to resist that wind load. In other words, a short building that is 35-feet wide has the same "sail area" – and receives the same wind load – as a long building that is 35-feet wide. Therefore, if the short building requires 12 feet of bracing, the long building should also require 12 feet of bracing. This reasoning conflicts with pre-2009 IRC bracing tables that based the amount of wind bracing on a percentage of the braced wall line <u>length</u>. This erroneously required more wind bracing for the long building than the short building. These different approaches are illustrated in **FIGURE 3.11.** In the 2012 wind bracing table, IRC Table R602.10.3(1) (**TABLE 3.3**), the user inputs braced wall line spacing (the building width) to determine the required bracing length in feet, regardless of building length.

FIGURE 3.11

**Wall bracing –
wind loads**

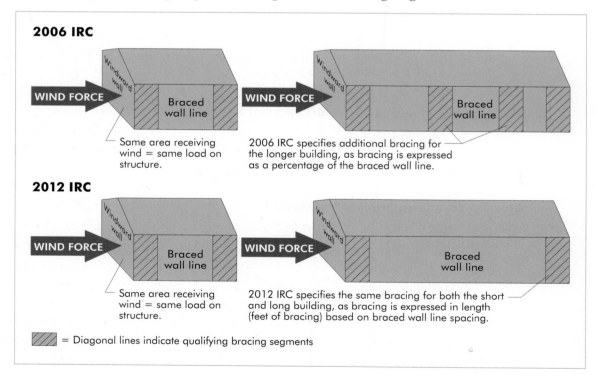

2006 IRC

WIND FORCE — Windward wall — Braced wall line

Same area receiving wind = same load on structure.

WIND FORCE — Windward wall — Braced wall line

2006 IRC specifies additional bracing for the longer building, as bracing is expressed as a percentage of the braced wall line.

2012 IRC

WIND FORCE — Windward wall — Braced wall line

Same area receiving wind = same load on structure.

WIND FORCE — Windward wall — Braced wall line

2012 IRC specifies the same bracing for both the short and long building, as bracing is expressed in length (feet of bracing) based on braced wall line spacing.

= Diagonal lines indicate qualifying bracing segments

There are two separate tables for computing bracing (ignoring for a moment the separate seismic bracing tables specifically for Method BV-WSP), because the development of bracing for seismic loads is conceptually the opposite of bracing for wind loads. When determining the amount of bracing required to resist seismic forces, the length of the building parallel to the direction of loading is the most important consideration. This is because mass is generally evenly distributed along the length and width of a building. For a given building width, the long building has more mass – and thus receives greater earthquake forces – than the short building. As a result, the long building requires a greater amount of bracing. For this reason, in the 2012 seismic bracing table (IRC Table R602.10.3(3), reproduced in **TABLE 3.5**), the user inputs the length of the braced wall line to determine the amount of bracing required. This is illustrated in **FIGURE 3.12**.

FIGURE 3.12

Wall bracing – seismic loads

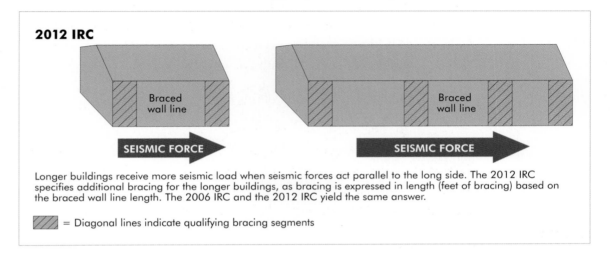

Longer buildings receive more seismic load when seismic forces act parallel to the long side. The 2012 IRC specifies additional bracing for the longer buildings, as bracing is expressed in length (feet of bracing) based on the braced wall line length. The 2006 IRC and the 2012 IRC yield the same answer.

= Diagonal lines indicate qualifying bracing segments

In previous versions of IRC, joint wind and seismic bracing tables were based on seismic loads, so – as with the 2012 IRC seismic bracing table – the amount of required bracing increased as the braced wall line length increased.

Also, unlike editions of the IRC prior to 2009, the amount of required bracing is provided in feet of bracing rather than a percentage of braced wall line length, eliminating the need for the user to compute the necessary feet of bracing.

Since wind and seismic loads act on a structure differently, a single table cannot accurately accommodate both forces of nature (as had been attempted in earlier versions of the IRC). The logical solution was to separate wind and seismic loads into two separate bracing tables. Like the 2009 IRC, the user may have to determine bracing length from both tables, and the required length of bracing for a given wall line is the greater of the two lengths.

What is the basis for the new tables? Although previous efforts were made to quantitatively fit wind bracing considerations for various SDCs into the IRC's earlier joint wind and seismic bracing tables, these tables were technically based only on seismic load considerations.

The ICC Ad Hoc Wall Bracing Committee realized the necessity of developing wind-load bracing tables based on engineering principles. The committee determined the actual loads that act on a structure within the range of wind speeds and building sizes covered by the IRC. They investigated structural resistance, evaluated and determined the capacities of existing bracing and proposed bracing methods. The committee also considered other factors that would impact the lateral performance of the structure beyond the designated braced wall panels, such as the strength contribution of interior walls and finishes, actual building performance compared with calculated performance, construction quality and factors of safety.

The wind bracing table that resulted from the Ad Hoc Committee's efforts was formatted to provide the user with the required bracing amount in total feet of bracing, based on the width of the building between braced wall lines. Although the basis for determining seismic load bracing did not change, the committee reformatted the seismic bracing table to also yield required bracing in feet, to be consistent with the wind bracing table.

TABLES 3.3 and **3.5** are the result of this multi-year project undertaken by a team of building officials, academics, design professionals, builders, structural engineers, ICC staff, product manufacturers and others. For each table, various adjustment factors must be applied. These adjustment factors – modifications to the amount of bracing based on variations in the structural geometry – are provided in tables immediately following the wind and seismic bracing tables, and are different for each table. These adjustment factors appear in IRC Tables R602.10.3(2) and R602.10.3(4), reproduced in **TABLES 3.4** and **3.6**.

It is important to note that neglecting an adjustment factor can result in insufficient bracing for a specific application. For example, the wind bracing tables are based on a roof eave-to-ridge height of 10 feet. If the roof height of a given single-story structure is 15 feet and 2012 IRC Table R602.10.3(2) is ignored, the required wall bracing will be insufficient by 30 percent. For this reason, all table footnotes and adjustment factors must be considered carefully.

How much bracing is needed for wind? The 2012 IRC wind bracing table (IRC Table R602.10.3(1)) is reproduced in **TABLE 3.3**. The adjustment factors (IRC Table R602.10.3(2)) for the required bracing lengths for wind are provided in **TABLE 3.4**. (Note that in **TABLE 3.3**, "story location" is represented by green shading in the building icon.)

As illustrated in **FIGURE 3.13**, the information in the wind bracing table is based on:

- Exposure Category B (explained in **CHAPTER 2**)
- 30-foot mean roof height
- 10-foot eave-to-ridge-height
- 10-foot wall height per story
- Two braced wall lines per direction of wind

FIGURE 3.13

Basis for wind bracing table

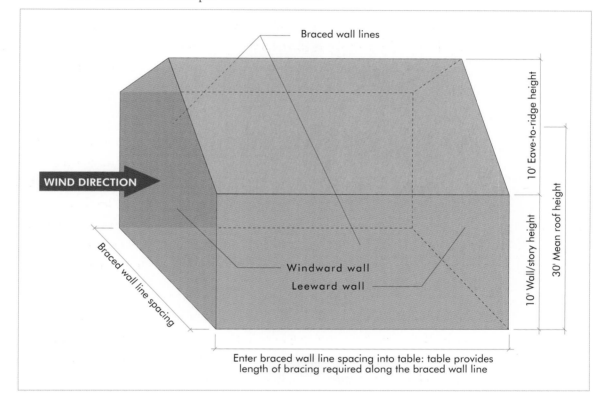

Enter braced wall line spacing into table: table provides length of bracing required along the braced wall line

TABLE 3.3

Unadjusted wind bracing requirements

IRC Table R602.10.3(1)

TABLE R602.10.3(1)
BRACING REQUIREMENTS BASED ON WIND SPEED

- Exposure Category B
- 30 Foot Mean Roof Height
- 10 Foot Eave-To-Ridge Height
- 10 Foot Wall Height
- 2 Braced Wall Lines

Minimum Total Length (feet) of Braced Wall Panels Required Along Each Braced Wall Line[a]

Basic Wind Speed (mph)	Story Location	Braced Wall Line Spacing (feet)	Method LIB[b]	Method GB	Methods DWB, WSP, SFB, PBS, PCP, HPS, CS-SFB[c]	Methods CS-WSP, CS-G, CS-PF
≤ 85		10	3.5	3.5	2.0	1.5
		20	6.0	6.0	3.5	3.0
		30	8.5	8.5	5.0	4.5
		40	11.5	11.5	6.5	5.5
		50	14.0	14.0	8.0	7.0
		60	16.5	16.5	9.5	8.0
		10	6.5	6.5	3.5	3.0
		20	11.5	11.5	6.5	5.5
		30	16.5	16.5	9.5	8.0
		40	21.5	21.5	12.5	10.5
		50	26.5	26.5	15.0	13.0
		60	31.5	31.5	18.0	15.5
		10	NP	9.0	5.5	4.5
		20	NP	17.0	10.0	8.5
		30	NP	24.5	14.0	12.0
		40	NP	32.0	18.0	15.5
		50	NP	39.0	22.5	19.0
		60	NP	46.5	26.5	22.5
≤ 90		10	3.5	3.5	2.0	2.0
		20	7.0	7.0	4.0	3.5
		30	9.5	9.5	5.5	5.0
		40	12.5	12.5	7.5	6.0
		50	15.5	15.5	9.0	7.5
		60	18.5	18.5	10.5	9.0
		10	7.0	7.0	4.0	3.5
		20	13.0	13.0	7.5	6.5
		30	18.5	18.5	10.5	9.0
		40	24.0	24.0	14.0	12.0
		50	29.5	29.5	17.0	14.5
		60	35.0	35.0	20.0	17.0
		10	NP	10.5	6.0	5.0
		20	NP	19.0	11.0	9.5
		30	NP	27.5	15.5	13.5
		40	NP	35.5	20.5	17.5
		50	NP	44.0	25.0	21.5
		60	NP	52.0	30.0	25.5

For SI: 1 inch = 25.4 mm, 1 foot = 305 mm, 1 mile per hour = 0.447 m/s.

a. Linear interpolation shall be permitted.

b. Method LIB shall have gypsum board fastened to at least one side with nails or screws in accordance with Table R602.3(1) for exterior sheathing or Table R702.3.5 for interior gypsum board. Spacing of fasteners at panel edges shall not exceed 8 inches.

c. Method CS-SFB does not apply where the wind speed is greater than 100 mph.

TABLE 3.3
(Continued)

Unadjusted wind bracing requirements

IRC Table R602.10.3(1)

TABLE R602.10.3(1)
BRACING REQUIREMENTS BASED ON WIND SPEED

- Exposure Category B
- 30 Foot Mean Roof Height
- 10 Foot Eave-To-Ridge Height
- 10 Foot Wall Height
- 2 Braced Wall Lines

Minimum Total Length (feet) of Braced Wall Panels Required Along Each Braced Wall Line[a]

Basic Wind Speed (mph)	Story Location	Braced Wall Line Spacing (feet)	Method LIB[b]	Method GB	Methods DWB, WSP, SFB, PBS, PCP, HPS, CS-SFB[c]	Methods CS-WSP, CS-G, CS-PF
≤ 100		10	4.5	4.5	2.5	2.5
		20	8.5	8.5	5.0	4.0
		30	12.0	12.0	7.0	6.0
		40	15.5	15.5	9.0	7.5
		50	19.0	19.0	11.0	9.5
		60	22.5	22.5	13.0	11.0
		10	8.5	8.5	5.0	4.5
		20	16.0	16.0	9.0	8.0
		30	23.0	23.0	13.0	11.0
		40	29.5	29.5	17.0	14.5
		50	36.5	36.5	21.0	18.0
		60	43.5	43.5	25.0	21.0
		10	NP	12.5	7.5	6.0
		20	NP	23.5	13.5	11.5
		30	NP	34.0	19.5	16.5
		40	NP	44.0	25.0	21.5
		50	NP	54.0	31.0	26.5
		60	NP	64.0	36.5	31.0
≤ 110[c]		10	5.5	5.5	3.0	3.0
		20	10.0	10.0	6.0	5.0
		30	14.5	14.5	8.5	7.0
		40	18.5	18.5	11.0	9.0
		50	23.0	23.0	13.0	11.5
		60	27.5	27.5	15.5	13.5
		10	10.5	10.5	6.0	5.0
		20	19.0	19.0	11.0	9.5
		30	27.5	27.5	16.0	13.5
		40	36.0	36.0	20.5	17.5
		50	44.0	44.0	25.5	21.5
		60	52.5	52.5	30.0	25.5
		10	NP	15.5	9.0	7.5
		20	NP	28.5	16.5	14.0
		30	NP	41.0	23.5	20.0
		40	NP	53.0	30.5	26.0
		50	NP	65.5	37.5	32.0
		60	NP	77.5	44.5	37.5

For SI: 1 inch = 25.4 mm, 1 foot = 305 mm, 1 mile per hour = 0.447 m/s.

a. Linear interpolation shall be permitted.

b. Method LIB shall have gypsum board fastened to at least one side with nails or screws in accordance with Table R602.3(1) for exterior sheathing or Table R702.3.5 for interior gypsum board. Spacing of fasteners at panel edges shall not exceed 8 inches.

c. Method CS-SFB does not apply where the wind speed is greater than 100 mph.

Footnote b is provided to remind the user that the capacity of let-in bracing (Method LIB) is predicated on the use of a gypsum board finish on either side of the wall at the Method LIB location. This gypsum board sheathing must be attached with a maximum fastener spacing of 8 inches on center.

Footnote c limits the use of Method CS-SFB (continuously sheathed structural fiberboard) to areas where wind speeds are less than or equal to 100 mph. While this limitation was formerly included in the text of the IRC, in the 2012 edition it is relegated to this footnote.

TABLE 3.4

Adjustment factors to the required wind bracing determined in Table 3.3

IRC Table R602.10.3(2)

TABLE R602.10.3(2)
WIND ADJUSTMENT FACTORS TO THE REQUIRED LENGTH OF WALL BRACING

❶ Adjustment Based On	❷ Story/ Supporting	Condition	Adjustment Factor[a, b] [multiply length from Table R602.10.3(1) by this factor]	Applicable Methods
❸ Exposure category	One-story structure	B	1.00	
		C	1.20	
		D	1.50	
	Two-story structure	B	1.00	
		C	1.30	
		D	1.60	
	Three-story structure	B	1.00	
		C	1.40	
		D	1.70	
❹ Roof eave-to-ridge height	Roof only	≤ 5 feet	0.70	All methods
		10 feet	1.00	
		15 feet	1.30	
		20 feet	1.60	
	Roof + 1 floor	≤ 5 feet	0.85	
		10 feet	1.00	
		15 feet	1.15	
		20 feet	1.30	
	Roof + 2 floors	≤ 5 feet	0.90	
		10 feet	1.00	
		15 feet	1.10	
		20 feet	Not permitted	
❺ Wall height adjustment	Any story	8 feet	0.90	
		9 feet	0.95	
		10 feet	1.00	
		11 feet	1.05	
		12 feet	1.10	
❻ Number of braced wall lines (per plan direction)[c]	Any story	2	1.00	
		3	1.30	
		4	1.45	
		≥ 5	1.60	

For SI: 1 inch = 25.4 mm, 1 foot = 305 mm, 1 pound = 4.48 N.
a. Linear interpolation shall be permitted.
b. The total adjustment factor is the product of all applicable adjustment factors.
c. The adjustment factor is permitted to be 1.0 when determining bracing amounts for intermediate braced wall lines provided the bracing amounts on adjacent braced wall lines are based on a spacing and number that neglects the intermediate braced wall line.

TABLE 3.4
(Continued)

**Adjustment
factors to
the required
wind bracing
determined in
Table 3.3**

**IRC Table
R602.10.3(2)**

TABLE R602.10.3(2)
WIND ADJUSTMENT FACTORS TO THE REQUIRED LENGTH OF WALL BRACING

	Adjustment Based On	Story/ Supporting	Condition	Adjustment Factor[a, b] [multiply length from Table R602.10.3(1) by this factor]	Applicable Methods
⑦	Additional 800-pound hold-down device	Top story only	Fastened to the end studs of each braced wall panel and to the foundation or framing below	0.80	DWB, WSP, SFB, PBS, PCP, HPS
⑧	Interior gypsum board finish (or equivalent)	Any story	Omitted from inside face of braced wall panels	1.40	DWB, WSP, SFB, PBS, PCP, HPS, CS-WSP, CS-G, CS-SFB
⑨	Gypsum board fastening	Any story	4 inches o.c. at panel edges, including top and bottom plates, and all horizontal joints blocked	0.7	GB

For SI: 1 inch = 25.4 mm, 1 foot = 305 mm, 1 pound = 4.48 N.
a. Linear interpolation shall be permitted.
⑩ b. The total adjustment factor is the product of all applicable adjustment factors.
c. The adjustment factor is permitted to be 1.0 when determining bracing amounts for intermediate braced wall lines provided the bracing amounts on adjacent braced wall lines are based on a spacing and number that neglects the intermediate braced wall line.

❶ **Adjustment based on** - IRC Table R602.10.3(2) includes adjustment factors to accommodate variations from IRC Table R602.10.3(1) assumptions for the wide range of residential structures covered by the IRC. Where appropriate, these adjustments are explained in the text below. Not all of these adjustments are new to the 2012 IRC; many have been taken from other sections of previous IRC editions and collected into this common location for the 2012 edition. This table also specifies when each adjustment applies to a bracing method.

❷ **Story/Supporting** - The second column in the table, *"Story/Supporting"*, refers to the construction that exists above the wall line for which the amount of bracing is being determined. Note also that when determining the amount of wind bracing required for the top story of a three-story building, the adjustment factor for a one-story building is appropriate. From the wind's perspective, the top story of the building is a single story tall. Similarly, for the middle story, the two-story adjustment is appropriate. Only for the bottom of a three-story building is the three-story adjustment required.

This adjustment is appropriate for all bracing methods.

❸ **Exposure category** - The exposure category adjustment factors are provided based on the number of stories (height of the structure) and the wind exposure category of the building's location. See **CHAPTER 2** of this guide for information on wind exposure.

Note that the wind bracing table (**TABLE 3.3**) is based on Exposure Category B. The exposure category for a given site is determined by the designer using the definitions in IRC Section R301.2.1.4, or a single wind exposure value is assigned in a jurisdiction by the building official. In the second case, the wind exposure is obtained from the building department's IRC Table R301.2(1).

As the number of stories increases (increasing the mean roof height), the adjustment factors increase. This is to accommodate the increased exposure to wind and larger sail area of the structure.

This adjustment is appropriate for all bracing methods.

❹ Roof eave-to-ridge height - Eave-to-ridge height is an important consideration because it increases the sail area of a structure, therefore increasing the wind load on the structure, as illustrated in **FIGURE 3.14**. Increasing eave-to-ridge height by as little as 5 feet, from 10 to 15 feet for example, can increase the required bracing panel length by 30 percent. Note that as the number of stories increases (the support conditions), the overall contribution of the roof eave-to-ridge height to the <u>total</u> sail area decreases. The increase caused by the greater eave height is "diluted" as the bracing requirements of subsequent stories are considered.

This adjustment is appropriate for all bracing methods.

FIGURE 3.14

Eave-to-ridge height

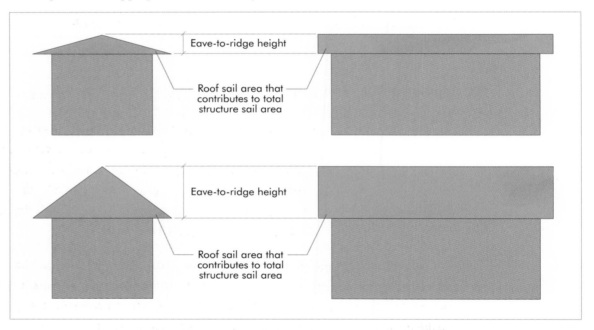

❺ Wall height adjustment - Like eave-to-ridge height, increasing the sail area of the structure by increasing the wall heights increases the wind load on the structure, thus requiring more bracing. The wind bracing table assumes a 10-foot wall height: taller walls require an adjustment to increase the amount of required bracing, while shorter walls are permitted an adjustment to decrease the amount of required bracing. This adjustment can be applied to each story individually. For example, in a house with a first-story wall height of 9 feet and a second-story wall height of 8 feet, the bracing amount for the first story can be reduced by five percent, and the bracing amount for the second story reduced by ten percent.

Note that wall height = stud height + bottom and top plates. It does not include depth of floor framing bearing on top of the wall.

This adjustment is appropriate for all bracing methods.

⑥ Number of braced wall lines (per plan direction) - At first glance, the adjustments based on the number of braced wall lines may give the impression that adding additional interior bracing walls is a disadvantage, because the amount of bracing in the wall lines must increase by an adjustment factor. Although true, this is somewhat misleading. The values in IRC Table R602.10.3(1) are actually based on the spacing of the braced wall lines. If, for example, the distance between two exterior walls in a home design requires a length of bracing that cannot be accommodated by the exterior wall lines alone, a braced wall line may be added through the interior of the structure. In this case, because the spacing of the braced wall lines decreases, the amount of bracing required for each of the braced wall lines also decreases. The adjustment factor is applied to the required bracing based on this <u>reduced</u> amount of bracing for the braced wall lines. This method is very conservative, but relatively easy to apply.

This adjustment is appropriate for all bracing methods.

Note Footnote c to Table R602.10.3(2), referenced by this adjustment:

> c. The adjustment factor is permitted to be 1.0 when determining bracing amounts for intermediate *braced wall lines* provided the bracing amounts on adjacent *braced wall lines* are based on a spacing and number that neglects the intermediate *braced wall line*.

This language is written in a confusing manner. Footnote c intends to cover unusual situations. For example, when a T or L-shaped building is broken into multiple sections to determine bracing, when the exterior wall of an upper story requires a braced wall line below to support the wall, or when an interior braced wall line is necessary for seismic loads but not necessary for wind loads. In each of these cases, you may have an interior braced wall line that does not need bracing, or only needs to be braced with an adjustment factor of 1.0.

In the first case, if you calculate the bracing required to the right of the intermediate braced wall line, then recalculate to the left of the intermediate braced wall line, then add the two amounts calculated for the intermediate braced wall line, an adjustment of 1.0 is permitted. See **FIGURE 3.15.** This concept is discussed in depth in **APPENDIX B**.

A second and equally appropriate interpretation of the footnote is that if an interior braced wall line is placed and the exterior braced wall line amounts are calculated in accordance with IRC Table R602.10.3(2), the total amount of bracing on the exterior walls need not be more than that required for the exterior walls if the interior braced wall line had not been used. An example of this could be when an interior braced wall line is placed in the first floor of a building just to support an exterior braced wall line in the story above. The lower story interior braced wall line would be required to meet the irregularity provisions of IRC Section R301.2.2.2.5 in a high SDC.

A third interpretation of the footnote is when an interior braced wall line is used for seismic bracing but is not necessary for wind bracing. In this instance, the braced wall line will not need to be checked nor any adjustment made.

The user must be careful, however, when ignoring the braced wall line length adjustments in IRC Tables R602.10.3(2) and R602.10.3(4) (**TABLE 3.4** and **3.6**) if the amount of bracing appears to be sufficient without adjustment. Some of the adjustments increase the amount of bracing required. For example, the eave-to-ridge adjustment in IRC Table R602.10.3(2) (**TABLE 3.4**): when the eave-to-ridge height is 10 feet or greater, the required bracing must be increased (to compensate for the increased surface area of the structure resisting the wind load).

FIGURE 3.15

Braced wall line spacing

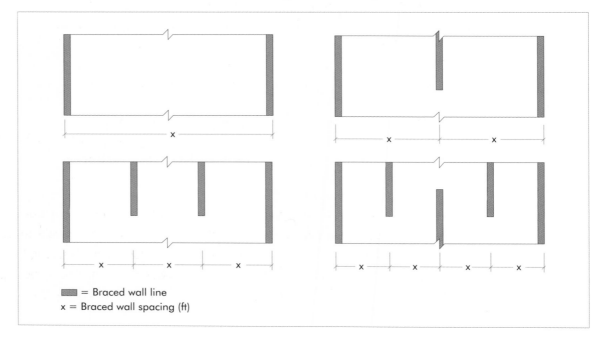

= Braced wall line
x = Braced wall spacing (ft)

❼ **Additional 800-pound hold-down device** - In developing the new wind bracing provisions, braced wall panels only supporting the roof above them (one-story buildings and the top story of multi-story buildings) were recognized to be only partially effective in resisting wind forces, as they are not being held down ("restrained") by the additional mass of a story above them. The use of an 800 lb hold-down device, installed in accordance with the manufacturer's recommendations, increases the capacity of bracing methods when supporting roof loads only. Adding such a hold-down device permits a 20 percent reduction in the length of bracing required. Note that the hold downs must be used at both ends of every bracing panel in the wall line and the hold-down anchorage must extend through all lower floors (if any) to provide a continuous load path until anchored into the foundation.

❽ **Interior gypsum board finish (or equivalent)** - The addition of "regular" interior gypsum wall board, even though not attached with the same quantity of fasteners as Method GB (gypsum board), does add some strength and stiffness to the bracing. Therefore, in cases in which gypsum board is not applied on the inside surface of braced wall panels, an adjustment must be made to reflect the reduction in strength and stiffness. In modern residential construction, the absence of gypsum board finish material is only likely to occur at gable end walls (above the top plates) and at exterior garage walls. Typically, in either of these applications, it is not difficult to increase the amount of bracing because such walls are unlikely to have many openings. This adjustment factor is appropriate for Methods DWB, WSP, SFB, PBS, PCP, HPS, CS-WSP, CS-G and CS-SFB. Note that Method LIB is not included because this method requires gypsum wall board on at least one side. See Footnote b of IRC Table R602.10.3(1).

⑨ Gypsum board fastening – The gypsum board fastening adjustment can be used to increase the effectiveness of Method GB bracing by decreasing the perimeter fastening of the gypsum board from 7 inches on center to 4 inches on center. Note that all field fastening must be maintained at 7 inches on center as is appropriate for Method GB wall bracing. This additional fastening permits the length of Method GB bracing to be multiplied by 0.7.

⑩ Footnote b – This significant footnote tells the user that the total length of bracing from IRC Table R602.10.3(1) shall be the product of <u>all</u> of the applicable adjustment factors. This means that the length from IRC Table R602.10.3(1) is multiplied by all appropriate factors, one after the other.

How much bracing is needed for seismic? For the 2009 IRC, the seismic bracing table underwent a major formatting revision with minor changes to the actual content. The table was reworked to provide the amount of required bracing in total feet of bracing length instead of a percentage of braced wall line length. This revision was accomplished by basing the table on the length of the braced wall line and fixing the braced wall line spacing at 25 feet.

The 2012 IRC seismic bracing table (IRC Table R602.10.3(3)) is essentially unchanged, except that SDC D_0 and D_1 have been separated into their own sections. This is reproduced in **TABLE 3.5**. (Note that in the table, the "story location" is represented by green shading in the building icon.)

IRC Section R301.2.2 exempts detached one- and two-family dwellings in SDC A, B and C and townhouses in SDC A and B from the seismic provisions of the IRC. In these cases, only the wind bracing requirements must be met.

As illustrated in **FIGURE 3.16**, the information in the seismic bracing table is based on:

- Soil site classification D (see Soil Site Classes sidebar)

> ### SOIL SITE CLASSES
>
> The seismic bracing requirements are based on soil site class D. Site classifications (discussed in the IBC, Section 1613.3.2) range from A to F. Soil site class A represents hard rock and site class F represents soils generally not considered suitable for construction. Site class D is the default soil condition and can be used for all cases, unless the building official or geotechnical survey determines that site class E or F are present. Site class E and F are very soft, loamy, sandy soils, and soils with soft and medium clays. These site classes are undesirable for prescriptive applications because softer soils amplify the earthquake ground motion. The local building official will know if such soils are present in a given area and will be familiar with the necessary requirements for building in such conditions. Contact your local building official for guidance.

- 10-foot wall height

- 10 psf floor dead load

- 15 psf roof and ceiling dead load

- Braced wall line spacing of 25 feet or less

FIGURE 3.16

Basis for seismic bracing table

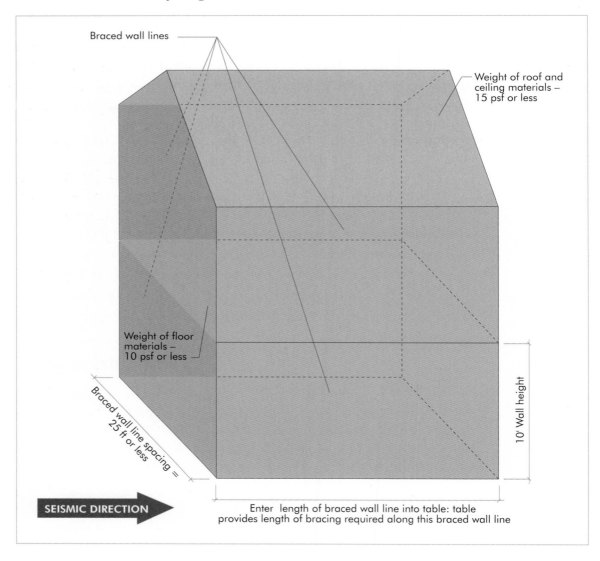

Braced wall lines

Weight of roof and ceiling materials – 15 psf or less

Weight of floor materials – 10 psf or less

Braced wall line spacing = 25 ft or less

10' Wall height

SEISMIC DIRECTION

Enter length of braced wall line into table: table provides length of bracing required along this braced wall line

The footnotes to the seismic bracing table include a clarification of the gypsum board requirements for Method LIB (let-in bracing) and a restriction on the use of Method CS-SFB (continuously sheathed structural fiberboard) to SDC C or less (see Footnote d to IRC Table R602.10.4). As in the 2009 IRC, adjustment factors are included separately in IRC Table R602.10.3(4) (**TABLE 3.6**). Not all of these adjustments are new to the IRC; many were taken from other sections and collected into a common location in the 2009 edition.

Footnote b of IRC Table R602.10.3(3) warrants some explanation. Soil site class D represents a fairly stiff soil (see "Soil Site Classes" on page 93). When the soil properties are not known in sufficient detail to determine a specific soil site class, site class D shall be used unless the building official or geotechnical data determines that site class E or F are present.

Footnote c reiterates the gypsum board requirements for Method LIB when permitted for use.

Footnote d restricts Method CS-SFB to townhouses in Seismic Design Category (SDC) C. (Detached one and two-family dwellings are exempt from the seismic requirements in SDC A-C (per IRC Section R301.2.2). Method CS-SFB is also restricted to areas where the wind speed is less than 100 mph.

TABLE 3.5

Unadjusted seismic bracing requirements

IRC Table R602.10.3(3)

TABLE R602.10.3(3)
BRACING REQUIREMENTS BASED ON SEISMIC DESIGN CATEGORY

- Soil Class D[b]
- Wall Height = 10 Feet
- 10 psf Floor Dead Load
- 15 psf Roof/Ceiling Dead Load
- Braced Wall Line Spacing ≤ 25 Feet

Minimum Total Length (feet) of Braced Wall Panels Required Along Each Braced Wall Line[a]

Seismic Design Category	Story Location	Braced Wall Line Length (feet)	Method LIB[c]	Method GB	Methods DWB, SFB, PBS, PCP, HPS, CS-SFB[d]	Method WSP	Methods CS-WSP, CS-G, CS-PF
C (townhouses only)		10	2.5	2.5	2.5	1.6	1.4
		20	5.0	5.0	5.0	3.2	2.7
		30	7.5	7.5	7.5	4.8	4.1
		40	10.0	10.0	10.0	6.4	5.4
		50	12.5	12.5	12.5	8.0	6.8
		10	NP	4.5	4.5	3.0	2.6
		20	NP	9.0	9.0	6.0	5.1
		30	NP	13.5	13.5	9.0	7.7
		40	NP	18.0	18.0	12.0	10.2
		50	NP	22.5	22.5	15.0	12.8
		10	NP	6.0	6.0	4.5	3.8
		20	NP	12.0	12.0	9.0	7.7
		30	NP	18.0	18.0	13.5	11.5
		40	NP	24.0	24.0	18.0	15.3
		50	NP	30.0	30.0	22.5	19.1
D_0		10	NP	2.8	2.8	1.8	1.6
		20	NP	5.5	5.5	3.6	3.1
		30	NP	8.3	8.3	5.4	4.6
		40	NP	11.0	11.0	7.2	6.1
		50	NP	13.8	13.8	9.0	7.7
		10	NP	5.3	5.3	3.8	3.2
		20	NP	10.5	10.5	7.5	6.4
		30	NP	15.8	15.8	11.3	9.6
		40	NP	21.0	21.0	15.0	12.8
		50	NP	26.3	26.3	18.8	16.0
		10	NP	7.3	7.3	5.3	4.5
		20	NP	14.5	14.5	10.5	9.0
		30	NP	21.8	21.8	15.8	13.4
		40	NP	29.0	29.0	21.0	17.9
		50	NP	36.3	36.3	26.3	22.3

For SI: 1 inch = 25.4 mm, 1 foot = 305 mm, 1 pound per square foot = 0.0479 kPa.

a. Linear interpolation shall be permitted.

b. Wall bracing lengths are based on a soil site class "D." Interpolation of bracing length between the S_{ds} values associated with the Seismic Design Categories shall be permitted when a site-specific S_{ds} value is determined in accordance with Section 1613.3 of the *International Building Code*.

c. Method LIB shall have gypsum board fastened to at least one side with nails or screws per Table R602.3(1) for exterior sheathing or Table R702.3.5 for interior gypsum board. Spacing of fasteners at panel edges shall not exceed 8 inches.

d. Method CS-SFB applies in SDC C only.

TABLE 3.5
(Continued)

Unadjusted seismic bracing requirements

IBC Table R602.10.3(3)

TABLE R602.10.3(3)
BRACING REQUIREMENTS BASED ON SEISMIC DESIGN CATEGORY

- Soil Class D[b]
- Wall Height = 10 Feet
- 10 psf Floor Dead Load
- 15 psf Roof/Ceiling Dead Load
- Braced Wall Line Spacing ≤ 25 Feet

Minimum Total Length (feet) of Braced Wall Panels Required Along Each Braced Wall Line[a]

Seismic Design Category	Story Location	Braced Wall Line Length (feet)	Method LIB[c]	Method GB	Methods DWB, SFB, PBS, PCP, HPS, CS-SFB[d]	Method WSP	Methods CS-WSP, CS-G, CS-PF
D₁		10	NP	3.0	3.0	2.0	1.7
		20	NP	6.0	6.0	4.0	3.4
		30	NP	9.0	9.0	6.0	5.1
		40	NP	12.0	12.0	8.0	6.8
		50	NP	15.0	15.0	10.0	8.5
		10	NP	6.0	6.0	4.5	3.8
		20	NP	12.0	12.0	9.0	7.7
		30	NP	18.0	18.0	13.5	11.5
		40	NP	24.0	24.0	18.0	15.3
		50	NP	30.0	30.0	22.5	19.1
		10	NP	8.5	8.5	6.0	5.1
		20	NP	17.0	17.0	12.0	10.2
		30	NP	25.5	25.5	18.0	15.3
		40	NP	34.0	34.0	24.0	20.4
		50	NP	42.5	42.5	30.0	25.5
D₂		10	NP	4.0	4.0	2.5	2.1
		20	NP	8.0	8.0	5.0	4.3
		30	NP	12.0	12.0	7.5	6.4
		40	NP	16.0	16.0	10.0	8.5
		50	NP	20.0	20.0	12.5	10.6
		10	NP	7.5	7.5	5.5	4.7
		20	NP	15.0	15.0	11.0	9.4
		30	NP	22.5	22.5	16.5	14.0
		40	NP	30.0	30.0	22.0	18.7
		50	NP	37.5	37.5	27.5	23.4
		10	NP	NP	NP	NP	NP
		20	NP	NP	NP	NP	NP
		30	NP	NP	NP	NP	NP
		40	NP	NP	NP	NP	NP
		50	NP	NP	NP	NP	NP
	Cripple wall below one- or two-story dwelling	10	NP	NP	NP	7.5	6.4
		20	NP	NP	NP	15.0	12.8
		30	NP	NP	NP	22.5	19.1
		40	NP	NP	NP	30.0	25.5
		50	NP	NP	NP	37.5	31.9

For SI: 1 inch = 25.4 mm, 1 foot = 305 mm, 1 pound per square foot = 0.0479 kPa.

a. Linear interpolation shall be permitted.

b. Wall bracing lengths are based on a soil site class "D." Interpolation of bracing length between the S_{ds} values associated with the Seismic Design Categories shall be permitted when a site-specific S_{ds} value is determined in accordance with Section 1613.3 of the *International Building Code*.

c. Method LIB shall have gypsum board fastened to at least one side with nails or screws per Table R602.3(1) for exterior sheathing or Table R702.3.5 for interior gypsum board. Spacing of fasteners at panel edges shall not exceed 8 inches.

d. Method CS-SFB applies in SDC C only.

TABLE 3.6

Adjustment factors to the required seismic bracing determined in Table 3.5

IRC Table R602.10.3(4)

TABLE R602.10.3(4)
SEISMIC ADJUSTMENT FACTORS TO THE REQUIRED LENGTH OF WALL BRACING

	Adjustment Based On:	Story/Supporting	Condition	Adjustment Factor[a, b] [Multiply length from Table R602.10.3(3) by this factor]	Applicable Methods
❶	Story height (Section 301.3)	Any story	≤ 10 ft > 10 ft and ≤ 12 ft	1.0 1.2	
❷	Braced wall line spacing, townhouses in SDC C	Any story	≤ 35 ft > 35 ft and ≤ 50 ft	1.0 1.43	
❸	Braced wall line spacing, in SDC D_0, D_1, D_2[c]	Any story	> 25 ft and ≤ 30 ft > 30 ft and ≤ 35 ft	1.2 1.4	All methods
❹	Wall dead load	Any story	> 8 psf and < 15 psf < 8 psf	1.0 0.85	
❺	Roof/ceiling dead load for wall supporting	Roof only or roof plus one or two stories	≤15 psf	1.0	
		Roof plus one or two stories	> 15 psf and ≤ 25 psf	1.1	
		Roof only	> 15 psf and ≤ 25 psf	1.2	
❻	Walls with stone or masonry veneer, townhouses in SDC C[d,e]			1.0	All intermittent and continuous methods
				1.5	
				1.5	
❼	Walls with stone or masonry veneer, detached one and two-family dwellings in SDC D_0 – D_2[d]	Any story	See Table R602.10.6.5		BV-WSP
❽	Interior gypsum board finish (or equivalent)	Any story	Omitted from inside face of braced wall panels	1.5	DWB, WSP, SFB, PBS, PCP, HPS, CS-WSP, CS-G, CS-SFB

For SI: 1 foot = 304.8 mm, 1 pound per square foot = 0.0479 kPa.
a. Linear interpolation shall be permitted.
b. The total length of bracing required for a given wall line is the product of all applicable adjustment factors.
c. The length-to-width ratio for the floor/roof *diaphragm* shall not exceed 3:1. The top plate lap splice nailing shall be a minimum of 12-16d nails on each side of the splice.
❾ d. Applies to stone or masonry veneer exceeding the first story height. See Section R602.10.6.5 for requirements when stone or masonry veneer does not exceed the first story height.
❿ e. The adjustment factor for stone or masonry veneer shall be applied to all exterior *braced wall lines* and all *braced wall lines* on the interior of the building, backing or perpendicular to and laterally supported veneered walls.

❶ **Story height (IRC Section R301.3)** – The amount of bracing required for seismic loads is directly related to the mass/weight of the structure and its elevation above grade. As a wall gets taller, its mass and distance above grade increases, thus requiring more bracing to resist the resulting seismic loads.

These adjustments are appropriate for all bracing methods.

❷ **Braced wall line spacing, townhouses in SDC C** – This adjustment factor only applies to townhomes in SDC C because of the seismic exception discussed previously. (Per IRC Section R301.2.2, detached one- and two-family dwellings in SDC A, B and C and townhouses in SDC A and B are exempt from the seismic requirements of the code.) Townhomes in SDC C are permitted a 35-foot to 50-foot braced wall line spacing using this adjustment factor.

These adjustments are appropriate for all bracing methods.

For simplicity, the 25-foot wall line spacing (first column heading in IRC Table R602.10.3(3), reproduced in **TABLE 3.5**) applies to detached one- and two-family dwellings in SDC D_0, D_1 and D_2 and townhouses in SDC C, D_0, D_1 and D_2. Braced wall line spacing requirements are expanded in the new IRC Table R602.10.1.3 (**TABLE 3.1**), where maximum braced wall line spacing for townhouses in SDC C is defined as 35 feet.

These adjustments are appropriate for all bracing methods.

❸ **Braced wall line spacing, SDC D_0-D_2** – This provision, along with the provisions in Footnote c below, formerly appeared in the text of the IRC (2009 IRC Section R602.10.1.5, Exception). These provisions, which amount to adjustments to the amount of bracing required, were moved to this table along with the other adjustments in an attempt to consolidate the bracing provisions in the 2012 IRC.

The basis for these adjustments is that, as the distance between the braced wall lines increases, greater load will be distributed into the braced wall lines from the roof or floor diaphragm above. Note that the adjustment in bracing length is made to the walls perpendicular to the braced wall line spacing.

Footnote c requires additional nailing at the top plate splices. As the braced wall lines are spaced farther apart, the roof or floor diaphragm grows longer and the tension requirements on the diaphragm chords (the double top plate) increases. To avoid having to engineer the chord splice, the 2012 IRC provides a prescriptive solution: "12-16d nails on each side of the splice" for this application.

Footnote c also places a 3:1 limit on the length-to-width ratio for the floor/roof diaphragm.

These adjustments are appropriate for all bracing methods.

④ Wall dead load – IRC Table R602.10.3(3) (**TABLE 3.5**) is based on a wall weight of 8 to 15 psf. If a lighter weight wall is used, a reduction is permitted in the amount of bracing required. (Again, more mass requires more bracing and less mass requires less bracing.) Note that a standard wood-framed stud wall has a weight of 11 to 12 psf (Table C3-1 of ASCE 7-10).

These adjustments are appropriate for all bracing methods.

⑤ Roof/ceiling dead load for wall supporting – IRC Table R602.10.3(3) (**TABLE 3.5**) is based on a roof/ceiling weight of 15 psf or less. As the roof weight/mass increases, so does the amount of bracing required. Note that a standard wood-framed roof ceiling with lightweight asphalt shingles or wood shingles has a weight that varies between 10 and 15 psf (Table C3-1 of ASCE 7-10).

These adjustments are appropriate for all bracing methods.

⑥ Walls with stone or masonry veneer, townhouses in SDC C – This is another case of more mass requiring more bracing. The requirements for stone and masonry veneer have been greatly simplified in the 2012 IRC. For SDC C, only townhouses are applicable, as IRC Section R301.2.2 exempts detached one- and two- family dwellings from the seismic design provisions. For townhouses in SDC C, any of the intermittent or continuous bracing methods may be used as long as the required seismic braced wall lengths are multiplied by the factors given in IRC Table R602.10.3(4) (**TABLE 3.6**). Note that there are two footnotes that are appropriate to these adjustment factors. Footnote d clarifies that the increases in bracing only apply when the stone or masonry veneer exceeds the first story height. (for example, the veneer extends up into the second or third story, or at a gable end over a single-story building wall). This is illustrated in the first row of ⑦, which shows an adjustment of 1.0 for this case. The second portion of Footnote d applies only to SDC D_0-D_2.

Footnote e clarifies that the bracing increases are only applicable to the walls that run perpendicular to the stone or masonry veneered wall, as well as to the wall immediately behind the veneer. Note that this is consistent with the engineering principles involved. The greater mass of the stone or masonry wall requires greater resistance when reacting to seismic loads. The bracing provisions are based on the assumption that it is only the perpendicular walls and the wall immediately behind the veneer that must resist that increased load. Therefore, in a structure with such veneer on the street-side of the building only, no additional bracing is required on the parallel "back wall".

⑦ Walls with stone or masonry veneer, detached one and two-family dwellings in SDC D_0-D_2 – Again, additional mass requires more bracing. In addition, higher SDCs require even more bracing. With the mass associated with stone and masonry veneer, conventional bracing is not sufficient for resisting the lateral loads in SDC D_0-D_2. For this reason, Method BV-WSP is required. Method BV-WSP is essentially a wood structural panel braced wall panel with hold-down straps on each end of each bracing panel. An engineer would immediately correctly recognize this as a shear wall. As discussed previously in this chapter, a separate seismic bracing table (IRC Table R602.10.6.5, reproduced in **TABLE 3.32**) has been added to the 2012 IRC for just these applications.

In this portion of IRC Table R602.10.3(4) **(TABLE 3.6)** only Footnote d is annotated. Footnote d clarifies that the increases in bracing only apply when the stone or masonry veneer exceeds the first story height. (for example, the veneer extends up into the second or third story, or at a gable end over a single-story building wall). If the veneer does extend past the first story, the requirements of IRC Section R602.10.6.5 and IRC Table R602.10.6.5 must be met.

The second portion of Footnote d permits the use of any type of bracing. Such walls may be braced in accordance with IRC Table R602.10.3(3) without adjustment for masonry, providing the stone or masonry veneer does not extend up past the first story.

While not referenced in ❼, from an engineering perspective, the braced wall line locations indicated in Footnote e are applicable to SDC D_0-D_2 as well. Footnote e clarifies that the bracing increases are only applicable to the walls that back or run perpendicular to the stone- or masonry-veneered wall. The greater mass of the stone or masonry wall require greater resistance when reacting to seismic loads. The bracing provisions are based on the assumption that it is only the perpendicular walls and the wall immediately behind the veneer that must resist that increased load. Therefore, in a structure with such veneer on the street-side of the building only, no additional bracing is required on the parallel "back wall". IRC Section R602.10.6.5 contains this requirement.

❽ **Interior gypsum board finish (or equivalent)** – This seismic bracing table adjustment factor for interior gypsum board finish is similar to an adjustment factor in the wind bracing table (IRC Table R602.10.3(2)), and it is appropriate for most panel-type bracing methods, both intermittent and continuous. If interior gypsum board finish is left off of the braced wall panels on any story, the length of seismic wall bracing for that braced wall line must be increased by a factor of 1.5. Note that the adjustment factor for wind is 1.4. This is not an error: gypsum wall board performs differently in wind and seismic situations and, as such, the adjustment factor for its omission varies for the two applications.

This provision was formerly in the text of 2009 IRC Section R602.10.2.1, Exception 3, and was not applicable to the continuous sheathing methods. For 2012, this provision has been correctly applied to the appropriate continuous sheathing methods and relocated here along with the rest of the adjustments appropriate for the seismic bracing length requirements.

As with the wind bracing adjustments, the addition of "regular" interior gypsum wall board, even though not attached with the same quantity of fasteners as Method GB (gypsum board) bracing, does add some strength and stiffness to the bracing. Therefore, in cases in which gypsum board is not applied on the inside surface of braced wall panels, an adjustment must be made to reflect the reduction in strength and stiffness. In modern residential construction, the absence of gypsum board finish material is only likely to occur at gable end walls (above the top plates) and at exterior garage walls. Typically, in either of these applications, it is not difficult to increase the amount of bracing because such walls are unlikely to have many openings. This adjustment factor is appropriate for Methods DWB, WSP, SFB, PBS, PCP, HPS, CS-WSP, CS-G and CS-SFB.

⑨ **Footnote d** – Note that IRC Section R602.10.6.5 redirects the user back to IRC Section R602.10.3 for situations where the stone or masonry veneer is properly installed (IRC Section R703.7) and covers the first story only. IRC Section R602.10.3 requires only the regular bracing of IRC Tables R602.10.3(1)-(4) *(TABLES 3.3-3.6)*, without additional masonry or brick veneer adjustments. Note that no provision for stone or masonry gable ends is made in this provision; it must be assumed that Footnote d does not apply to single-story stone or masonry walls when they extend up into the gable.

⑩ **Footnote e** – Although worded awkwardly ("laterally supported" should read "laterally supporting", per IRC Section R602.10.6.5), the intent of this footnote is that, when considering a single wall with stone or masonry veneer, only the bracing on the frame wall to which the veneer is applied, and the braced wall lines perpendicular (both interior and exterior) to it, are impacted by its mass in a seismic event. Thus, only those walls need to have additional bracing hold downs applied.

Certainly, if the veneer is on two, three or four sides of the building, all braced wall lines are impacted; however, if just one side of the structure has stone or masonry veneer, the walls parallel to the veneered wall do not have to comply with the additional bracing requirements. This can reduce construction costs.

The user must be careful, however, when ignoring the braced wall line length adjustments in IRC Tables R602.10.3(2) and R602.10.3(4) *(TABLE 3.4* and *3.6)* if the amount of bracing appears to be sufficient without adjustment. Some of the adjustments increase the amount of bracing required. For example, the story height adjustment in IRC Table R602.10.3(4): when the story height is greater than 10 feet, the required bracing must be increased (to compensate for the increased distance the roof diaphragm is above grade, increasing the seismic force on the structure).

Examples: Determining length of bracing

The following several examples explain how to use the bracing length tables as well as the adjustment tables.

Example 3.1: SDC A, Wind Exposure B, 105 mph

Determining length of bracing using intermittent Method SFB (structural fiberboard sheathing).

Given:

- The detached house is in SDC A with a 105 mph Exposure B design wind speed.

- 48-inch Method SFB bracing is used.

- Braced wall line has no stories above it.

- The distance between braced wall lines is 30 feet.

- The garage is 30 feet deep.

- Roof eave-to-ridge height is 10 feet.

- ***FIGURE 3.17***.

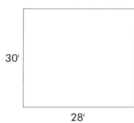

30'

28'

FIGURE 3.17

Example using Method SFB (structural fiberboard sheathing)

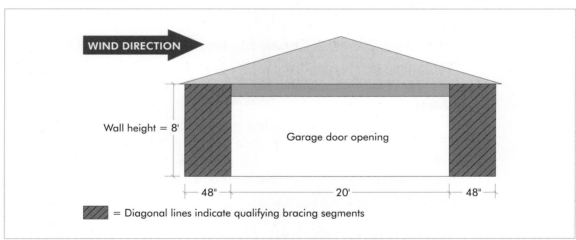

Solution:

STEP 1. Determine which bracing tables, wind and/or seismic, are required for analysis.

The wall line is part of a detached one- or two-family residence. In accordance with IRC Section R301.2.2, it is exempt from seismic design (it is located in SDC A) so only the wind bracing tables apply.

STEP 2. Determine how much wind bracing is required.

- From IRC Table R602.10.3(1) (**TABLE 3.3**), we can see that for a wall line in a single-story structure, Method SFB bracing, wind speeds less than 110 mph (Exposure B), and a braced wall line spacing of 30 feet: <u>8.5 feet of bracing is required</u> and braced wall panels shall not be spaced greater than 20 feet between adjacent edges.

- Adjust values:

    - In accordance with the "wall height adjustment" of IRC Table R602.10.3(2) (**TABLE 3.4**), use of a wall height of 8 feet permits a reduction in bracing length by multiplying length by 0.9.

$$8.5 \text{ feet} \times 0.90 = 7.65 \text{ feet}$$

STEP 3. Determine how much qualified bracing is present in the braced wall line.

$$\frac{(48 \text{ inches} + 48 \text{ inches})}{12 \text{ inches per foot}} = 8 \text{ feet of bracing available}$$

STEP 4. This braced wall line meets the minimum bracing requirement for the given conditions: the 8 feet of bracing provided is more than the 7.65 feet required.

Example 3.2: SDC D$_0$, Wind Exposure B, 90 mph

Determining length of bracing using Method PBS (particleboard sheathing) in a 10-foot tall wall.

Given:

- The structure is a single-family residence in SDC D$_0$ with a 90 mph Exposure B design wind speed.

- 48-inch Method PBS bracing is used.

- Braced wall line has one story above it.

- Roof eave-to-ridge height is 7 feet.

- Light-weight wood construction with asphalt shingles.

- The distance between braced wall lines is 30 feet.

- **FIGURE 3.18**.

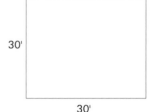

30'

30'

FIGURE 3.18

Example using Method PBS (particleboard sheathing)

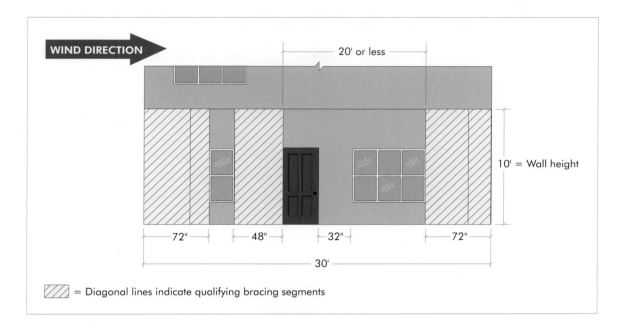

= Diagonal lines indicate qualifying bracing segments

Solution:

STEP 1. Determine which bracing tables, wind and/or seismic, are required for analysis.

The wall line is assumed to be a part of a detached one- or two-family residence. In accordance with IRC Section R301.2.2, this structure is located in SDC D$_0$ and therefore not exempt from seismic design. Both wind and seismic bracing tables must be considered.

STEP 2. Determine how much wind bracing is required.

- From IRC Table R602.10.3(1) (**TABLE 3.3**), we can see that for a first-story wall line of a two-story structure, 10-foot tall wall, Method PBS bracing, 90 mph winds (Exposure B), and a braced wall line spacing of 30 feet: <u>10.5 feet of bracing is required</u> and braced wall panels shall not be spaced greater than 20 feet between adjacent edges.

- Adjust values:

  ○ In accordance with "Roof eave-to-ridge height" IRC Table R602.10.3(2) (**TABLE 3.4**), for a two-story building with a 7-foot ridge height, multiply the required bracing length by 0.91 by interpolation (see **APPENDIX C**).

    10.5 feet x 0.91 = 9.56 feet of wind bracing required

STEP 3. Determine how much seismic bracing is required.

- From IRC Table R602.10.3(3) (**TABLE 3.5**), for a first-story wall line of a two-story structure, 10-foot tall wall, Method PBS bracing, SDC D$_0$, a braced wall line spacing of 30 feet, and a braced wall line length of 30 feet: <u>15.8 feet of bracing is required</u>.

- Adjust values:

  - The required bracing is based on a braced wall spacing less than or equal to 25 feet. For braced wall line spacing of 30 feet in accordance with IRC Table R602.10.3(4) (**TABLE 3.6**), an adjustment factor of 1.2 is required.

    15.8 feet x 1.2 = 19 feet of seismic bracing is required

STEP 4. Determine how much qualified bracing is present in the braced wall line.

$$\frac{(72 \text{ inches} + 72 \text{ inches} + 48 \text{ inches})}{12 \text{ inches per foot}} = 16 \text{ feet of bracing available}$$

STEP 5. Of the two determined bracing wall lengths, the seismic requirement is greater and controls at 19 feet; however, the braced wall line does not meet this requirement for the given conditions. The 16 feet of bracing present is less than the 19 feet required. Possible solutions include:

- Add additional bracing panel length (an unlikely solution as the braced wall line length is 30 feet long and 19 feet is required).

- For seismic applications, IRC Table R602.10.1.3 (**TABLE 3.1**) provides for braced wall lines to be spaced up to 30 feet apart adjacent to a single room (not to exceed 900 square feet) in each dwelling unit, as long as all of the other braced wall lines in that unit are spaced at 25 feet or less. As a solution for this example, ensure that other braced wall lines in the structure do not exceed 25 feet on center spacing, then the 1.2 multiplier applied to the required amount of bracing need not be applied to the amount of seismic bracing required. As such, 15.8 feet of bracing is required.

- However, the requirements can also be met with Method WSP (requires 13.5 feet of bracing) or Methods CS-WSP or CS-SFB (requires 11.5 feet of bracing). All three of these methods provide sufficient bracing, assuming the 900 square foot provisions have been met.

- Switching to Method CS-WSP, with the 1.2 adjustment factor for 30 foot braced wall line spacing, is another solution.

Example 3.3: SDC A, Wind Exposure B, 90 mph

Determining length of bracing using Method HPS (hardboard panel siding), located away from corner, in 9-foot tall wall with offsets in braced wall line.

Given:

- The house is in SDC A with a 90 mph Exposure B design wind speed.

- 48-inch-wide Method HPS bracing is used.

- Braced wall line has one story above it.

- Lightweight wood construction with asphalt shingles.

- Roof eave-to-ridge height is 9 feet.

- The distance between braced wall lines is 25 feet.

- ***FIGURE 3.19***.

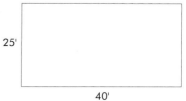

FIGURE 3.19

Example using Method HPS (hardboard panel siding)

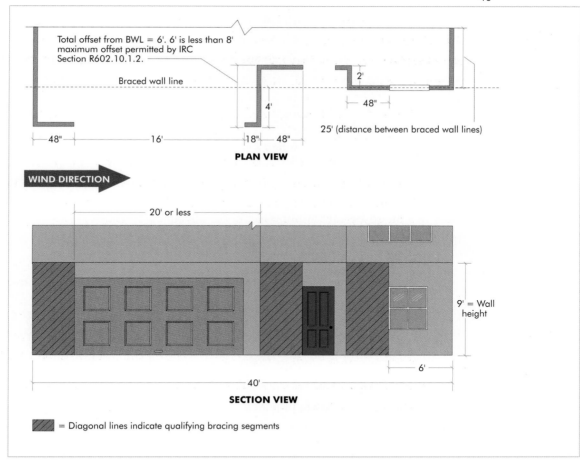

Solution:

STEP 1. Determine which bracing tables, wind and/or seismic, are required for analysis.

The wall line is assumed to be a part of a detached one-or two-family residence. In accordance with typical IRC Section R301.2.2, it is exempt from seismic design (it is located in SDC A) so only the wind bracing tables apply.

STEP 2. Determine how much wind bracing is required.

- From IRC Table R602.10.3(1) (**TABLE 3.3**), we can see that for a first-story wall line of a two-story structure, 9-foot tall wall, Method HPS bracing, 90 mph winds (Exposure B), and a braced wall line spacing of 25 feet: 9 feet of bracing is required by interpolation (see **APPENDIX C**) (7.5 feet required for 20 foot spacing and 10.5 feet required for 30 foot spacing; interpolation yields 9 feet).

- Adjust values:

    ○ In accordance with IRC Table R602.10.3(2) (**TABLE 3.4**), the use of 9-foot tall walls permits an adjustment of 0.95.

    $$9 \text{ feet} \times 0.95 = 8.6 \text{ feet of bracing required}$$

    ○ In accordance with IRC Table R602.10.3(2) (**TABLE 3.4**), an eave-to-ridge height of 9 feet permits an adjustment of 0.97, by interpolation.

    $$8.6 \text{ feet} \times 0.97 = 8.3 \text{ feet of bracing required}$$

STEP 3. Determine how much qualified bracing is present in the braced wall line.

Note that all offsets are within 4 feet of the effective (imaginary) braced wall line, so all qualified full-width panels on all three wall sections count towards bracing the braced wall line.

$$\frac{(48 \text{ inches} + 48 \text{ inches} + 48 \text{ inches})}{12 \text{ inches per foot}} = 12 \text{ feet of bracing available}$$

Note that, with respect to the middle 48-inch bracing segment, it would be improper (IRC Section R602.10.2) to add the adjacent 18-inch section to that segment.

STEP 4. This braced wall line meets the minimum bracing requirements for the given conditions: the 12 feet of bracing provided is more than the 8.3 feet required. The existing bracing is sufficient.

Note that the panel on the right is located 6 feet away from one end of the braced wall line. This meets both the IRC Section R602.10.2.2 location requirements (a braced wall panel shall begin within 10 feet from each end of a braced wall line) and the IRC Section R602.10.1.2 offset requirements (all wall lines occur within 4 feet of designated braced wall line).

Example 3.4: SDC B, Wind Exposure C, 105 mph

Determining length of bracing using Method PCP (Portland cement plaster).

Given:

- The house is in SDC B with a 105 mph Exposure C design wind speed.

- Method PCP bracing is used. Method PCP adds 10.4 psf to the weight of the wall. The weight associated with the plaster does not require an adjustment factor within SDC B, as one- and two-family residences are exempt from seismic requirements (per IRC Section R301.2.2).

- Light-weight roof construction with asphalt shingles.

- Roof eave-to-ridge height is 7 feet.

- Braced wall line has one story above it.

- The distance between braced wall lines is 40 feet.

- ***FIGURE 3.20***.

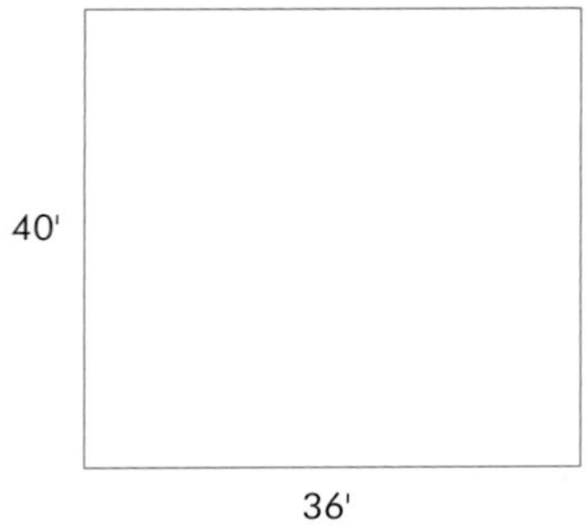

40'

36'

FIGURE 3.20

Example using Method PCP (Portland cement plaster)

WIND DIRECTION

8' = Wall height

7'   8'   6'   8'   7'

36'

▨ = Diagonal lines indicate qualifying bracing segments

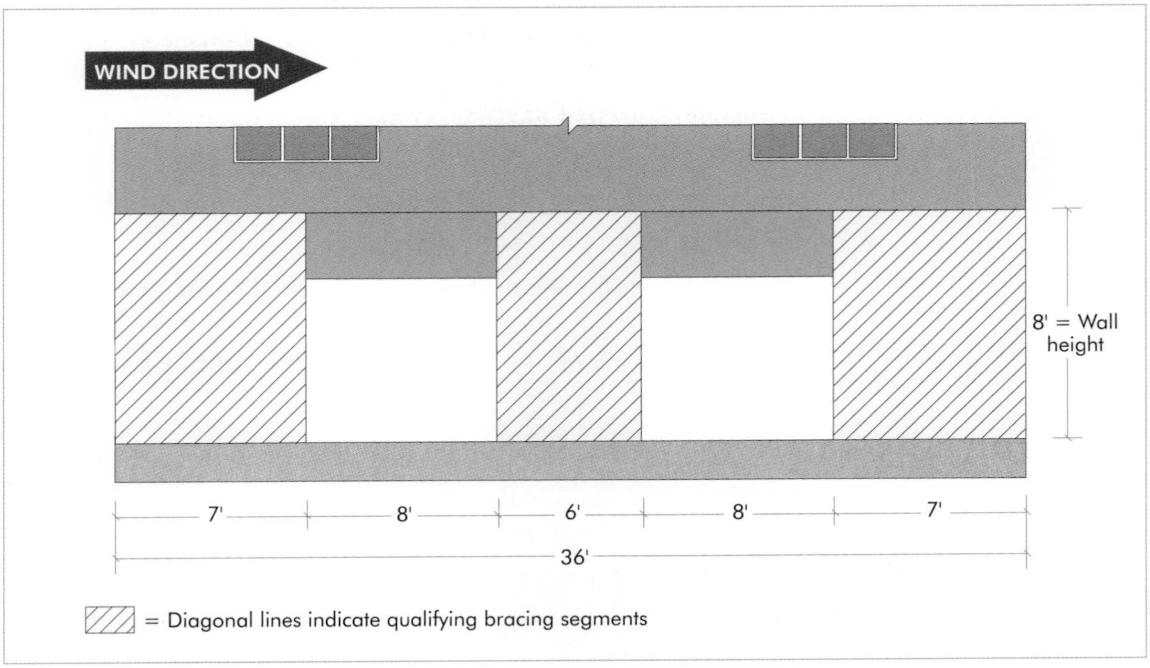

Solution:

STEP 1. Determine which bracing tables, wind and/or seismic, are required for analysis.

As the wall line is located in a SDC B, all structures covered by the IRC are exempt from seismic design. Only the wind bracing tables apply.

STEP 2. Determine how much wind bracing is required.

- From IRC Table R602.10.3(1) (**TABLE 3.3**), we can see that for a first-story wall line of a two-story structure, Method PCP bracing, 105 mph winds (Exposure B), and a braced wall line spacing of 40 feet. If using the 110 mph portion of IRC Table R602.10.3(1), 20.5 feet of bracing is required. If, however, interpolation (see **APPENDIX C**) is used between the 100 mph and the 110 mph portions of the table, only 18.75 feet of bracing is required. For this example, interpolation will not be used, even though it provides a workable solution. Instead, this example illustrates the addition of an interior braced wall line in the solution.

- Adjust values:

    ○ In accordance with IRC Table R602.10.3(2) (**TABLE 3.4**), a two-story Exposure C building requires an adjustment of 1.3.

    20.5 feet x 1.3 = 26.7 feet of bracing required

    ○ In accordance with IRC Table R602.10.3(2) (**TABLE 3.4**), for eave-to-ridge height of 7 feet, by interpolation:

    26.65 feet x 0.91 = 24.3 feet of bracing required

    ○ In accordance with IRC Table R602.10.3(2) (**TABLE 3.4**), for an 8-foot maximum wall height:

    24.25 feet x 0.90 = 21.8 feet of bracing required

STEP 3. Determine how much qualified bracing is present in the braced wall line.

(7 feet + 6 feet + 7 feet) = 20 feet of bracing available

STEP 4. This braced wall line does not meet the minimum bracing requirement for the given conditions: the 20 feet of bracing present is less than the 21.8 feet required. One possible solution is to add an interior braced wall line as shown in **FIGURE 3.21**. This results in braced wall line spacings of 25 and 15 feet. Repeat steps 2-4 for braced wall line spacing of 25 feet.

FIGURE 3.21

Adding a braced wall line to the interior of the structure to reduce bracing on exterior wall lines

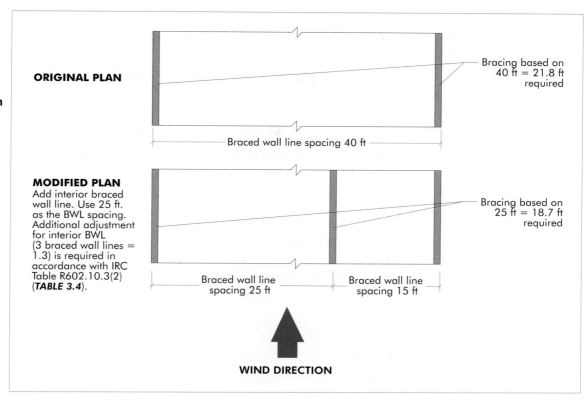

ORIGINAL PLAN

Bracing based on 40 ft = 21.8 ft required

Braced wall line spacing 40 ft

MODIFIED PLAN
Add interior braced wall line. Use 25 ft. as the BWL spacing. Additional adjustment for interior BWL (3 braced wall lines = 1.3) is required in accordance with IRC Table R602.10.3(2) (**TABLE 3.4**).

Bracing based on 25 ft = 18.7 ft required

Braced wall line spacing 25 ft

Braced wall line spacing 15 ft

WIND DIRECTION

STEP 2 (REPEAT). Determine how much wind bracing is required.

- From IRC Table R602.10.3(1) (**TABLE 3.3**), we can see that for a first-story wall line of a two-story structure, Method PCP bracing, 105 mph winds, and a braced wall line spacing of 25 feet: <u>13.5 feet of bracing is required</u> by interpolation (see **APPENDIX C**) (11 feet required for 20 foot spacing and 16 feet required for 30 foot spacing; interpolation yields 13.5 feet). Note that the next largest wind speed 110 mph – was used for this example. Interpolation between 100 mph and 110 mph could have been used for a reduced braced wall line requirement.

- Adjust values:

  ○ In accordance with IRC Table R602.10.3(2) (**TABLE 3.4**), a two-story Exposure C building requires an adjustment of 1.3.

    13.5 feet x 1.3 = 17.6 feet of bracing required

  ○ In accordance with IRC Table R602.10.3(2) (**TABLE 3.4**), for an eave-to-ridge height of 7 feet, by interpolation:

    17.6 feet x 0.91 = 16 feet of bracing required

  ○ In accordance with IRC Table R602.10.3(2) (**TABLE 3.4**), for an 8 foot maximum wall height:

    16 feet x 0.90 = 14.4 feet of bracing required

○ In accordance with IRC Table R602.10.3(2) (**TABLE 3.4**), three braced wall lines require an additional adjustment of 1.3.

14.4 feet x 1.3 = 18.7 feet of bracing required

STEP 3 (REPEAT). See Step 3 above.

STEP 4 (REPEAT). This braced wall line meets the minimum bracing requirement for the given conditions: the 20 feet of bracing present is more than the 18.7 feet required.

Note that once the braced wall line length requirement has been met by the braced wall length provided, it is unnecessary to seek additional reductions to the required braced wall line length.

Examples: Determining length of bracing when using narrow-width panels

The following several examples explain how to use the bracing length tables as well as the adjustment tables to determine the length of bracing when using narrow-width (less than 48 inches wide) braced wall panels.

Example 3.5: SDC C, Wind Exposure B, 90 mph

Determining length of bracing using Method CS-G (continuously sheathed wood structural panel adjacent to garage openings)

Method CS-G permits bracing panels on either side of single-story garages that have a 4:1 height-to-length ratio – the tabular values based on wall height are provided in IRC Table R602.10.5 (**TABLE 3.28**). This bracing option is included in IRC Table R602.10.4 (**TABLE 3.22**) and can only be used when the wall line is continuously sheathed with wood structural panels (Method CS-WSP) in accordance with IRC Section R602.10.4.2. Note the Footnote b requires a 3 psf limitation on roof mass when in SDCs D_0, D_1 and D_2. The limitation does not apply to the selection of wind bracing or lower SDCs. An increase in roof mass increases seismic loads only.

Given:

- The single-family garage is located in SDC C with a 90 mph Exposure B design wind speed.

- Method CS-G bracing is used per IRC Section R602.10.4 (see also IRC Table R602.10.4 (**TABLE 3.24**)).

- The braced wall line has a roof with a dead load of 15 psf. (Note that Footnote b of IRC Table R602.10.4 (**TABLE 3.7**) is a seismic requirement and does not apply in this case (per IRC Section R301.2.2) because the structure is a single-family garage located in SDC C.)

- The distance between braced wall lines is 25 feet.

- Roof eave-to-ridge height is 6 feet.

- **FIGURE 3.22**.

25'

20'

FIGURE 3.22

Example using Method CS-G (continuously sheathed wood structural panel adjacent to garage openings)

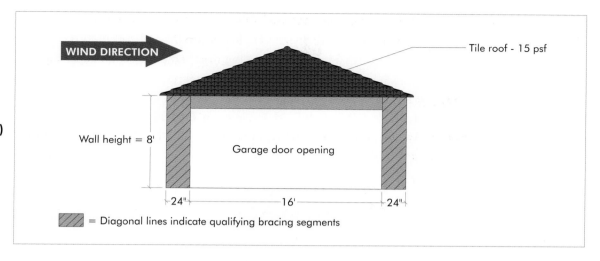

Solution:

STEP 1. Determine which bracing tables, wind and/or seismic, are required for analysis.

As the wall line is a part of a single-family residence in SDC C, it is exempt from seismic design. Only the wind bracing tables apply.

STEP 2. Determine how much wind bracing is required.

- From IRC Table R602.10.3(1) (**TABLE 3.3**), we can see that for continuous sheathing, braced wall line spacing of 25 feet, and wind speeds of 90 mph or less (Exposure B): <u>4.25 feet of bracing is required</u> by interpolation (see **APPENDIX C**) (3.5 feet required for 20 foot spacing and 5 feet required for 30 foot spacing; interpolation yields 4.25 feet).

- Note also that a qualified return corner (IRC Figure R602.10.7) (**FIGURES 3.49-3.53**) is also required at each end of the braced wall line. In lieu of a return corner, a minimum 800 lb capacity hold down must be attached to the corner studs.

- Adjust values:

  ○ In accordance with IRC Table R602.10.3(2) (**TABLE 3.4**), a single-story building with a 6-foot eave-to-ridge height is permitted an adjustment of 0.76 by interpolation.

    4.25 feet x 0.76 = 3.23 feet of bracing required

  ○ In accordance with IRC Table R602.10.3(2) (**TABLE 3.4**), a building with an 8-foot wall height is permitted an adjustment of 0.90.

    3.23 feet x 0.90 = 2.91 feet of bracing required

STEP 3. Determine how much qualified bracing is present in the braced wall line. In accordance with IRC Table R602.10.5 (**TABLE 3.28**), the minimum length of a braced wall panel for Method CS-G on an 8-foot wall height is 24 inches.

    24 inches + 24 inches = 48 inches = 4 feet of bracing available

STEP 4. This braced wall line meets the minimum bracing requirement for the given conditions: the 4 feet of bracing present is more than the 2.91 feet required. Note that IRC Section R602.10.2.3 requires a minimum bracing requirement after all adjustments of two braced wall panels for each braced wall line. This additional requirement is met by the two CS-G panels.

Example 3.6: SDC A, Wind Exposure B, 100 mph

Determining length of bracing using Method CS-SFB (continuously sheathed structural fiberboard).

Given:

- The house is in SDC A with a 100 mph Exposure B design wind speed.

- Method CS-SFB braced panel length per IRC Section R602.10.5 (see also IRC Table R602.10.5 (***TABLE 3.28***))

- Braced wall line has one story above it.

- The distance between braced wall lines is 20 feet.

- Roof eave-to-ridge height is 5 feet.

- ***FIGURE 3.23***.

FIGURE 3.23

Example using Method CS-SFB (continuously sheathed structural fiberboard)

Solution:

STEP 1. Determine which bracing tables, wind and/or seismic, are required for analysis.

As the wall line is a part of a single-family residence in SDC B, it is exempt from seismic design. Only the wind bracing tables apply.

STEP 2. Determine how much wind bracing is required.

- From IRC Table R602.10.3(1) (**TABLE 3.3**), we can see that for a first-story wall line in a two-story residence, a 100 mph basic wind speed (Exposure B), continuously sheathed with a wall bracing spacing of 20 feet: <u>9 feet of bracing is required</u>.

- Adjust values:

  - In accordance with IRC Table R602.10.3(2) (**TABLE 3.4**), for an eave-to-ridge height of 5 feet:

$$9 \text{ feet} \times 0.85 = 7.7 \text{ feet of bracing required}$$

  - In accordance with IRC Table R602.10.3(2) (**TABLE 3.4**), for a wall height of 8 feet:

$$7.7 \text{ feet} \times 0.9 = 6.9 \text{ feet of bracing required}$$

STEP 3. Determine how much qualified bracing is present in the braced wall line.

Check full-height segment lengths to ensure that they meet minimum length requirements (per IRC Table R602.10.5) (**TABLE 3.28**) for the size of the window or door opening adjacent. Note that the 24-inch wall segment adjacent to the door is too narrow to count. A braced wall panel adjacent to an 80-inch clear height opening requires a minimum length of 32 inches.

$$\frac{(32 \text{ inches} + 32 \text{ inches} + 32 \text{ inches})}{12 \text{ inches per foot}} = 8 \text{ feet of bracing available}$$

STEP 4. This braced wall line meets the minimum bracing requirement for the given conditions: the 8 feet of bracing present is more than the 6.9 feet required.

Note that the adjustments to the required bracing length that reduce its required length are necessary, as it was determined that 8 feet of bracing is available, and the braced wall length requirement from IRC Table R602.10.3(1) (**TABLE 3.3**) is 9 feet. The user must be careful, however, when ignoring the braced wall line length adjustments in IRC Tables R602.10.3(2) and R602.10.3(4) (**TABLE 3.4** and **3.6**) if the amount of bracing appears to be sufficient without adjustment. Some of the adjustments increase the amount of bracing required. For example, the eave-to-ridge adjustment in IRC Table R602.10.3(2): when the eave-to-ridge height is 10 feet or greater, the required bracing must be increased (to compensate for the increased surface area of the structure resisting the wind load).

Note that a qualified return corner (IRC Figure R602.10.7, reproduced in **FIGURES 3.49-3.53**) is required at each end of the braced wall line. In lieu of a return corner, a minimum 800 lb capacity hold down must be attached to the corner studs.

Example 3.7: SDC B, Wind Exposure B, 85 mph

Determining length of bracing using Method CS-PF (continuously sheathed portal frame)

Given:

- The structure is a single-family residence in SDC B with an 85 mph Exposure B design wind speed.

- 10-foot wall height.

- Method CS-PF bracing is used per IRC Table R602.10.6.4 (**TABLE 3.7**) (see also IRC Tables R602.10.5 and R602.10.6.4 (**TABLES 3.25** and **3.28**) for minimum length requirements).

- Braced wall line has one story above it.

- The distance between braced wall lines is 20 feet.

- Roof eave-to-ridge height is 6 feet.

- ***FIGURE 3.24***.

FIGURE 3.24

Example using Method CS-PF (continuously sheathed portal frame) at garage wall

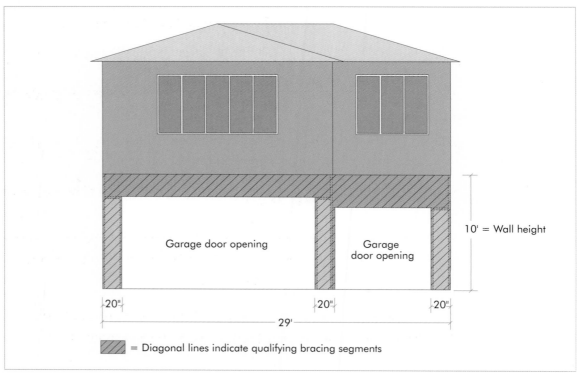

Solution:

STEP 1. Determine which bracing tables, wind and/or seismic, are required for analysis.

As the wall line is a part of a single-family residence in SDC B, it is exempt from seismic design. Only the wind bracing tables apply.

STEP 2. Determine how much wind bracing is required.

- From IRC Table R602.10.3(1) (**TABLE 3.3**), we can see that for a first-story wall line of a two-story structure, 10-foot tall wall, 85 mph Exposure B wind zone, Method CS-PF bracing, and a braced wall line spacing of 20 feet: <u>5.5 feet of bracing is required</u>. Note also that a qualified return corner (IRC Figure R602.10.7, reproduced in **FIGURES 3.49-3.53**) is also required at each end of the braced wall line. In lieu of a return corner, a minimum 800 lb capacity hold down must be attached to the corner studs.

- Adjust values:

    ○ In accordance with IRC Table R602.10.3(2) (**TABLE 3.4**), for a two-story building with an a eave-to-ridge height of 6 feet, by interpolation (see **APPENDIX C**):

        5.5 feet x 0.88 = 4.8 feet of bracing required

STEP 3. Check minimum length requirement for Method CS-PF.

Per IRC Table R602.10.5 (**TABLE 3.28**), for a 10-foot tall wall, the minimum length permitted for this segment is 20 inches.

STEP 4. Determine how much qualified bracing is present in the braced wall line.

$$\frac{(20\text{ inches} + 20\text{ inches} + 20\text{ inches})}{12\text{ inches per foot}} = 5\text{ feet of bracing available}$$

When a pony wall is used to increase the wall height with respect to the clear height of the garage door opening, IRC Table R602.10.6.4 (**TABLE 3.31**) provides the necessary provisions for selection of required strapping to resist wind loads.

STEP 5. This braced wall line meets the minimum bracing requirement for the given conditions: the 5 feet of bracing present is more than the 4.8 feet feet required.

Example 3.8: SDC C, Wind Exposure C, 90 mph

Determining length of bracing using Method CS-PF (continuously sheathed portal frame) and Method CS-WSP (continuously sheathed wood structural panel) with offsets in braced wall line for a single-story structure.

Given:

- The structure is a one-story, single-family residence in SDC C with a 90 mph Exposure C design wind speed.

- 9-foot wall height.

- Method CS-PF and CS-WSP bracing are used, per IRC Section R602.10.4.2 (see also IRC Tables R602.10.4 (***TABLE 3.7***) and R602.10.6.4 (***TABLE 3.31***)).

- Braced wall line supports a roof only.

- The distance between braced wall lines is 30 feet.

- Roof eave-to-ridge height is 7.5 feet.

- ***FIGURE 3.25***.

FIGURE 3.25

Example using Method CS-PF (continuously sheathed portal frame) at offset wall line

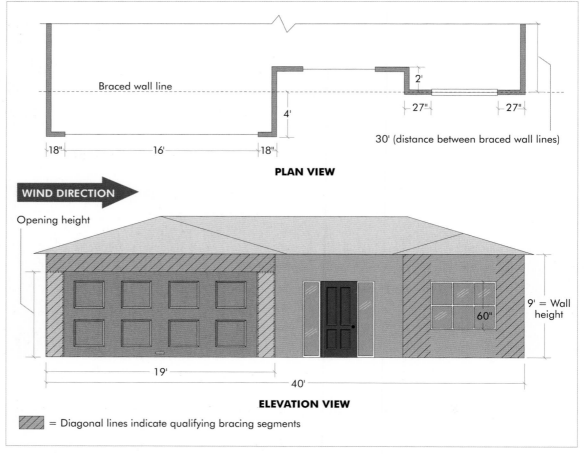

PLAN VIEW

WIND DIRECTION

ELEVATION VIEW

= Diagonal lines indicate qualifying bracing segments

Solution:

Note that the two wall lines with braced wall panels are within 4 feet of the designated braced wall line, thus acceptable per IRC Section R602.10.1.2 and IRC Figure R602.10.1.1 (**FIGURE 3.2**).

STEP 1. Determine which bracing tables, wind and/or seismic, are required for analysis.

As the wall line is a part of a single-family residence in SDC C, it is exempt from seismic design. Only the wind bracing tables apply.

STEP 2. Determine how much wind bracing is required.

- From IRC Table R602.10.3(1) (**TABLE 3.3**), we can see that for a single-story structure, 9-foot tall wall, 90 mph Exposure B wind zone, continuously sheathed bracing, and a braced wall line spacing of 30 feet: <u>5 feet of bracing is required</u>.

- Adjust values:

   ○ In accordance with IRC Table R602.10.3(2) (**TABLE 3.4**), for a single-story building with an eave-to-ridge height of 7.5 feet, by interpolation (see **APPENDIX C**):

$$5 \text{ feet} \times 0.85 = 4.25 \text{ feet of bracing required}$$

   ○ In accordance with IRC Table R602.10.3(2) (**TABLE 3.4**), use of 9-foot tall walls permits an adjustment of 0.95:

$$4.25 \text{ feet} \times 0.95 = 4 \text{ feet of bracing required}$$

   ○ In accordance with IRC Table R602.10.3(2) (**TABLE 3.4**), use of Exposure C requires an adjustment of 1.2:

$$4 \text{ feet} \times 1.2 = 4.8 \text{ feet of bracing required}$$

STEP 3. Check garage wall minimum length requirement for Method CS-PF.

Per IRC Table R602.10.5 (**TABLE 3.28**), for a 9-foot tall wall, the minimum length permitted for this segment is 18 inches. The minimum length for Method CS-PF is met in the example.

STEP 4. Check living space wall bracing minimum length requirement for Method CS-WSP.

IRC Table R602.10.5 (**TABLE 3.28**) permits the use of a 27-inch segment in a 9-foot tall wall adjacent to a clear opening height that is less than or equal to 64 inches. In this case, the clear opening height is the 60-inch high window in the exterior wall. The minimum panel length for Method CS-WSP is met in the living-space portion of the structure.

STEP 5. Determine how much qualified bracing is present in the braced wall line.

$$\frac{(18 \text{ inches} + 18 \text{ inches} + 27 \text{ inches} + 27 \text{ inches})}{12 \text{ inches per foot}} = 7.5 \text{ feet of bracing available}$$

STEP 6. This braced wall line meets the minimum bracing requirements for the given conditions: the 7.5 feet of bracing present is more than the 4.8 feet required. The distance between the adjacent edges of braced wall panels is not more than 20 feet. The existing bracing is sufficient. Note that a qualified return corner (IRC Figure R602.10.7, reproduced in **FIGURES 3.49-3.53**) is also required at each end of each braced wall line. In lieu of a return corner, a minimum 800 lb capacity hold down must be attached to the corner studs.

When a pony wall is used to increase the wall height with respect to the clear height of the garage door opening, IRC Table R602.10.6.4 (**TABLE 3.31**) provides the necessary provisions for selection of required strapping to resist wind loads.

Example 3.9: SDC B, Wind Exposure B, 90 mph

Determining length of bracing using Method ABW (alternate braced wall) at garage wall.

Given:

- The single-family residence is in SDC B with a 90 mph Exposure B design wind speed.

- 10-foot wall height.

- Method ABW with hold downs and wood structural panel sheathing is used, per IRC Section R602.10.6.1, IRC Figure R602.10.6.1 (**FIGURE 3.44**), and IRC Table R602.10.6.1 (**TABLE 3.30**).

- Braced wall line has one story above it.

- Roof eave-to-ridge height is 5.5 feet.

- The distance between braced wall lines is 20 feet.

- **FIGURE 3.26**.

FIGURE 3.26

Example using Method ABW (alternate braced wall) at garage wall

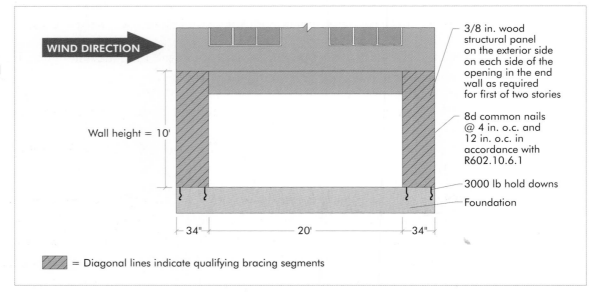

Solution:

STEP 1. Determine which bracing tables, wind and/or seismic, are required for analysis.

As the wall line is a part of a single-family residence in SDC B, it is exempt from seismic design. Only the wind bracing tables apply.

STEP 2. Determine how much wind bracing is required.

- From IRC Table R602.10.3(1) (**TABLE 3.3**), we can see that for the first of two stories, 10-foot tall wall, 90 mph Exposure B wind zone, Method WSP bracing (or any of the panel-type bracing methods, except Method GB), and a braced wall line spacing of 20 feet: 7.5 feet of bracing is required. (Note that Method ABW is discussed in detail under IRC Section R602.10.6, later in this chapter. Although not specifically listed in IRC Table R602.10.3(1), determination of the total bracing length requirement for Method ABW, when used by itself, is accomplished by using values established for Method WSP. It is an alternate (like Method PFH) to other wall bracing methods and if it were to be used, for example, in a Method PCP wall, the length of bracing for the Method PCP wall would be the required bracing for the wall. Method ABW bracing could be used to replace four feet of the Method PCP wall each time it was used.)

- Adjust values:

  ○ In accordance with IRC Table R602.10.3(2) (**TABLE 3.4**), for a two-story structure with an eave-to-ridge height of 5.5 feet, by interpolation (see **APPENDIX C**):

$$7.5 \text{ feet} \times 0.865 = 6.5 \text{ feet of bracing required}$$

STEP 3. Check minimum length requirement for Method WSP.

In accordance with IRC Table R602.10.5 (**TABLE 3.28**), for a 10-foot braced wall, a minimum panel length of 34 inches is required. Minimum braced panel length is met.

STEP 4. Determine how much qualified bracing is present in the braced wall line.

- Note that each 34-inch segment, for the purpose of determining total required length of bracing per IRC Table R602.10.5 (**TABLE 3.28**), is equivalent to 48 inches of bracing.

$$\frac{(48 \text{ inches} + 48 \text{ inches})}{12 \text{ inches per foot}} = 8 \text{ feet of bracing available}$$

STEP 5. This braced wall line meets the minimum bracing requirements for the given conditions: the 8 feet of bracing present is more than the 6.5 feet required. The existing bracing is sufficient. Note that a 3,000 lb hold down (IRC Table R602.10.6.1) (**TABLE 3.30**) is required at each end of each braced panel when using this method. Foundation reinforcement is also required in accordance with IRC Section R602.10.6.1 and IRC Figure R602.10.6.1 (**FIGURE 3.40**) when Method ABW is used. As ABW is installed at the bottom of two stories, the panel edges require nailing at 4 inches o.c.

Example 3.10: SDC D$_2$, Wind Exposure C, 110 mph

Determining length of bracing using Method PFH (portal frame with hold downs) at garage wall.

Given:

- The house is in SDC D$_2$ with a 110 mph Exposure C design wind speed.

- 8-foot wall height.

- Method PFH with hold downs is used, per IRC Section R602.10.6.2, Intermittent Method WSP is used on the structure.

- Braced wall line has one story above it.

- The distance between braced wall lines is 20 feet.

- Roof eave-to-ridge height is 8 feet.

- *FIGURE 3.27*.

FIGURE 3.27

Example using Method PFH (portal frame with hold downs) with hold downs at garage wall

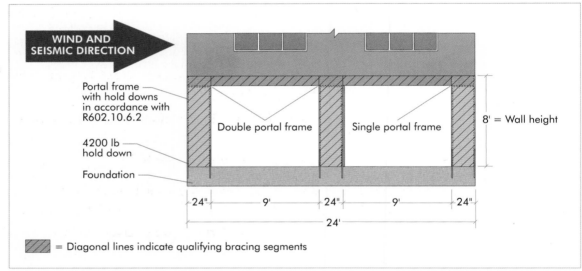

Note that when using Method CS-PF, a continuous header across both openings is not permitted. In the figure above, one header spans the double portal frame and the header for the single portal frame bears on the left side on an additional jack stud(s). This is how a double opening with Method CS-PF should be fabricated.

Solution:

STEP 1. Determine which bracing tables, wind and/or seismic, are required for analysis.

In accordance with IRC Section R301.2.2, this structure is located in SDC D$_2$ and therefore not exempt from seismic design. Both wind and seismic bracing tables must be considered.

STEP 2. Determine how much wind bracing is required.

- From IRC Table R602.10.3(1) (**TABLE 3.3**), we can see that for the first-story braced wall line in a two-story structure, 8-foot tall wall, intermittent Method WSP bracing, 110 mph wind Exposure B, and a braced wall line spacing of 20 feet: <u>11 feet of bracing is required</u>. As with Method ABW, discussed above, Method PFH is not specifically listed in IRC Table R602.10.3(1). Again, determination of the total bracing length requirement for Method PFH wind bracing is accomplished by using values established for Method WSP.

- Adjust values:

  - In accordance with IRC Table R602.10.3(2) (**TABLE 3.4**), a two-story Exposure C building requires an adjustment of 1.3.

    $$11 \text{ feet x } 1.3 = 14.3 \text{ feet of wind bracing is required}$$

  - In accordance with IRC Table R602.10.3(2) (**TABLE 3.4**), for a two-story building with an eave-to-ridge height of 8 feet, by interpolation (see **APPENDIX C**):

    $$14.3 \text{ feet x } 0.94 = 13.4 \text{ feet of bracing required}$$

  - In accordance with IRC Table R602.10.3(2) (**TABLE 3.4**), use of 8-foot tall walls permits an adjustment of 0.9.

    $$13.4 \text{ feet x } 0.90 = 12.1 \text{ feet of wind bracing is required}$$

STEP 3. Determine how much seismic bracing is required.

- From IRC Table R602.10.3(3) (**TABLE 3.5**), for a first-story wall line of a two-story structure, Method WSP bracing, SDC D$_2$, a braced wall line length of 24 feet, and a braced wall line spacing of less than 25 feet: <u>13.2 feet of bracing is required</u> by interpolation.

- Adjust values:

  - No applicable seismic adjustment factors.

STEP 4. Determine how much qualified bracing is present in the braced wall line. Per IRC Table R602.10.5 (**TABLE 3.28**), the minimum length required for a Method PFH on a 9-foot tall wall supporting one story and a roof is 24 inches.

- Note that each 24-inch segment, for the purpose of determining the total length of bracing provided, is equivalent to 48 inches of bracing.

  $$\frac{(48 \text{ inches} + 48 \text{ inches} + 48 \text{ inches})}{12 \text{ inches per foot}} = 12 \text{ feet of bracing available}$$

STEP 5. Of the two determined wall bracing lengths, the seismic bracing requirement is greater and controls at 13.2 feet. The braced wall line does not meet the requirement for the given conditions: the 12 feet of bracing present is less than the 13.2 feet required.

A possible solution is to reduce the length of the garage wall line to 22 feet while maintaining the same bracing, which would reduce the amount of required bracing 12.1 feet. As 12 feet are provided and this is less than one percent deficient, this would probably be considered sufficient.

R602.10.4 Construction methods for *braced wall panels*

R602.10.4 Construction methods for *braced wall panels*. Intermittent and continuously sheathed *braced wall panels* shall be constructed in accordance with this section and the methods listed in Table R602.10.4.

The 2012 IRC bracing methods are essentially the same as those in the 2009, although a new method has been added and the continuous and intermittent methods, formerly listed in separate locations in the bracing provisions, are now listed together in one table.

There are still just two types of bracing: intermittent bracing and continuous sheathing. Intermittent bracing refers to bracing methods that can be used in discrete locations along a braced wall line. Intermittent methods permit the option of using nonstructural sheathing in areas of the wall where bracing is not required. Continuous sheathing bracing methods require that the whole wall line be sheathed, including above and below openings and at gable ends, if present. The continuous methods require less bracing and permit the use of narrower bracing panels, allowing home designers greater flexibility in selecting the size and location of doors and windows. Continuous methods may also provide a substrate suitable for the attachment of nonstructural siding materials in areas exposed to higher wind speeds.

Intermittent bracing methods

The twelve intermittent bracing methods listed in IRC Section R602.10.4 of the 2012 IRC include the eleven intermittent methods from 2009 plus one "new" method. The eleven intermittent methods from the 2009 IRC are:

1. Let-in bracing (Method LIB)

2. Diagonal wood boards (Method DWB)

3. Wood structural panel (plywood or OSB) (Method WSP)

4. Structural fiberboard (Method SFB)

5. Interior gypsum board or gypsum sheathing (Method GB)

6. Particleboard sheathing (Method PBS)

7. Portland cement plaster (Method PCP)

8. Hardboard panel siding (Method HPS)

9. Alternate braced wall (Method ABW)

10. Portal frame with hold downs (Method PFH)

11. Portal frame at garage door openings in Seismic Design Categories A, B and C (Method PFG)

12. Wood structural panels with stone or masonry veneer (Method BV-WSP)

The 12th intermittent bracing method, Method BV-WSP (wood structural panels with stone or masonry veneer) is new to this section and was taken from the text of the existing bracing provisions for structures with stone and masonry veneer. These provisions were previously located in the 2009 IRC Section R602.12 and are essentially unchanged, although they have been clarified and better integrated into the body of the bracing provisions. Method BV-WSP will be discussed in detail later in this chapter.

As the name implies, intermittent bracing methods are meant to be used intermittently along the wall line (as shown in *FIGURE 3.28*). For these methods, the minimum length required for a single braced wall panel segment ranges from 16 to 96 inches. Beginning with the 2009 IRC, slightly shorter panel lengths are permitted for the standard 48 inch bracing methods, but with a penalty. For example, a 42-inch particleboard sheathing (Method PBS) panel may be used as a bracing panel, but when computing the required length of bracing, it is equivalent to only 36 inches of wall bracing. (See IRC Section R602.10.5.2.)

FIGURE 3.28

Example of "intermittent" Method WSP (wood structural panel) braced wall panel

Intermittent bracing need only occur in isolated, specified locations

TABLE 3.7

Intermittent Bracing Methods

Excerpt from IRC Table R602.10.4

TABLE R602.10.4
BRACING METHODS

Methods, Material	Minimum Thickness	Figure	Connection Criteria[a]	
			Fasteners	Spacing
LIB Let-in-bracing	1 × 4 wood or approved metal straps at 45° to 60° angles for maximum 16" stud spacing		Wood: 2-8d common nails or 3-8d (2-1/2" long x 0.113" dia.) nails	Wood: per stud and top and bottom plates
			Metal strap: per manufacturer	Metal: per manufacturer
DWB Diagonal wood boards	3/4"(1" nominal) for maximum 24" stud spacing		2-8d (2-1/2" long × 0.113" dia.) nails or 2 - 1-3/4" long staples	Per stud
WSP Wood structural panel (See Section R604)	3/8"		Exterior sheathing per Table R602.3(3)	6" edges 12" field
			Interior sheathing per Table R602.3(1) or R602.3(2)	Varies by fastener
BV-WSP[e] Wood structural panels with stone or masonry veneer (see Section R602.10.6.5)	7/16"	See figure R602.10.6.5	8d common (2-1/2" × 0.131) nails	4" at panel edges 12" at intermediate supports 4" at braced wall panel end posts
SFB Structural fiberboard sheathing	1/2" or 25/32" for maximum 16" stud spacing		1-1/2" long × 0.12" dia. (for 1/2" thick sheathing) 1-3/4" long × 0.12" dia. (for 25/32" thick sheathing) galvanized roofing nails or 8d common (2-1/2" long × 0.131" dia.) nails	3" edges 6" field
GB Gypsum board	1/2"		Nails or screws per Table R602.3(1) for exterior locations	For all braced wall panel locations: 7" edges (including top and bottom plates) 7" field
			Nails or screws per Table R702.3.5 for interior locations	
PBS Particleboard sheathing (see Section R605)	3/8" or 1/2" for maximum 16" stud spacing		For 3/8", 6d common (2" long × 0.113" dia.) nails For 1/2", 8d common (2-1/2" long × 0.131" dia.) nails	3" edges 6" field
PCP Portland cement plaster	See Section R703.6 for maximum 16" stud spacing		1-1/2" long, 11 gage, 7/16" dia. head nails or 7/8" long, 16 gage staples	6" o.c. on all framing members
HPS Hardboard panel siding	7/16" for maximum 16" stud spacing		0.092" dia., 0.225" dia. head nails with length to accommodate 1-1/2" penetration into studs	4" edges 8" field

(left margin label: Intermittent Bracing Method)

For SI: 1 inch = 25.4 mm, 1 foot = 305 mm, 1 degree = 0.0175 rad, 1 pound per square foot = 47.8 N/m², 1 mile per hour = 0.447 m/s.
a. Adhesive attachment of wall sheathing, including Method GB, shall not be permitted in Seismic Design Categories C, D_0, D_1 and D_2.
e. Method applies to detached one- and two-family dwellings in Seismic Design Categories D_0 through D_2 only.

TABLE 3.7
(Continued)

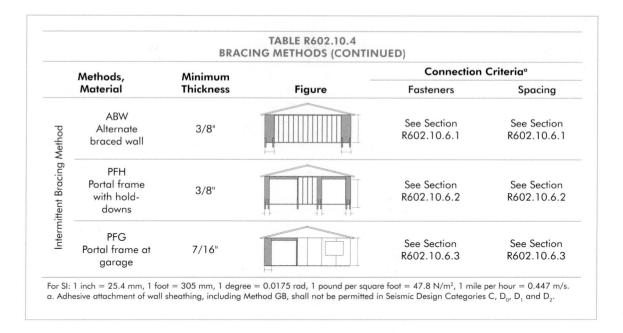

TABLE R602.10.4
BRACING METHODS (CONTINUED)

Methods, Material	Minimum Thickness	Figure	Connection Criteria[a]	
			Fasteners	Spacing
Intermittent Bracing Method — ABW Alternate braced wall	3/8"		See Section R602.10.6.1	See Section R602.10.6.1
PFH Portal frame with hold-downs	3/8"		See Section R602.10.6.2	See Section R602.10.6.2
PFG Portal frame at garage	7/16"		See Section R602.10.6.3	See Section R602.10.6.3

For SI: 1 inch = 25.4 mm, 1 foot = 305 mm, 1 degree = 0.0175 rad, 1 pound per square foot = 47.8 N/m², 1 mile per hour = 0.447 m/s.

a. Adhesive attachment of wall sheathing, including Method GB, shall not be permitted in Seismic Design Categories C, D_0, D_1 and D_2.

TABLE 3.7 displays the twelve intermittent bracing methods contained in the 2012 IRC. Much of the included content, including minimum thickness information and connection requirements, is a carry-over from the 2009 IRC. The following pages contain several additional tables and figures that further detail these methods. Although the methods are, in most cases, not detailed in paragraph form, appropriate sections of the code are referenced as needed.

Method LIB (Let-in bracing)

Note the maximum stud spacing is 16 inches. See **TABLE 3.8** and **FIGURE 3.29**.

TABLE 3.8

Method LIB

Excerpt from IRC Tables R602.10.4 and R602.10.5

Method, Material	Minimum Thickness	Figure	Connection Criteria[a]	
			Fasteners	Spacings
LIB Let-in bracing	1x4 wood or approved metal straps at 45° to 60° angles for maximum 16″ stud spacing		Wood: 2-8d common nails or 3-8d (2-1/2″ long x 0.113″ dia.) nails	Wood: per stud including top and bottom plate
			Metal straps: per manufacturer	Metal: per manufacturer

a. Adhesive attachment of wall sheathing, including Method GB, shall not be permitted In Seismic Design Categories C, D_0, D_1 and D_2.

Minimum length per IRC Table R602.10.5 (TABLE 3.28)	Minimum Length[a] (in.)					Contributing Length (in.)
	Wall Height					
	8 ft	9 ft	10 ft	11 ft	12 ft	
LIB	55	62	69	NP	NP	Actual[b]

NP = Not permitted
a. Linear interpolation shall be permitted.
b. Use actual length when it is greater than or equal to the minimum length.

FIGURE 3.29

Method LIB (let-in bracing)

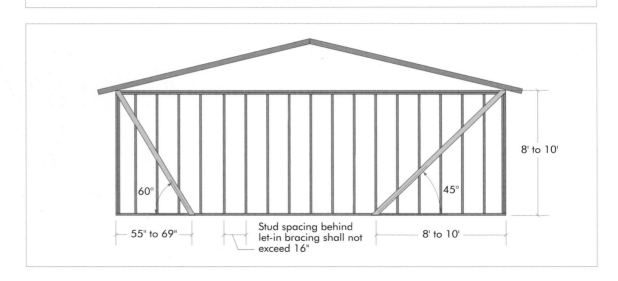

FIGURE 3.35

**Method GB
(gypsum board)
– two faces
sheathed**

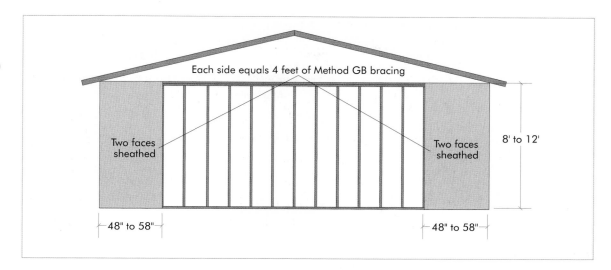

Note that the connection criteria for Method GB in IRC Table R602.10.4 specifies a nail and/or screw schedule of 7 inches at all panel edges and 7 inches in the field of the panel; however, there is not sufficient space in the table to provide all of the permitted fastener types. Two additional tables (referenced under "Connection Criteria" in **TABLE 3.13**) addressing fastener requirements for gypsum sheathing and gypsum wall board are shown in **TABLES 3.14** and **3.15**. Gypsum sheathing, formulated for enhanced moisture and fire resistance, is primarily intended for protected exterior wall applications.

TABLE 3.14

**Fastener
description for
Method GB
(gypsum board)
– gypsum
sheathing**

**Excerpt from IRC
Table R602.3(1)**

Item	Description of Building Materials	Description of Fastener[b]
	Other wall sheathing[h]	
37	1/2" gypsum sheathing[d]	1-1/2" galvanized roofing nail; staple galvanized, 1-1/2" long; 1-1/4" screws, Type W or S
38	5/8" gypsum sheathing[d]	1-3/4" galvanized roofing nail; staple galvanized, 1-5/8" long; 1-5/8" screws, Type W or S

b. Staples are 16-gage wire and have a minimum 7/16-inch on diameter crown width.
d. Four-foot-by-8-foot or 4-foot-by-9-foot shall be applied vertically.
h. Gypsum sheathing shall conform to ASTM C 1396 and shall be installed in accordance with GA 253.

TABLE 3.15

Fastener description for Method GB (gypsum board) – interior gypsum board

Excerpt from IRC Table R702.3.5

Thickness of Gypsum Board (inches)	Appli-cation	Orientation of Gypsum Board to Framing	Size of Nails for Application to Wood Framing
			Application with or without adhesive
1/2	Wall	Either direction	13 gage, 1-3/8" long, 19/64" head; 0.098" diameter, 1-1/4" long, annular-ringed; 5d cooler nail, 0.086" diameter, 1-5/8" long, 15/64"
	Wall	Either direction	head; or gypsum board nail, 0.086" diameter, 1-5/8" long, 9/32" head
5/8	Wall	Either direction	13 gage, 1-5/8" long, 19/64" head; 0.098" diameter, 1-3/8" long, annular-ringed; 6d cooler nail, 0.092" diameter, 1-7/8" long, 1/4" head;
	Wall	Either direction	or gypsum board nail, 0.0915" diameter, 1-7/8" long, 19/64" head

The lengths indicated in *FIGURE 3.34* are for single-sided gypsum bracing panels. IRC Table R602.10.5 (*TABLE 3.28*) permits a minimum length of 4 feet for Method GB bracing placed on just one face of the wall; however, this counts as just 2 feet of bracing. A wall element with both faces sheathed with Method GB fastening requirements, as shown in *FIGURE 3.35*, provides a length of bracing equal to the actual length of the bracing element.

For the 2012 IRC, the prohibition against adhesive attachment of bracing panels in areas of high seismicity (SDC D_0, D_1 and D_2) was relocated to Footnote a of Table R602.10.4 (*TABLE 3.7*). In addition, clarification was added that this prohibition <u>includes</u> Method GB. This was specifically clarified because when attaching gypsum wall board with adhesives, it is important to note that the gypsum wall board so applied cannot be considered bracing Method GB, even if the 7-inch on center nailing pattern is used in addition to the adhesive (a common practice). The basis for the original provision was a similar IBC provision prohibiting the use of adhesives for braced wall panels in SDC D and higher.

Method PBS (Particleboard sheathing)

See **TABLE 3.16** and **FIGURE 3.36**.

Note the maximum stud spacing is 16 inches.

TABLE 3.16

Method PBS

Excerpt from IRC Tables R602.10.4 and R602.10.5

Method, Material	Minimum Thickness	Figure	Connection Criteria[a]	
			Fasteners	Spacings
PBS Particleboard sheathing (see Section R605)	3/8" or 1/2" for maximum 16" stud spacing	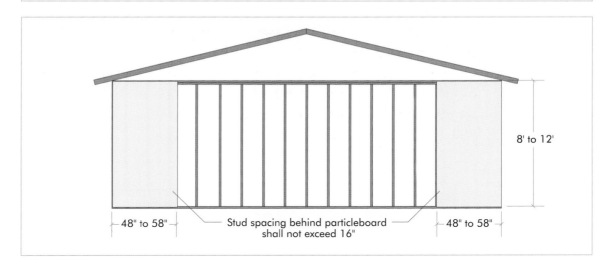	For 3/8", 6d common (2" long x 0.113" dia.) nails. For 1/2", 8d common (2-1/2" x 0.131") nails	3" edges 6" field

a. Adhesive attachment of wall sheathing, including Method GB, shall not be permitted In Seismic Design Categories C, D_0, D_1 and D_2.

Minimum length per IRC Table R602.10.5 (TABLE 3.28)	Minimum Length[a] (in.)					Contributing Length (in.)
	Wall Height					
	8 ft	9 ft	10 ft	11 ft	12 ft	
PBS	48	48	48	53	58	Actual[b]

a. Linear interpolation shall be permitted.
b. Use actual length when it is greater than or equal to the minimum length.

FIGURE 3.36

Method PBS (particleboard sheathing)

Note that in the 2009 IRC, the nail size and schedule was changed for particleboard where it is used for bracing. The traditional nailing schedule, per IRC Table R602.3(1) (6d common nails (2 inches x 0.113 inches) with a 6-inch and 12-inch schedule for panel edges and interior supports respectively), can still be used where the particleboard is <u>not used</u> for bracing.

The attachment schedule for particleboard sheathing when used as bracing has been increased to permit grouping of braced wall panel methods in IRC Tables R602.10.3(1) (**TABLE 3.3**) and R602.10.3(3) (**TABLE 3.5**). Closer nailing gives particleboard the same capacity as the other bracing methods.

Method PCP (Portland cement plaster)

See **TABLE 3.17** and **FIGURE 3.37**.

Note the maximum stud spacing is 16 inches.

TABLE 3.17

Method PCP

Excerpt from IRC Tables R602.10.4 and R602.10.5

Method, Material	Minimum Thickness	Figure	Connection Criteria[a]	
			Fasteners	Spacings
PCP Portland cement plaster	See Section R703.6 for maximum 16" stud spacing		1-1/2", 11 gage, 7/16" dia. head nails or 7/8" long, 16 gage staples	6" o.c. on all framing members

a. Adhesive attachment of wall sheathing, including Method GB, shall not be permitted In Seismic Design Categories C, D_0, D_1 and D_2.

Minimum length per IRC Table R602.10.5 (TABLE 3.28)	Minimum Length[a] (in.)					Contributing Length (in.)
	Wall Height					
	8 ft	9 ft	10 ft	11 ft	12 ft	
PCP	48	48	48	53	58	Actual[b]

a. Linear interpolation shall be permitted.
b. Use actual length when it is greater than or equal to the minimum length.

FIGURE 3.37

Method PCP (Portland cement plaster)

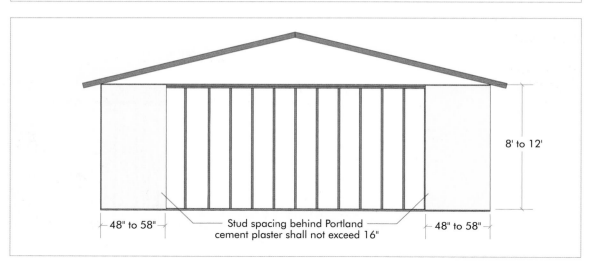

8' to 12'

48" to 58"   Stud spacing behind Portland cement plaster shall not exceed 16"   48" to 58"

IRC Section R703.6 is referenced in the Minimum Thickness column. This section of the code includes additional thickness information and connection criteria.

Fastening requirements for bracing Method PCP:

R703.6 EXTERIOR PLASTER. Installation of these materials shall be in compliance with ASTM C 926 and ASTM C 1063 and the provisions of this code.

R703.6.1 LATH. All lath and lath attachments shall be of corrosion-resistant materials. Expanded metal or woven wire lath shall be attached with 1-1/2-inch-long (38 mm), 11-gage nails having a 7/16-inch (11.1 mm) head, or 7/8-inch-long (22.2 mm), 16-gage staples, spaced at no more than 6 inches (152 mm), or as otherwise approved.

Method HPS (Hardboard panel siding)

See **TABLE 3.18** and **FIGURE 3.38**

Note the maximum stud spacing is 16 inches.

TABLE 3.18

Method HPS

Excerpt from IRC Tables R602.10.4 and R602.10.5

Method, Material	Minimum Thickness	Figure	Connection Criteria[a]	
			Fasteners	**Spacings**
HPS Hardboard panel siding	7/16" for maximum 16" stud spacing	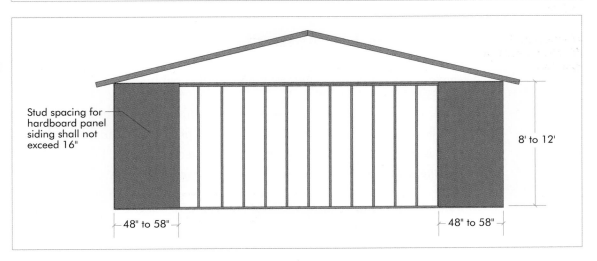	0.092" dia., 0.225" head nails with length to accommodate 1-1/2" penetration into studs	4" edges 8" field

a. Adhesive attachment of wall sheathing, including Method GB, shall not be permitted In Seismic Design Categories C, D_0, D_1 and D_2.

Minimum length per IRC Table R602.10.5 (TABLE 3.28)	Minimum Length[a] (in.)					Contributing Length (in.)
	Wall Height					
	8 ft	**9 ft**	**10 ft**	**11 ft**	**12 ft**	
HPS	48	48	48	53	58	Actual[b]

a. Linear interpolation shall be permitted.
b. Use actual length when it is greater than or equal to the minimum length.

FIGURE 3.38

Method HPS (hardboard panel siding)

Stud spacing for hardboard panel siding shall not exceed 16"

8' to 12'

48" to 58"   48" to 58"

Method ABW (Alternate braced wall)

See **TABLE 3.19** and **FIGURE 3.44**.

TABLE 3.19

Method ABW

Excerpt from IRC Tables R602.10.4 and R602.10.5

Method, Material	Minimum Thickness	Figure	Connection Criteria[a]	
			Fasteners	Spacings
ABW Alternate braced wall	3/8"		See Section R602.10.6.1	See Section R602.10.6.1

a. Adhesive attachment of wall sheathing, including Method GB, shall not be permitted In Seismic Design Categories C, D_0, D_1 and D_2.

Minimum length per IRC Table R602.10.5 (TABLE 3.28)		Minimum Length[a] (in.)					Contributing Length (in.)
		Wall Height					
		8 ft	9 ft	10 ft	11 ft	12 ft	
ABW	SDC A, B and C, wind speed < 110 mph	28	32	34	38	42	48
	SDC D_0, D_1 and D_2, wind speed < 110 mph	32	32	34	NP	NP	

NP = Not permitted
a. Linear interpolation shall be permitted.

Method ABW (alternate braced wall) (IRC Section R602.10.6.1) has been in the IRC in one form or another since 2000 and was often referred to as the "32-inch alternate with hold downs." Method ABW panels are typically used when bracing is needed in a wall area that is not long enough to accommodate a 4-foot braced wall panel.

In the 2012 IRC, Method ABW was grouped with the intermittent wall bracing methods because it may be substituted on a one-for-one basis for a braced wall panel from any other bracing method, and, as such, it is used intermittently. An updated figure (IRC Figure R602.10.6.1, reproduced in **FIGURE 3.44**) clarifies the method and reduces redundancy.

For purposes of computing the required length of bracing, a single Method ABW panel is considered to be equivalent to 4 feet of bracing, regardless of its actual length. (See Table R602.10.5 of the 2012 IRC.)

Method PFH (Portal frame with hold downs)

See **TABLE 3.20** and **FIGURE 3.45**.

TABLE 3.20

Method PFH

Excerpt from IRC Tables R602.10.4 and R602.10.5

Method, Material	Minimum Thickness	Figure	Connection Criteria[a]	
			Fasteners	Spacings
PFH Portal frame with hold downs	3/8"		See Section R602.10.6.2	See Section R602.10.6.2

a. Adhesive attachment of wall sheathing, including Method GB, shall not be permitted In Seismic Design Categories C, D_0, D_1 and D_2.

Minimum length per IRC Table R602.10.5 (TABLE 3.28)		Minimum Length[a] (in.)					Contributing Length (in.)
		Wall Height					
		8 ft	9 ft	10 ft	11 ft	12 ft	
PFH	Supporting roof only	16	16	16	18[c]	20[c]	48
	Supporting one story and roof	24	24	24	27[c]	29[c]	48

a. Linear interpolation shall be permitted.
c. Maximum header height for PFH is 10' per Figure R602.10.6.2, but wall height may be increased to 12' with pony wall.

Method PFH is illustrated and described in full in IRC Section R602.10.6.2 (reproduced in **FIGURE 3.45**).

WHAT IS A HOLD DOWN?

A hold down is a prefabricated metal anchoring device that attaches the framing of a wall system to the structure below. Ultimately, the hold down load path must extend down into the foundation. The hold down prevents uplift of the studs and, thus, overturning of the wall segment. One of a number of types is shown.

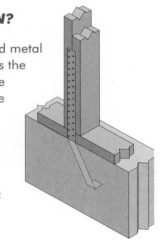

Method PFG (Portal frame at garage door openings in Seismic Design Categories A, B and C)

See **TABLE 3.21** and **FIGURE 3.46**.

TABLE 3.21

Method PFG

Excerpt from IRC Tables R602.10.4 and R602.10.5

Method, Material	Minimum Thickness	Figure	Connection Criteria[a]	
			Fasteners	Spacings
PFG Portal frame at garage	7/16"		See Section R602.10.6.3	See Section R602.10.6.3

a. Adhesive attachment of wall sheathing, including Method GB, shall not be permitted In Seismic Design Categories C, D_0, D_1 and D_2.

Minimum lengths per IRC Table R602.10.5 (TABLE 3.28)	Minimum Length[a] (in.)					Contributing Length (in.)
	Wall Height					
	8 ft	9 ft	10 ft	11 ft	12 ft	
PFG	24	27	30	33[d]	36[d]	1.5 x Actual[b]

a. Linear interpolation shall be permitted.
b. Use actual length when it is greater than or equal to the minimum length.
d. Maximum header height for PFG is 10' per Figure R602.10.6.3, but wall height may be increased to 12' with pony wall.

A second intermittent portal frame method, Method PFG (portal frame at garage door openings in Seismic Design Categories A, B and C), was added in the 2009 IRC. Method PFG does not require hold downs, has a minimum length requirement of 24 inches, and is permitted for use only in SDC A, B and C. In addition, this method may only be used adjacent to a garage door and to support a roof and/or one story above. For the purposes of computing the required length of bracing, a single unit of this method is equivalent to 1.5 times its actual length.

Method PFG is illustrated and described in full in IRC Section R602.10.6.3 and Figure R602.10.3 (see **FIGURE 3.46**).

Continuous sheathing bracing methods

For the 2012 IRC, the three wood structural panel continuous sheathing methods (CS-WSP, CS-G and CS-PF) and the fiberboard continuous sheathing method (CS-SFB) have been merged with the rest of the bracing methods. See **TABLE 3.22**.

TABLE 3.22

Continuous sheathing bracing methods

IRC Table R602.10.4 (Continued)

TABLE R602.10.4
BRACING METHODS (CONTINUED)

Methods, Material	Minimum Thickness	Figure	Connection Criteria[a]	
			Fasteners	Spacing
CS-WSP Continuously sheathed wood structural panel	3/8"		Exterior sheathing per Table R602.3(3)	6" edges 12" field
			Interior sheathing per Table R602.3(1) or R602.3(2)	Varies by fastener
CS-G[b, c] Continuously sheathed wood structural panel adjacent to garage openings	3/8"		See Method CS-WSP	See Method CS-WSP
CS-PF Continuously sheathed portal frame	7/16"		See Section R602.10.6.4	See Section R602.10.6.4
CS-SFB[d] Continuously sheathed structural fiberboard	1/2" or 25/32" for maximum 16" stud spacing		1-1/2" long × 0.12" dia. (for 1/2" thick sheathing) 1-3/4" long × 0.12" dia. (for 25/32" thick sheathing) galvanized roofing nails or 8d common (2-1/2" long × 0.131" dia.) nails	3" edges 6" field

Continuous Sheathing Methods

For SI: 1 inch = 25.4 mm, 1 foot = 305 mm, 1 degree = 0.0175 rad, 1 pound per square foot = 47.8 N/m², 1 mile per hour = 0.447 m/s.
a. Adhesive attachment of wall sheathing, including Method GB, shall not be permitted in Seismic Design Categories C, D_0, D_1 and D_2.
b. Applies to panels next to garage door opening when supporting gable end wall or roof load only. May only be used on one wall of the garage. In Seismic Design Categories D_0, D_1 and D_2, roof covering dead load may not exceed 3 psf.
c. Garage openings adjacent to a Method CS-G panel shall be provided with a header in accordance with Table R502.5(1). A full height clear opening shall not be permitted adjacent to a Method CS-G panel.
d. Method CS-SFB does not apply in Seismic Design Categories D_0, D_1 and D_2 and in areas where the wind speed exceeds 100 mph.

The two basic continuous sheathing bracing methods, Method CS-WSP (continuously sheathed wood structural panel) and Method CS-SFB (continuously sheathed structural fiberboard) (described in IRC Sections R602.10.4.2 and R602.10.7) require braced wall lines, including areas above and below openings and at gable ends, to be fully sheathed with a minimum of 3/8-inch wood structural panel sheathing (as shown in **FIGURE 3.40**), or 1/2-inch structural fiberboard sheathing.

FIGURE 3.39

Example of continuously sheathed braced walls

Gone for 2012 are the special corner details required for continuous sheathing bracing methods. The important part of these corner figures was the nailing requirement between end studs of adjacent intersecting walls. The ICC Ad Hoc Wall Bracing Committee members felt that these were considered minimal attachment requirements, and criteria for 16d nails at 12 inches on center was added to 2012 IRC Table R602.3(1), Item 8 for all construction.

The importance of the corner attachment for the continuous sheathing bracing methods is to connect the intersecting walls together to create a stronger, box-like structure that will perform better during high wind or seismic events. This corner attachment requires a minimum of a single row of 16d nails at 12 inches on center. A double row of 16d nails at 24 inches on center, framing member orientation permitting, is considered equivalent.

Because of the added strength and stiffness of wood structural panels and structural fiberboard sheathing when applied to all exterior surfaces (that are not window or door openings), narrower bracing panels may be used, allowing for additional architectural latitude. Wood structural panel lengths as narrow as 24 inches in length (4:1 aspect ratio) can be used adjacent to garage door openings (Method CS-G). Due to the required 4:1 aspect ratio, taller walls require longer braced panels. In addition, the minimum length of the bracing panel depends on the size of the opening next to the bracing panel as can be seen in IRC Table R602.10.5 (**TABLE 3.28**).

The 2012 IRC also permits the use of site-built portal frames without hold downs adjacent to openings with an aspect ratio of 6:1 (Method CS-PF). These portal frames may be used on any story, over elevated floors; however, no more than four may be used in any single wall line. (IRC Section R602.10.6.4.)

Method CS-WSP (Continuously sheathed wood structural panel)

See **TABLE 3.23** and **FIGURE 3.40**.

TABLE 3.23

Method CS-WSP

Excerpt from IRC Tables R602.10.4 and R602.10.5

Method, Material	Minimum Thickness	Figure	Connection Criteria[a]	
			Fasteners	**Spacings**
CS-WSP Continuously sheathed wood structural panel	3/8"		Exterior sheathing see Table R602.3(3)	6" spacing (panel edges); 12" spacing (intermediate supports)
			Interior sheathing see Table R602.3(1) or Table R602.3(2)	Varies by fastener

a. Adhesive attachment of wall sheathing, including Method GB, shall not be permitted In Seismic Design Categories C, D_0, D_1 and D_2.

Minimum length per IRC Table R602.10.5 (TABLE 3.28)	Adjacent clear opening height (in.)	Minimum Length[a] (in.)					Contributing Length (in.)
		Wall Height					
		8 ft	**9 ft**	**10 ft**	**11 ft**	**12 ft**	
	< 64	24	27	30	33	36	
	68	26	27	30	33	36	
	72	27	27	30	33	36	
	76	30	29	30	33	36	
	80	32	30	30	33	36	
	84	35	32	32	33	36	
	88	38	35	33	33	36	
	92	43	37	35	35	36	
	96	48	41	38	36	36	
	100		44	40	38	38	
CS-WSP	104		49	43	40	39	Actual[b]
	108		54	46	43	41	
	112			50	45	43	
	116			55	48	45	
	120			60	52	48	
	124				56	51	
	128				61	54	
	132				66	58	
	136					62	
	140					66	
	144					72	

a. Linear interpolation shall be permitted.
b. Use actual length when it is greater than or equal to the minimum length.

FIGURE 3.40

Method CS-WSP (continuously sheathed wood structural panel)

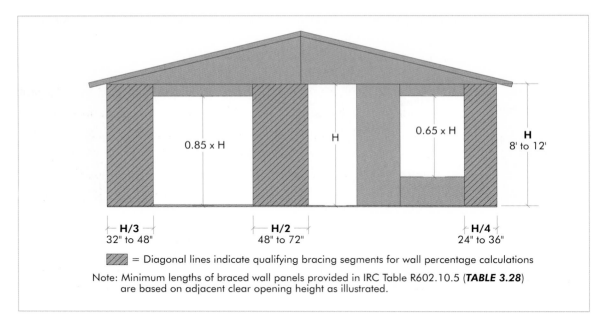

= Diagonal lines indicate qualifying bracing segments for wall percentage calculations

Note: Minimum lengths of braced wall panels provided in IRC Table R602.10.5 (**TABLE 3.28**) are based on adjacent clear opening height as illustrated.

This portion of the 2012 IRC includes only minor changes (primarily formatting). As with all continuous sheathing methods, Method CS-WSP is permitted to be used on a wall line-by-wall line basis, and, on a story-by-story basis, in SDC D_0, D_1 and D_2 or areas where the basic wind speed exceeds 100 mph.

Mixing bracing methods is covered in Section R602.10.4.1 of the 2012 IRC and is addressed later in this chapter, but the only limitation that is specific to the continuous bracing methods is that only the continuously sheathed portal frames (Methods CS-G and CS-FP) can be mixed with Method CS-WSP along a braced wall line.

Method CS-WSP can be placed away from corners, as is permitted for intermittent methods. A number of details have been added to the 2012 IRC Figure R602.10.7 (**FIGURES 3.49-3.53**) to clarify the corner attachment requirements of the continuous sheathing provisions.

Method CS-G (Continuously sheathed wood structural panel adjacent to garage openings)

See *TABLE 3.24* and *FIGURE 3.41*.

Method CS-G (continuously sheathed wood structural panel adjacent to garage openings) is a narrow-width panel that can be used with Method CS-WSP (continuously sheathed wood structural panel). This method permits the use of a panel length as short as 24 inches for an 8-foot wall, but because the length of the wall is linked to an aspect ratio (height/length = 4/1), the segment is required to grow longer as the wall gets taller. Method CS-G is not a portal frame. It is a sheathed section of wall with a normal-length header, just long enough to be supported by the cripple studs.

TABLE 3.24

Method CS-G

Excerpt from IRC Tables R602.10.4 and R602.10.5

Method, Material	Minimum Thickness	Figure	Connection Criteria[a]	
			Fasteners	Spacings
CS-G[b,c] Continuously sheathed wood structural panel adjacent to garage openings	3/8"		See Method CS-WSP	See Method CS-WSP

a. Adhesive attachment of wall sheathing, including Method GB, shall not be permitted In Seismic Design Categories C, D_0, D_1 and D_2.
b. Applies to panels next to garage door opening when supporting gable end wall or roof load only. May only be used on one wall of the garage. In Seismic Design Categories D_0, D_1 and D_2 roof covering dead load may not exceed 3 psf.
c. Garage openings adjacent to a Method CS-G panel shall be provided with a header in accordance with Table R502.5(1). A full height clear opening shall not be permitted adjacent to a Method CS-G panel.

Minimum length per IRC Table R602.10.5 (TABLE 3.28)	Minimum Length[a] (in.)					Contributing Length (in.)
	Wall Height					
	8 ft	9 ft	10 ft	11 ft	12 ft	
CS-G	24	27	30	33	36	Actual[b]

a. Linear interpolation shall be permitted.
b. Use actual length when it is greater than or equal to the minimum length.

FIGURE 3.41

Method CS-G (continuously sheathed wood structural panel adjacent to garage openings)

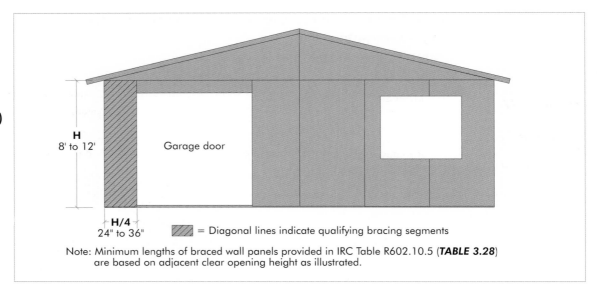

H 8' to 12'

Garage door

H/4 24" to 36"

= Diagonal lines indicate qualifying bracing segments

Note: Minimum lengths of braced wall panels provided in IRC Table R602.10.5 (**TABLE 3.28**) are based on adjacent clear opening height as illustrated.

Pay particular attention to Footnotes b and c of IRC Table R602.10.4 (**TABLE 3.24**). The first does not permit the use of 4:1 aspect ratio narrow wall panels on more than one wall of a garage. In other words, the braced panel may only be used around the garage door opening. If garage door openings occur in two walls of the garage, only one wall may use the Method CS-G panel. This should not be interpreted to mean that narrow wall segments cannot be used on both sides of a garage door within a single wall; rather, that is their designed use. Footnote b further restricts the Method CS-G to single story structures ("supporting gable end wall or roof load only"). In areas of high seismicity (SDC D_0-D_2) the roof covering is restricted to a total weight of 3 psf. Relatively light roofing materials minimize the seismic weight (mass) of the roof in a seismic event. As such, this restriction is only applicable to structures that are not exempt from the seismic bracing requirements of the IRC.

Footnote c is provided to clarify that Method CS-G is not to be used adjacent to a full-height opening. A header must be in place and sized in accordance with IRC Section R502.5(1) to restrict the clear opening height.

Method CS-G can only be used with Method CS-WSP (IRC Section R602.10.4.1, Item 4). For purposes of determining length of bracing in a wall line, use the actual length of the narrow braced wall panel(s). Of course, the required length of bracing must be met for any wall in the structure; this provision simply permits the use of smaller segments to make up the required length of bracing.

2012 IRC BRACING PROVISIONS **149**
R602.10.4

Method CS-PF (Continuously sheathed portal frame)

See **TABLE 3.25** and **FIGURE 3.42**.

TABLE 3.25

Method CS-PF

Excerpt from IRC Tables R602.10.4 and R602.10.5

Method, Material	Minimum Thickness	Figure	Connection Criteria[a]	
			Fasteners	Spacings
CS-PF Continuously sheathed portal frame	7/16"		See Section R602.10.6.4	See Section R602.10.6.4

a. Adhesive attachment of wall sheathing, including Method GB, shall not be permitted In Seismic Design Categories C, D_0, D_1 and D_2.

Minimum length per IRC Table R602.10.5 (TABLE 3.28)	Minimum Length[a] (in.)					Contributing Length (in.)
	Wall Height					
	8 ft	9 ft	10 ft	11 ft	12 ft	
CS-PF	16	16	20	22[e]	24[e]	Actual[b]

a. Linear interpolation shall be permitted.
b. Use actual length when it is greater than or equal to the minimum length.
e. Maximum opening height for CS-PF is 10' per Figure R602.10.6.4, but wall height may be increased to 12' with pony wall.

FIGURE 3.42

Method CS-PF (continuously sheathed portal frame)

Excerpt from IRC Section R602.10.6.4

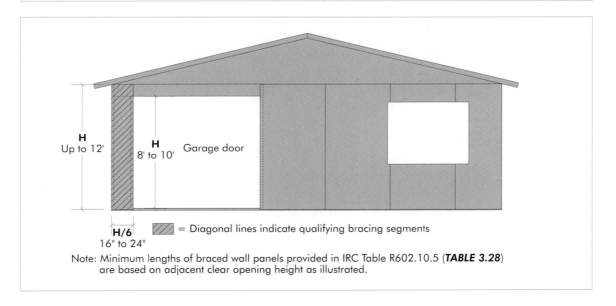

= Diagonal lines indicate qualifying bracing segments

Note: Minimum lengths of braced wall panels provided in IRC Table R602.10.5 (**TABLE 3.28**) are based on adjacent clear opening height as illustrated.

Method CS-PF can only be used with Method CS-WSP (see IRC Section R602.10.4.1, Item 4).

Continued in the 2012 IRC are provisions for the use of a pony wall directly over the portal frame (See IRC Figure R602.10.6.4). These provisions have been added to the other portal frame methods (Methods PFH and PFG), and are also applicable to Method ABW as well as any conventional garage header application. This pony wall is often a means of elevating the second story of the structure over the garage in a home with a split-level entry. The tension strap provisions are meant to address the problem of a structural hinge created over a door or window header that can result in the header bulging in or out due to wind loads blowing directly against the wall, or even differential moisture conditions. In severe cases, it can lead to structural problems. Often in garages, these areas are braced back to the ceiling with framing to prevent such an occurrence.

Method CS-SFB (Continuously sheathed structural fiberboard)

See **TABLE 3.26**.

Method, Material	Minimum Thickness	Figure	Connection Criteria[a]	
			Fasteners	Spacings
CS-SFB[d] Continuously sheathed structural fiberboard	1/2" or 25/32" for 16" stud spacing only		1-1/2" long × 0.12" dia. (for 1/2" thick sheathing) 1-3/4" long × 0.12" dia. (for 25/32" thick sheathing) galvanized roofing nails or 8d common (2-1/2" long × 0.131" dia.) nails	3" edges 6" field

a. Adhesive attachment of wall sheathing, including Method GB, shall not be permitted In Seismic Design Categories C, D_0, D_1 and D_2.
d. Method CS-SFB does not apply in Seismic Design Categories D_0, D_1 and D_2 and in areas where the wind speed exceeds 100 mph.

Minimum length per IRC Table R602.10.5 (TABLE 3.28)	Adjacent clear opening height (in.)	Minimum Length[a] (in.)					Contributing Length (in.)
		Wall Height					
		8 ft	9 ft	10 ft	11 ft	12 ft	
CS-SFB	< 64	24	27	30	33	36	Actual[b]
	68	26	27	30	33	36	
	72	27	27	30	33	36	
	76	30	29	30	33	36	
	80	32	30	30	33	36	
	84	35	32	32	33	36	
	88	38	35	33	33	36	
	92	43	37	35	35	36	
	96	48	41	38	36	36	
	100		44	40	38	38	
	104		49	43	40	39	
	108		54	46	43	41	
	112			50	45	43	
	116			55	48	45	
	120			60	52	48	
	124				56	51	
	128				61	54	
	132				66	58	
	136					62	
	140					66	
	144					72	

For SI: 1 inch = 24.5 mm, 1 foot = 304.8 mm, 1 mile per hour = 0.447 m/s.
a. Linear interpolation shall be permitted.
b. Use actual length when it is greater than or equal to the minimum length.

As with Method CS-WSP, other bracing methods may not be used in a Method CS-SFB wall line. Mixing bracing methods is described in IRC Section R602.10.4.1.

Also, like Method CS-WSP wall lines, Method CS-SFB wall lines are permitted on a line-by-line basis. Method CS-SFB can also be placed away from corners, as is permitted for intermittent methods. A number of figures have been added to the 2012 IRC Figure R602.10.7 (**FIGURES 3.49-3.53**) to clarify the corner condition requirements of the continuous sheathing provisions.

There are some limitations on the use of Method CS-SFB bracing that set it apart from Method CS-WSP. Method CS-SFB is not permitted to be used in areas with wind speeds of greater than 100 mph or in SDC D_0, D_1 or D_2. Return corners and narrow wall segments adjacent to a corner without a hold down shall be not less than 32 inches (as shown in 2012 IRC Figure R602.10.7) See **FIGURES 3.49** and **3.52**.

R602.10.4.1 Mixing methods. Mixing of bracing methods shall be permitted as follows:

1. Mixing intermittent bracing and continuous sheathing methods from story to story shall be permitted.

Mixing bracing methods from story-to-story is permitted. An example is using Method WSP (wood structural panel) bracing on the bottom of a three-story building while using Method PBS (particleboard sheathing) or Method GB (gypsum board) bracing on the top and/or second story.

2. Mixing intermittent bracing methods from *braced wall line* to *braced wall line* within a story shall be permitted. Within Seismic Design Categories A, B and C ~~or~~ _and_ in regions where the basic wind speed is less than or equal to 100 mph (45 m/s), mixing of intermittent bracing and continuous sheathing methods from *braced wall line* to *braced wall line* within a story shall be permitted.

Note that in the code excerpt above, we have changed the "or" to an "and". This is to correct a typographical error in the code: the intent of the code is that when both of the requirements are met – the basic wind speed is less than 100 mph and the SDC is C or less – mixing is permitted. A builder is allowed to use different bracing methods on different braced wall lines within a story. For example, in a "window wall", a designer may use choose to Method WSP (wood structural panel) bracing along one wall line of a story because its lower bracing length requirements can help to accommodate additional windows. On other walls that have fewer windows, the designer may use Method GB.

This item specifically permits, in areas of low or moderate seismicity and wind speeds of 100 mph or less, continuous sheathing bracing methods to be used with other bracing methods on other walls of the same story and on other stories. What is inferred by this section is that, in areas of high seismicity or high wind zones, mixing intermittent bracing methods with continuous sheathing methods (CS-WSP, CS-PF and CS-G) is not permitted on the same story. Note that Method CS-SFB is not permitted in high seismic or high wind zones.

As such, in high seismic and high wind zones, all <u>exterior</u> walls of a given level must be continuously sheathed if a single wall on that level is continuously sheathed. However, in Seismic Design Categories C and below, walls inside the building or walls on other levels may use whatever bracing meets the requirements for that wall or level.

3. Mixing intermittent bracing methods along a *braced wall line* shall be permitted in Seismic Design Categories A and B, and detached dwellings in Seismic Design Category C provided the length of required bracing in accordance with Table R602.10.3(1) or R602.10.3(3) is the highest value of all intermittent bracing methods used.

The builder is permitted to mix various types of intermittent braced wall panels in a single braced wall line in areas of low to moderate seismicity, as long as two provisions are met. First, this is permitted for all structures covered by the IRC in SDC A and B. Detached one- and two-family dwellings are further permitted to use this provision in SDC C.

Second, the <u>greatest</u> minimum length of all of the intermittent bracing methods used in the braced wall line will be applied to all methods.

For example, a single-family dwelling meets the SDC requirements allowing Methods WSP and GB to be used on a braced wall line. From 2012 IRC Table R602.10.3(1) and (2) (**TABLE 3.3** and **TABLE 3.4**), it is determined that 13 feet and 7.5 feet of Methods GB and WSP bracing, respectively, will be required for a specific braced wall line. As both methods are to be used, the greater of the two length requirements, 13 feet of bracing, will be the required total bracing length in that braced wall line.

Note that, even though this single-family dwelling is exempt from seismic requirements (IRC Section R302.2), the limitations on the wind load bracing amounts of the section still apply. If the structure in this example was a townhouse in SDC C, both the wind and seismic bracing amounts would be impacted by this provision.

4. Mixing of continuous sheathing methods CS-WSP, CS-G and CS-PF along a *braced wall line* shall be permitted.

The builder may use CS-G and CS-PF in a line with CS-WSP. This is a logical interpretation as these portal methods were developed for use with the Method CS-WSP system; however, these portal methods are currently not permitted to used with the Method CS-SFB system, as deflection compatibility for these three systems has not been established.

5. In Seismic Design Categories A and B, and for detached one- and two-family dwellings in Seismic Design Category C, mixing of intermittent bracing methods along the interior portion of a *braced wall line* with continuous sheathing methods CS-WSP, CS-G and CS-PF along the exterior portion of the same *braced wall line* shall be permitted. The length of required bracing shall be the highest value of all intermittent bracing methods used in accordance with Table R602. 10.3(1) or R602.10.3(3) as adjusted by Table R602.10.3(2) and R602.10.3(4), respectively. The requirements of Section R602.10.7 shall apply to each end of the continuously sheathed portion of the *braced wall line*.

This new provision is a special case for T- and L-shaped buildings, where an exterior braced wall line continues into the interior of the structure. As gypsum wall board is typically used on the interior it is reasonable to use Method GB on the interior braced wall regardless of what is used on the exterior walls. Without this provision, this would not be permitted if the exterior walls were continuously sheathed (see Item 4 above).

While this provision permits mixing, note that the amount of bracing required (based on IRC Tables R602.10.3(1) through (4) (**TABLE 3.3** through **3.6**) shall be the longest length required of all the intermittent values used in that braced wall line.

Note that, in accordance with IRC Section R301.2.2, one- and two-family dwellings in SDC A, B and C are exempt from the seismic provisions of the code, as are townhouse structures in SDC A and B. While the amount of bracing in the IRC Tables R602.10.3(3) and (4) (**TABLE 3.5** and **3.6**) does not apply to these structures, the provisions for mixing bracing types do apply for these areas of low to moderate seismicity. This provision is meant to ensure that the bracing that is applied for wind loads will act to protect the structure from seismic loads as well.

What is missing from these mixing method provisions is permission for the use of Method GB interior shear/bracing walls regardless of what method is used on the exterior walls in high seismic areas. This practice is generally considered acceptable in the design community in high wind and moderate-to-high Seismic Design Categories (D_0-D_2), and is especially popular in townhouse construction where sound attenuation requirements between units necessitate the use of double-layer gypsum party walls. While Method GB is not very effective in areas of high seismicity, there is often enough length and layers available in party walls to make the method viable. As Method GB is used only for the interior shear/braced walls, building symmetry is generally not an issue.

The mixing bracing provisions are tabulated in **TABLE 3.27**. A graphic representation of these provisions is provided in **APPENDIX E**.

TABLE 3.27

**Mixing
possibilities and
their limitations**

See also
APPENDIX E
for a graphic
representation of
the mixing bracing
provisions

Mixing Locations	Mixing Limitations	SDC A-B	SDC C Detached	SDC C Townhouses	SDC D₀-D₂
Story to Story	Mixing intermittent and continuous sheathing methods	•	•	•	•
BWL to BWL	Mixing intermittent methods	•	•	•	•
BWL to BWL	Mixing intermittent and continuous sheathing methods	•	•	•	
Within BWL	Mixing intermittent methods in a single wall line	•	•		
Within BWL	Mixing continuous sheathing methods using wood structural panels only (mixing CS-WSP, CS-G and CS-PF)	•	•	•	•
Within BWL	Mixing an intermittent method on an interior portion and CS-WSP, CS-PF and CS-G on an exterior portion of a wall line	•	•		

BWL = Braced Wall Line

R602.10.4.2 Continuous sheathing methods. Continuous sheathing methods require structural panel sheathing to be used on all sheathable surfaces on one side of a *braced wall line* including areas above and below openings and gable end walls and shall meet the requirements of Section R602.10.7.

In the 2012 IRC, continuously sheathed braced wall lines are permitted on a wall line-by-wall line basis. For example, just the front side of a one- or two-family dwelling or townhouse with an attached garage could be continuously sheathed to permit narrow walls on either side of the garage door, while the remaining walls of the house could use other IRC-approved bracing methods. Of course, IRC Figure R602.10.7 corner requirements (***FIGURES 3.49-3.53***) must be met for continuously sheathed wall lines. Note that in SDC D or in areas where the basic wind speed is greater than 100 mph, mixing of continuous and intermittent bracing methods within a single story is not permitted (see IRC Section R602.10.4.1, Item 2).

Four continuous sheathing bracing methods have been brought forward from the 2009 IRC. In the 2012 IRC, the continuously sheathed structural fiberboard method (Method CS-SFB) is incorporated into the existing table of continuous sheathing methods. The four bracing methods are added to the bracing methods table, IRC Table R602.10.4 (***TABLE 3.22***). These methods have their roots in various provisions of previous editions of the IRC, but are clarified in the latest edition.

1. Method CS-WSP (continuously sheathed wood structural panel)
2. Method CS-G (continuously sheathed wood structural panel adjacent to garage openings)
3. Method CS-PF (continuously sheathed portal frame)
4. Method CS-SFB (continuously sheathed structural fiberboard)

R602.10.4.3 Braced wall panel interior finish material. *Braced wall panels* shall have gypsum wall board installed on the side of the wall opposite the bracing material. Gypsum wall board shall be not less than 1/2 inch (12.7 mm) in thickness and be fastened with nails or screws in accordance with Table R602.3(1) for exterior sheathing or Table R702.3.5 for interior gypsum wall board. Spacing of fasteners at panel edges for gypsum wall board opposite Method LIB bracing shall not exceed 8 inches (203 mm). Interior finish material shall not be glued in Seismic Design Categories D_0, D_1 and D_2.

Exceptions:

1. Interior finish material is not required opposite wall panels that are braced in accordance with Methods GB, BV-WSP, ABW, PFH, PFG and CS-PF, unless otherwise required by Section R302.6.

2. An approved interior finish material with an in-plane shear resistance equivalent to gypsum board shall be permitted to be substituted, unless otherwise required by Section R302.6.

3. Except for Method LIB, gypsum wall board is permitted to be omitted provided the required length of bracing in Tables R602.10.3(1) and R602.10.3(3) is multiplied by the appropriate adjustment factor in Tables R602.10.3(2) and R602.10.3(4) respectively, unless otherwise required by Section R302.6.

Updated in the 2012 IRC is the specific requirement for gypsum wall board as an interior finish for all intermittent and continuous sheathing methods. This provision includes a number of exceptions, as listed above. Methods GB, BV-WSP, ABW, PFH, PFG and CS-PF are excepted (IRC Section R602.10.4.3, Exception 1) as these methods were not tested or developed with gypsum wall board on one side. IRC Section R302.6, referenced in the exception, is the dwelling/garage fire separation provision, reproduced in **CHAPTER 2** of this guide: this provision, which requires gypsum wall board between the garage and living spaces of the structure, takes precedence over the exception when applicable.

The second exception, brought forward from 2009, permits an alternative inside covering to be substituted for gypsum wall board, as long as it has the same in-plane shear resistance (IRC Section R602.10.4.3, Exception 2). Also carried over from 2009 is the exception that permits the elimination of the gypsum wall board (again, provided it is not otherwise required by IRC Section R302.6) if the length of bracing used is in excess of that required by IRC Tables IRC Tables R602.10.3(1) or (3) (**TABLES 3.3** or **3.5**), adjusted by the factors listed in IRC Tables R602.10.3(2) (**TABLE 3.4**), a factor of 1.4, and R602.10.3(4) (**TABLE 3.6**), a factor of 1.5, respectively. Note that this requirement is for the use of standard gypsum wall board, not Method GB bracing. Interior finish gypsum wall board can be attached in accordance with IRC Section R702.3.5 (the more restrictive 7-inch minimum on center attachment required for Method GB is not necessary).

R602.10.5 Minimum length of a braced wall panel

R602.10.5 Minimum length of a *braced wall panel*. The minimum length of a *braced wall panel* shall comply with Table R602.10.5. For Methods CS-WSP and CS-SFB, the minimum panel length shall be based on the adjacent clear opening height in accordance with Table R602.10.5 and Figure R602.10.5. When a panel has an opening on either side of differing heights, the taller opening height shall be used to determine the panel length. (See **TABLE 3.28**.)

TABLE 3.28

Minimum length of braced wall panels and contributing length

IRC Table R602.10.5

TABLE R602.10.5
MINIMUM LENGTH OF BRACED WALL PANELS

Method (See Table R602.10.4)		Minimum Length[a] (inches)					Contributing Length (Inches)
		Wall Height					
		8 ft	9 ft	10 ft	11 ft	12 ft	
DWB, WSP, SFB, PBS, PCP, HPS, BV-WSP		48	48	48	53	58	Actual[b]
GB		48	48	48	53	58	Double sided = Actual Single sided = 0.5 × Actual
LIB		55	62	69	NP	NP	Actual[b]
ABW	SDC A, B and C, wind speed < 110 mph	28	32	34	38	42	48
	SDC D_0, D_1 and D_2, wind speed < 110 mph	32	32	34	NP	NP	
PFH	Supporting roof only	16	16	16	18[c]	20[c]	48
	Supporting one story and roof	24	24	24	27[c]	29[c]	48
PFG		24	27	30	33[d]	36[d]	1.5 × Actual[b]
CS-G		24	27	30	33	36	Actual[b]
CS-PF		16	18	20	22[e]	24[e]	Actual[b]

For SI: 1 inch = 25.4 mm, 1 foot = 304.8 mm, 1 mile per hour = 0.447 m/s.
NP = Not Permitted.
a. Linear interpolation shall be permitted.
b. Use the actual length when it is greater than or equal to the minimum length.
c. Maximum header height for PFH is 10 feet in accordance with Figure R602.10.6.2, but wall height may be increased to 12 feet with pony wall.
d. Maximum opening height for PFG is 10 feet in accordance with Figure R602.10.6.3, but wall height may be increased to 12 feet with pony wall.
e. Maximum opening height for CS-PF is 10 feet in accordance with Figure R602.10.6.4, but wall height may be increased to 12 feet with pony wall.

TABLE 3.28
(Continued)

Minimum length of braced wall panels and contributing length

IRC Table R602.10.5

TABLE R602.10.5
MINIMUM LENGTH OF BRACED WALL PANELS

Method (See Table R602.10.4)	Minimum Length[a] (inches) Wall Height					Contributing Length (Inches)
	8 ft	9 ft	10 ft	11 ft	12 ft	
Adjacent clear opening height (inches)						
≤ 64	24	27	30	33	36	
68	26	27	30	33	36	
72	27	27	30	33	36	
76	30	29	30	33	36	
80	32	30	30	33	36	
84	35	32	32	33	36	
88	38	35	33	33	36	
92	43	37	35	35	36	
96	48	41	38	36	36	
CS-WSP, CS-SFB 100	—	44	40	38	38	
104	—	49	43	40	39	Actual[b]
108	—	54	46	43	41	
112	—	—	50	45	43	
116	—	—	55	48	45	
120	—	—	60	52	48	
124	—	—	—	56	51	
128	—	—	—	61	54	
132	—	—	—	66	58	
136	—	—	—	—	62	
140	—	—	—	—	66	
144	—	—	—	—	72	

For SI: 1 inch = 25.4 mm, 1 foot = 304.8 mm, 1 mile per hour = 0.447 m/s.
NP = Not Permitted.
a. Linear interpolation shall be permitted.
b. Use the actual length when it is greater than or equal to the minimum length.
c. Maximum header height for PFH is 10 feet in accordance with Figure R602.10.6.2, but wall height may be increased to 12 feet with pony wall.
d. Maximum opening height for PFG is 10 feet in accordance with Figure R602.10.6.3, but wall height may be increased to 12 feet with pony wall.
e. Maximum opening height for CS-PF is 10 feet in accordance with Figure R602.10.6.4, but wall height may be increased to 12 feet with pony wall.

The minimum length of a braced wall panel shall comply with IRC Table R602.10.5. For Methods CS-WSP and CS-SFB, the minimum panel length shall be based on the adjacent clear opening height in accordance with this table and IRC Figure R602.10.5 (**FIGURE 3.43**). When a panel has an opening on either side of differing heights, the taller opening height shall be used to determine the panel length.

FIGURE 3.43

**Panel lengths
- continuous
sheathing**

**IRC Figure
R602.10.5**

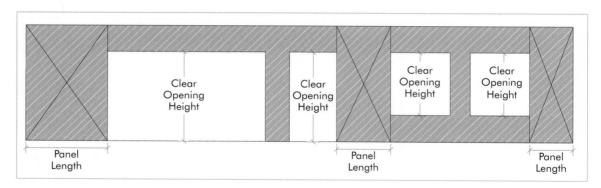

FIGURE R602.10.5
BRACED WALL PANELS WITH CONTINUOUS SHEATHING

R602.10.5.1 Contributing length. For purposes of computing the required length of bracing in Tables R602.10.3(1) and R602.10.3(3), the contributing length of each *braced wall panel* shall be as specified in Table R602.10.5.

New in the 2012 IRC is Table R602.10.5 (**TABLE 3.28**). It includes minimum length requirements for all 16 bracing methods in one table to facilitate the selection of braced wall panels by the designer. It is important to note that the minimum lengths given are just that – the minimum required length to establish a qualified braced wall panel for the intermittent methods or a qualified full-height segment for a continuous sheathing method. Any length over the minimum can be counted toward the required length of bracing specified in IRC Tables R602.10.3(1)-(4) (**TABLES 3.3-3.6**). There are two exceptions, however. Methods ABW and PFH each count as 48 inches of bracing, even when fabricated longer than the minimum length requirement. The "contributing length" column of the table is provided to simplify the determination. The following examples provide some insights on interpreting minimum length requirements:

In an 8-foot-tall wall line, 54 inches of Method WSP braced wall exceeds the minimum length requirement of 48 inches, but contributes the entire 54 inches toward the amount of bracing required.

In the same wall line, a Method PFG garage portal is used. The length of the vertical leg of this portal is 30 inches. This exceeds the minimum length requirement of 24 inches and contributes (30 x 1.5 =) 45 inches towards the amount of bracing required.

A Method PFH portal frame is used on the first of a two-story building. The portal frame is constructed with a 32-inch-long vertical leg. From IRC Table R602.10.5 (**TABLE 3.28**) we see that this meets the minimum leg length of 24 inches, but contributes 48 inches towards the length of bracing required. Increasing the length of a Method PFH portal frame beyond the minimum length required will not increase the amount of bracing contributed to the total.

Method GB warrants a special mention. Forty-eight inches of Method GB contributes 48 inches of bracing, as long as both sides of the wall are constructed with Method GB. If the wall has Method GB on one side only, than the 48 inches of Method GB is only "worth" 24 inches of bracing. In terms of minimum length required, however, the table <u>does</u> permit the use of 48 inches of single-sided Method GB as a qualifying bracing unit, but it contributes only 24 inches.

Note that the use of Method GB on both sides is not to be confused with Method GB on one side and interior finish per IRC Section 602.10.4.3 on the other. Gypsum wall board meeting the interior finish requirements is not sufficiently attached to the framing to be considered Method GB bracing. Gypsum used for interior finish can be attached with nails or screws spaced as far apart as 24 inches, but the Method GB attachment requirement calls for fasteners at 7 inches on center along all panel edges and in the field. Floating corners are not permitted with Method GB; however, this method does meet the interior finishing requirements of IRC Section R702.3.5.

R602.10.5.2 Partial credit. For Methods DWB, WSP, SFB, PBS, PCP and HPS in Seismic Design Categories A, B and C, panels between 36 inches and 48 inches (914 mm and 1219 mm) in length shall be considered a *braced wall panel* and shall be permitted to partially contribute toward the required length of bracing in Tables R602.10.3(1) and R602.10.3(3), and the contributing length shall be determined from Table R602.10.5.2.

Also brought forward from the 2009 IRC is the concept that, in regions of low to moderate seismicity, reductions in the minimum panel length of some intermittent bracing methods can be accepted as bracing panels with an effective length less than their actual length. These less-than-full-length panels are known to contribute to the lateral resistance of a wall, but due to their reduced stiffness (by virtue of their reduced length) they cannot contribute their full length to the amount of bracing required. As such, only a portion of their length may be used, as shown in IRC Table R602.10.5.2 (**TABLE 3.29**). The value for 48 inches is provided for interpolation purposes (see **APPENDIX C**).

TABLE 3.29

Partial credit for intermittent braced wall panels less than 48 inches in length

IRC Table R602.10.5.2

TABLE R602.10.5.2
PARTIAL CREDIT FOR BRACED WALL PANELS LESS THAN 48 INCHES IN ACTUAL LENGTH

Actual Length of Braced Wall Panel (inches)	Contributing Length of Braced Wall Panel (inches)[a]	
	8-foot Wall Height	9-foot Wall Height
48	48	48
42	36	36
36	27	N/A

For SI: 1 inch = 25.4 mm, 1 foot = 304.8 mm.
N/A = Not Applicable.
a. Linear interpolation shall be permitted.

R602.10.6 Construction of Methods ABW, PFH, PFG, CS-PF and BV-WSP

R602.10.6 Construction of Methods ABW, PFH, PFG, CS-PF and BV-WSP. Methods ABW, PFH, PFG, CS-PF and BV-WSP shall be constructed as specified in Sections R602.10.6.1 through R602.10.6.5.

For 2012, bracing methods that warranted a specific figure or limitation were collected here. Every attempt was made to unify the formats and look of these figures in the code. For this guide, the figures have been enlarged, reformatted, and colorized for easier reading.

R602.10.6.1 Method ABW: Alternate *braced wall panels*. Method ABW *braced wall panels* shall be constructed in accordance with Figure R602.10.6.1. The hold-down force shall be in accordance with Table R602.10.6.1.

Method ABW (alternate braced wall) has been in the IRC in one form or another since 2000 and is often referred to as the "32-inch alternate with hold downs.") See IRC Table R602.10.6.1. Method ABW panels are typically used when bracing is needed in a wall area that is not long enough to accommodate a 4-foot braced wall panel.

In the 2012 IRC, Method ABW is grouped with the intermittent bracing methods because it may be substituted on a one-for-one basis for a braced wall panel from any other bracing method, and, as such, it is used intermittently. An updated figure (IRC Figure R602.10.6.1, reproduced in **FIGURE 3.44**) clarifies the method and reduces redundancy.

For purposes of computing the required length of bracing, a single Method ABW panel is considered to be equivalent to 4 feet of bracing, regardless of its actual length. Note that this method utilizes hold-down framing anchors to develop its capacity (see IRC Table R602.10.6.1, reproduced in **TABLE 3.30**).

TABLE 3.30

Sizing hold-down anchors for Method ABW

IRC Table R602.10.6.1

		Hold Down Force (pounds)				
Seismic Design Category And Wind Speed	**Supporting/Story**	**Height of Braced Wall Panel**				
		8 feet	9 feet	10 feet	11 feet	12 feet
SDC A, B and C Wind speed < 110 mph	One story	1,800	1,800	1,800	2,000	2,200
	First of two stories	3,000	3,000	3,000	3,300	3,600
SDC D_0, D_1 and D_2 Wind speed < 110 mph	One story	1,800	1,800	1,800	NP	NP
	First of two stories	3,000	3,000	3,000	NP	NP

TABLE R602.10.6.1
MINIMUM HOLD-DOWN FORCES FOR METHOD ABW BRACED WALL PANELS

For SI: 1 inch = 25.4 mm, 1 foot = 304.8 mm, 1 pound = 4.45 N, 1 mile per hour = 0.447 m/s.
NP = Not Permitted.

Brought forward from the 2009 IRC are tension strap provisions for the use of a pony wall directly over a portal frame. For 2012, these provisions have been applied to all the portal bracing methods (Methods PFH, PFG and CS-PF). While not specifically referenced in the IRC, these provisions also apply to any conventional garage header application. This pony wall is often a means of elevating the second story of the structure over the garage in a home with a split-level entry. The tension strap provisions are meant to address the problem of a structural hinge created over a door or window header that can result in the header bulging in or out due to wind loads blowing directly against the wall, or even differential moisture conditions. In severe cases, it can lead to structural problems. Often in garages, these areas are braced back to the ceiling with framing to prevent such an occurrence.

IRC Table R602.10.6.4 (**TABLE 3.31**) provides the required strap capacities for various stud sizes, pony wall heights, opening widths and wind speeds.

When "bracing back the header" detailing is not desired, the information provided in IRC Figures R602.10.6.2, R602.10.6.3 and R602.10.6.4 (**FIGURES 3.44-3.47**) and in IRC Table R602.10.6.4 can be used to determine portal frame design wind loads and exposures. While not specifically permitted in the IRC, from an engineering perspective, interpolation of the variables in the table is appropriate (see **APPENDIX C**).

TABLE 3.31

Tension strap requirements for pony walls

IRC Table R602.10.6.4

TABLE R602.10.6.4
TENSION STRAP CAPACITY REQUIRED FOR RESISTING WIND PRESSURES PERPENDICULAR TO METHOD PFH, PFG AND CS-PF BRACED WALL PANELS

Minimum Wall Stud Framing Nominal Size and Grade	Maximum Pony Wall Height (feet)	Maximum Total Wall Height (feet)	Maximum Opening Width (feet)	Tension Strap Capacity Required (pounds)[a, b]					
				Basic Wind Speed (mph)					
				85	90	100	85	90	100
				Exposure B			Exposure C		
2 × 4 No. 2 Grade	0	10	18	1,000	1,000	1,000	1,000	1,000	1,000
	1	10	9	1,000	1,000	1,000	1,000	1,000	1,275
			16	1,000	1,000	1,750	1,800	2,325	3,500
			18	1,000	1,200	2,100	2,175	2,725	DR
	2	10	9	1,000	1,000	1,025	1,075	1,550	2,500
			16	1,525	2,025	3,125	3,200	3,900	DR
			18	1,875	2,400	3,575	3,700	DR	DR
	2	12	9	1,000	1,200	2,075	2,125	2,750	4,000
			16	2,600	3,200	DR	DR	DR	DR
			18	3,175	3,850	DR	DR	DR	DR
	4	12	9	1,775	2,350	3,500	3,550	DR	DR
			16	4,175	DR	DR	DR	DR	DR
2 × 6 Stud Grade	2	12	9	1,000	1,000	1,325	1,375	1,750	2,550
			16	1,650	2,050	2,925	3,000	3,550	DR
			18	2,025	2,450	3,425	3,500	4,100	DR
	4	12	9	1,125	1,500	2,225	2,275	2,775	3,800
			16	2,650	3,150	DR	DR	DR	DR
			18	3,125	3,675	DR	DR	DR	DR

For SI: 1 inch = 25.4 mm, 1 foot = 304.8 mm, 1 pound = 4.45 N.
a. DR = design required.
b. Strap shall be installed in accordance with manufacturer's recommendations.

As stated previously, the pony wall information in IRC Table R602.10.6.4 (***TABLE 3.31***) may be used for pony walls over any conventional header within the scope of the table as long as used in conjunction with wood structural panels on the opposite side of the studs from the straps, as shown in ***FIGURES 3.45-3.47***. For conventionally framed headers, the table is slightly conservative, but it is the only prescriptive guidance available for pony walls over headers. The use of this table will ensure that the header/pony wall assembly has sufficient strength and stiffness to prevent a hinge from forming at the header-to-pony wall joint when subjected to wind loads acting against the wall.

R602.10.6.5 Wall bracing for dwellings with stone and masonry veneer in Seismic Design Categories D_0, D_1 and D_2.
Where stone and masonry veneer are installed in accordance with Section R703.7, wall bracing on exterior braced wall lines and braced wall lines on the interior of the building, backing or perpendicular to and laterally supporting veneered walls shall comply with this section.

Although worded awkwardly, the intent of the first paragraph of IRC Section R602.10.6.5 is that, when considering a single wall with stone or masonry veneer, only the bracing on the wall to which the veneer is applied and the braced wall lines perpendicular ("backing or perpendicular to and laterally supporting veneered walls") to it are impacted by its mass in a seismic event. Thus, only those walls need to have additional bracing hold downs applied. See IRC Figure R602.10.6.5 (*FIGURE 3.48*).

Certainly, if the veneer is on two, three or four sides of the building, all braced wall lines are impacted; however, if just one side of the structure has stone or masonry veneer, the wall parallel to the veneered wall does not have to comply with the additional bracing requirements. This can reduce construction costs.

> Where dwellings in Seismic Design Categories D_0, D_1 and D_2 have stone or masonry veneer installed in accordance with Section R703.7, and the veneer does not exceed the first-story height, wall bracing shall be in accordance with Section R602.10.3.

IRC Section R602.10.6.5 refers the user back to IRC Section R602.10.3 for situations where the stone or masonry veneer is properly installed (IRC Section R703.7) and covers part or all of the first story wall height <u>only</u>. IRC Section R602.10.3 requires standard bracing per IRC Tables R602.10.3(1)-(4) (*TABLES 3.3-3.6*) without additional adjustments beyond those required by IRC Tables R602.10.3(2) and R602.10.3(4). Note that no provision for stone or masonry gable ends is made and it must be assumed that this provision <u>does not</u> apply to single-story stone or masonry walls when they extend up into the gable.

> Where detached one- or two-family dwellings in Seismic Design Categories D_0, D_1 and D_2 have stone or masonry veneer installed in accordance with Section R703.7, and the veneer exceeds the first-*story height*, wall bracing at exterior *braced wall lines* and *braced wall lines* on the interior of the building shall be constructed using Method BV-WSP in accordance with this section and Figure R602.10.6.5. Cripple walls shall not be permitted, and required interior *braced wall lines* shall be supported on continuous foundations.

These provisions for the use of Method BV-WSP are clearly defined as applicable to only detached one- and two-family dwellings and only when the stone or masonry veneer <u>exceeds</u> the first story height. As no exception for single stories with stone or masonry extending up into the gable is provided in the previous paragraph, it must be assumed that the intent of the code is to consider the gable end wall the first of a two-story building when gable end veneers are present.

Hold down location and capacity requirements are provided in IRC Table R602.10.6.5 (*TABLE 3.32*) and Figure R602.10.6.5 (*FIGURE 3.48*). As illustrated in IRC Figure R602.10.6.5, the capacity of the hold down is determined by the relationship of the ends of braced wall panels between stories. When Method BV-WSP panel ends are stacked above one another, the cumulative hold-down force provided in IRC Table R602.10.6.5 is required for the lower braced wall panels.

When the ends of braced wall lines are not vertically aligned (for example, one panel ends at a different location along the wall line than the panel below) then the single-story hold-down capacity given in IRC Table R602.10.6.5 is used. When Method BV-WSP is installed above the first story, the hold-down anchorage must be continued down to the foundation. For example, if a hold down is installed on the second or third story, each story below must have a single-story-force hold down that is vertically aligned with the hold down on the story above. If a braced wall panel at the story below ends at the same location along the wall line, the hold-down capacity should be greater than or equal to the cumulative hold-down force.

Note that while wood structural panel sheathing may be used over the whole wall, including above and below openings, hold downs only need to be applied to the ends of those elements that are required for intermittent bracing. This is an important consideration when bracing lengths greater than 48 inches are used. For example, if a wall line has a 6-foot length of Method BV-WSP wall bracing, consisting of one 4-foot and one 2-foot piece attached to a common stud, the hold downs are only required at the start and end of the 6-foot length, and not at 4-foot intervals.

The use of stone and masonry veneer in SDC D_0, D_1 and D_2 requires that interior braced wall lines be supported on continuous foundations regardless of plan dimension length. In addition, cripple walls are not permitted to be used.

FIGURE 3.48

Method BV-WSP - Wall bracing for dwellings with stone or masonry veneer in SDC D_0, D_1 and D_2

Adapted from IRC Figure R602.10.6.5

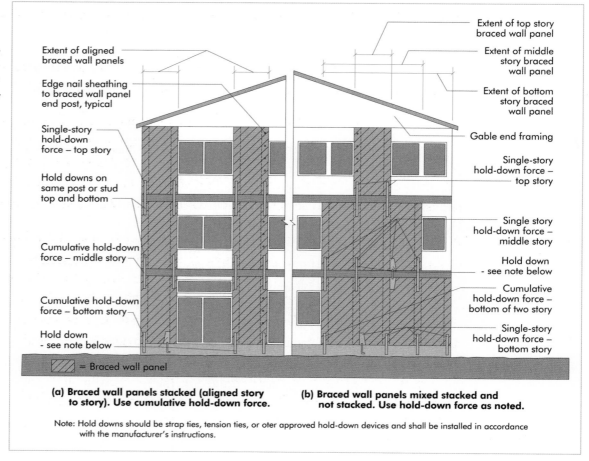

(a) Braced wall panels stacked (aligned story to story). Use cumulative hold-down force.

(b) Braced wall panels mixed stacked and not stacked. Use hold-down force as noted.

Note: Hold downs should be strap ties, tension ties, or oter approved hold-down devices and shall be installed in accordance with the manufacturer's instructions.

Townhouses in Seismic Design Categories D_0, D_1 and D_2 with stone or masonry veneer exceeding the first-story height shall be designed in accordance with accepted engineering practice.

This provision reiterates what was inferred by the preceding paragraphs: in the higher Seismic Design Categories, there are no prescriptive solutions for townhouses and they must be engineered when the veneer exceeds the first-story height.

> **R602.10.6.5.1 Length of bracing.** The length of bracing along each *braced wall line* shall be the greater of that required by the design wind speed and *braced wall line* spacing in accordance with Table R602.10.3(1) as adjusted by the factors in the Table R602.10.3(2) or the Seismic Design Category and *braced wall line* length in accordance with Table R602.10.6.5. Angled walls shall be permitted to be counted in accordance with Section R602.10.1.4, and *braced wall panel* location shall be in accordance with Section R602.10.2.2.1. The seismic adjustment factors in Table R602.10.3(4) shall not be applied to the length of bracing determined using Table R602.10.6.5. In no case shall the minimum total length of bracing in a *braced wall line*, after all adjustments have been taken, be less than 48 inches (1219 mm) total.

(Editorial note: For clarity, we have changed the reference in the code excerpt above from IRC Section R602.10.2.2 to R602.10.2.2.1. This corrects a typographical error in the code. IRC Section R602.10.2.2.1, the correct reference, provides the Seismic Design Category provisions for IRC Section R602.10.2.2.)

IRC Section R602.10.6.5.1 applies to stone and masonry veneer construction and is applicable for detached one- and-two family dwellings in SDC D_0, D_1 and D_2 only.

In this section, the standard seismic bracing requirements (IRC Table R602.10.3(3), reproduced in **TABLE 3.5**) do not apply because of the increased mass of the veneer when that veneer exceeds the first story height. IRC Table R602.10.6.5 (**TABLE 3.32**) was developed for these applications. Note that the adjustments to the standard bracing table (IRC Table R602.10.3(4), reproduced in **TABLE 3.6**) do not apply to the Method BV-WSP seismic bracing table.

In short, when determining the amount of bracing required for a detached one- or two-family dwelling in SDC D_0, D_1 or D_2, and the stone or masonry veneer <u>exceeds</u> the first story in height, IRC Tables R602.10.3(1) and (2) (**TABLE 3.3** and **3.4**) are used to determine the amount of wind bracing required, and IRC Table R602.10.6.5 (**TABLE 3.32**), without adjustment, is used for determining the amount of seismic bracing. For each wall, the most restrictive of the adjusted wind or the unadjusted seismic bracing length requirements shall be used.

If the stone or masonry veneer <u>does not</u> exceed the first story in height, IRC Table R602.10.3(3) (**TABLE 3.5**) and the adjustments in IRC Table R602.10.3(4) (**TABLE 3.6**) provide the required amount of seismic bracing.

TABLE 3.32

Method BV-WSP wall bracing requirements

Adapted from IRC Table R602.10.6.5

Seismic Design Category	Story	Braced Wall Line Length (feet)					Single-Story Hold-Down Force (pounds)[a]	Cumulative Hold-Down Force (pounds)[b]
		10	20	30	40	50		
		Minimum Total Length (feet) of Braced Wall Panels Required Along Each Braced Wall Line						
D₀		4.0	7.0	10.5	14.0	17.5	N/A	—
		4.0	7.0	10.5	14.0	17.5	1900	—
		4.5	9.0	13.5	18.0	22.5	3500	5400
		6.0	12.0	18.0	24.0	30.0	3500	8900
D₁		4.5	9.0	13.5	18.0	22.5	2100	—
		4.5	9.0	13.5	18.0	22.5	3700	5800
		6.0	12.0	18.0	24.0	30.0	3700	9500

For SI: 1 inch = 25.4 mm, 1 foot = 304.8 mm, 1 pound per square foot = 0.479 kPa, 1 pound-force = 4.448 N.
NP = Not Permitted.
N/A = Not Applicable.

❶ a. Hold-down force is minimum allowable stress design load for connector providing uplift tie from wall framing at end of braced wall panel at the noted story to wall framing at end of braced wall panel at the story below, or to foundation or foundation wall. Use single-story hold-down force where edges of braced wall panels do not align; a continuous load path to the foundation shall be maintained.

❷ b. Where hold-down connectors from stories above align with stories below, use cumulative hold-down force to size middle- and bottom-story hold-down connectors.

TABLE 3.32
(Continued)

Method BV-WSP wall bracing requirements

Adapted from IRC Table R602.10.6.5

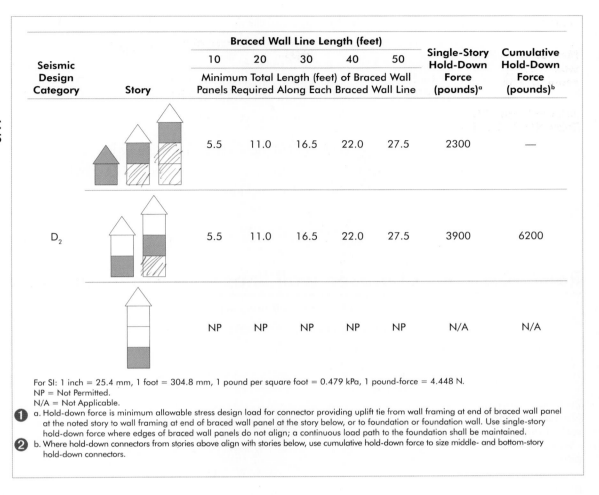

	Seismic Design Category	Story	Braced Wall Line Length (feet)					Single-Story Hold-Down Force (pounds)[a]	Cumulative Hold-Down Force (pounds)[b]
			10	20	30	40	50		
			Minimum Total Length (feet) of Braced Wall Panels Required Along Each Braced Wall Line						
			5.5	11.0	16.5	22.0	27.5	2300	—
	D₂		5.5	11.0	16.5	22.0	27.5	3900	6200
			NP	NP	NP	NP	NP	N/A	N/A

For SI: 1 inch = 25.4 mm, 1 foot = 304.8 mm, 1 pound per square foot = 0.479 kPa, 1 pound-force = 4.448 N.
NP = Not Permitted.
N/A = Not Applicable.

❶ a. Hold-down force is minimum allowable stress design load for connector providing uplift tie from wall framing at end of braced wall panel at the noted story to wall framing at end of braced wall panel at the story below, or to foundation or foundation wall. Use single-story hold-down force where edges of braced wall panels do not align; a continuous load path to the foundation shall be maintained.

❷ b. Where hold-down connectors from stories above align with stories below, use cumulative hold-down force to size middle- and bottom-story hold-down connectors.

❶ **Footnote a** – The basis for this footnote is that the lateral force acting on the braced wall panel creates an overturning force at the end of the braced wall panel. This overturning force is used to select the single-story and cumulative story hold-down force in IRC Table R602.10.6.5. The overturning force increases proportionally to the increase in height. In prescriptive terms, a bracing panel on the top floor requires more hold-down force to prevent its rotation at the foundation than does the same bracing panel on the first floor. When the "edges" (ends) of the bracing panels on subsequent floors do not align, the "single story hold-down force" shown is appropriate for the braced wall panel to be distributed to the foundation. For lower stories, although the single story force for a panel on that story would be less than the force required for a panel on the upper story, the listed single story force is large enough to resist upper story panel overturning forces that are being transferred to the foundation.

❷ **Footnote b** – when the braced wall panel ends on all floors line up/align with panels above and below, the individual panel hold-down requirement is combined with the hold-down requirement of the aligned braced wall panel. This value is shown in the "cumulative hold-down force" column. Note that where panel ends do not line up, it is not uncommon to see an upper-story braced wall panel hold down extend down through the middle of subsequent braced wall panels, or even areas with no bracing at all, until it reaches the foundation. In that case, the Footnote a provisions are appropriate.

While IRC Table R602.10.6.5 doesn't contain a footnote for interpolation, interpolation between braced wall line lengths is clearly permitted based on engineering principles (see ***APPENDIX C***).

In ***TABLE 3.32***, we have adjusted the shading of the figures in the top row of SDC D_0 to recognize the code requirement for the use of IRC Table R602.10.6.5 only when the veneer extends above the first story height. This includes gable ends as well as stories above. Once this correction has been made to D_0 and subsequent SDCs, it will be possible in future editions of the IRC to eliminate this extra row in SDC D_0.

R602.10.7 Ends of *braced wall lines* with continuous sheathing

R602.10.7 Ends of *braced wall lines* with continuous sheathing. Each end of a *braced wall line* with continuous sheathing shall have one of the conditions shown in Figure R602.10.7. (See ***FIGURES 3.49-3.53***.)

FIGURE 3.49

End Condition 1: Narrow braced wall panel with corner-return panel

IRC Figure R602.10.7

END CONDITION 1

a. Return panel: 24" for braced wall lines sheathed with wood structural panels
32" for braced wall lines sheathed with structural fiberboard

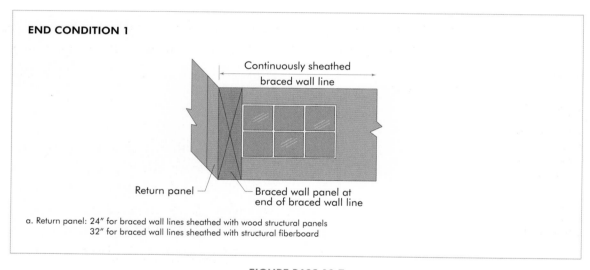

FIGURE R602.10.7
END CONDITIONS FOR BRACED WALL LINES WITH CONTINUOUS SHEATHING

END CONDITION 1 (FIGURE 3.49) - A continuously sheathed braced wall line must have a qualifying continuously sheathed braced panel at each end of the braced wall line and a qualifying return panel at each corner. The minimum return panel is 24-inches long for wood structural panels or 32-inches long for structural fiberboard sheathing.

FIGURE 3.50

End Condition 2: Narrow braced wall panel with 800 lb hold down

IRC Figure R602.10.7 (Continued)

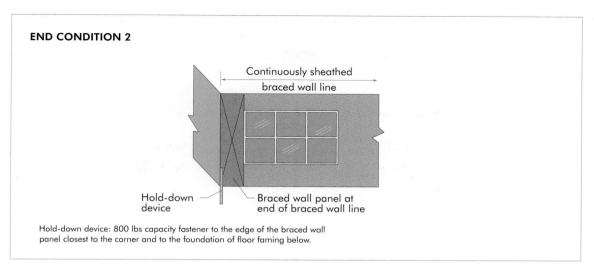

FIGURE R602.10.7 (CONTINUED)
END CONDITIONS FOR BRACED WALL LINES WITH CONTINUOUS SHEATHING

END CONDITION 2 (FIGURE 3.50) - This end condition provides for an 800 lb hold down in lieu of the return corner required in End Condition 1.

Note that if the adjacent wall is also a continuously sheathed wall without a braced wall panel at the corner, the adjacent wall will have to meet the requirements of End Condition 5.

FIGURE 3.51

End Condition 3: Full length panel at corner - no return corner or hold down required

IRC Figure R602.10.7 (Continued)

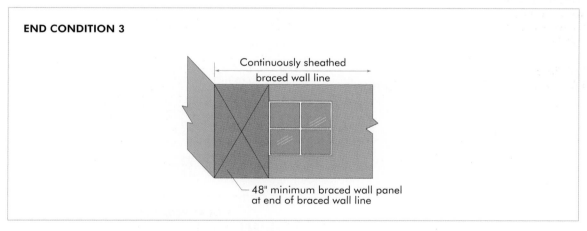

FIGURE R602.10.7 (CONTINUED)
END CONDITIONS FOR BRACED WALL LINES WITH CONTINUOUS SHEATHING

END CONDITION 3 (FIGURE 3.51) - Neither a corner return or hold down is required at the end of a continuously sheathed braced wall line if the braced wall panel at the corner is 48 inches long. This is because a full-length braced wall panel provides at least as much anchorage for the continuously sheathed braced wall line as does End Condition 1 or 2. This condition assumes proper nailing of the corner studs in accordance with IRC Table R602.3(1), Item 8.

FIGURE 3.52

End Condition 4: First braced wall panel away from corner requires "D" length panel on each side of corner

IRC Figure R602.10.7 (Continued)

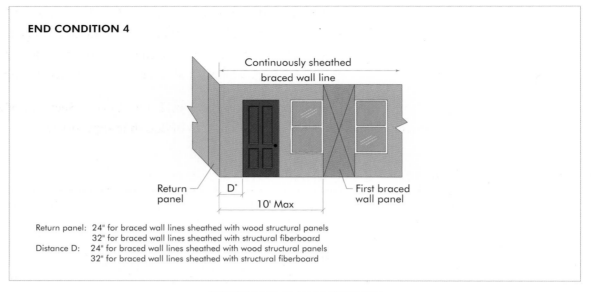

FIGURE R602.10.7 (CONTINUED)
END CONDITIONS FOR BRACED WALL LINES WITH CONTINUOUS SHEATHING

END CONDITION 4 (FIGURE 3.52) - Like intermittent braced wall lines, continuously sheathed braced wall lines are permitted to start away from the corner/end of the braced wall line by as much as 10 feet, providing a full-height panel segment of length "D" is placed at each side of the affected corner. The length of D and the return corner are defined in IRC Figure R602.10.7 (*FIGURE 3.52*). Note that neither the return corner nor D have to meet the minimum length requirements of the continuous sheathing methods.

FIGURE 3.53

End Condition 5: First braced wall panel away from corner requires 800 lb hold down if sheathed corner provisions not met

IRC Figure R602.10.7 (Continued)

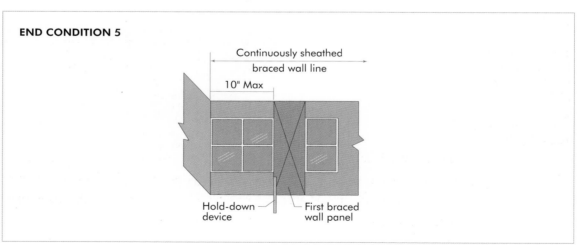

FIGURE R602.10.7 (CONTINUED)
END CONDITIONS FOR BRACED WALL LINES WITH CONTINUOUS SHEATHING

END CONDITION 5 (FIGURE 3.53) — As an option to End Condition 4, a hold-down device may be substituted for the return corner and corner sheathing of length D. Note that if the adjacent wall is also continuously sheathed, it does not have the structural advantage offered by the return corner. As such, the adjacent wall must also have a hold-down attachment.

In SDC D_0, D_1 and D_2, the hold-down capacity must be 1,800 lb (Section R602.10.2.2.1, Exception 2). For other applications a capacity of 800 lb is appropriate.

R602.10.8 Braced wall panel connections

R602.10.8 Braced wall panel connections. *Braced wall panels* shall be connected to floor framing or foundations as follows:

IRC Table R602.3(1), Item 16 provides the basic nailing schedule for attaching braced wall panels to the floor below and the ceiling or floor above. The sole plate (or bottom plate) of the braced wall panels is required to be nailed with three 16d nails every 16 inches on center into the joist or blocking below the braced wall panels. See **TABLE 3.33**.

Note that the nails do not have to be clustered every 16 inches on center: there just have to be three nails in every 16 inch-length of braced wall panel. In fact, clustering the nails may not be a good idea if, for example, they are going into a rim board. In other cases, clustering may be needed, such as an interior braced wall parallel to and situated between floor framing: clustering may be necessary to attach the braced wall to the blocking. See IRC Figures R602.10.8(1) and (2) (**FIGURES 3.54** and **3.55**).

TABLE 3.33

Attachment of braced wall panels at sole plate

Item	Description Of Building Elements	Member And Type Of Fastener	Spacing Of Fasteners
16	Sole plate to joist or blocking, at braced wall panels	3-16d (3-1/2" x 0.135")	16" o.c.

Excerpt from IRC Table R602.3(1)

For a braced wall panel to provide lateral load resistance to the structure, it is essential that lateral loads transfer into the panel at its top and out to the framing members below at its bottom. Appropriate connections are necessary to complete this lateral load path and are addressed in the braced wall panel connection provisions.

1. Where joists are perpendicular to a *braced wall panel* above or below, a rim joist, band joist or blocking shall be provided along the entire length of the *braced wall panel* in accordance with Figure R602.10.8(1). Fastening of top and bottom wall plates to framing, rim joist, band joist and/or blocking shall be in accordance with Table R602.3(1).

FIGURE 3.54

Braced wall panel connection when perpendicular to floor/ceiling framing

Adapted from IRC Figure R602.10.8(1)

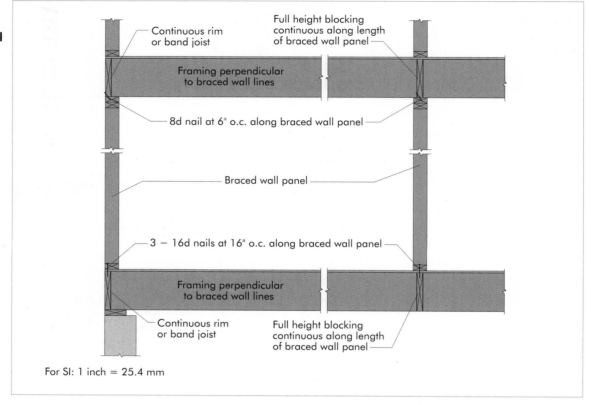

2. Where joists are parallel to a *braced wall panel* above or below, a rim joist, end joist or other parallel framing member shall be provided directly above and below the *braced wall panel* in accordance with Figure R602.10.8(2). Where a parallel framing member cannot be located directly above and below the panel, full-depth blocking at 16-inch (406 mm) spacing shall be provided between the parallel framing members to each side of the *braced wall panel* in accordance with Figure R602.10.8(2). Fastening of blocking and wall plates shall be in accordance with Table R602.3(1) and Figure R602.10.8(2).

FIGURE 3.55

Braced wall panel connection when parallel to floor/ceiling framing

Adapted from IRC Figure R602.10.8(2)

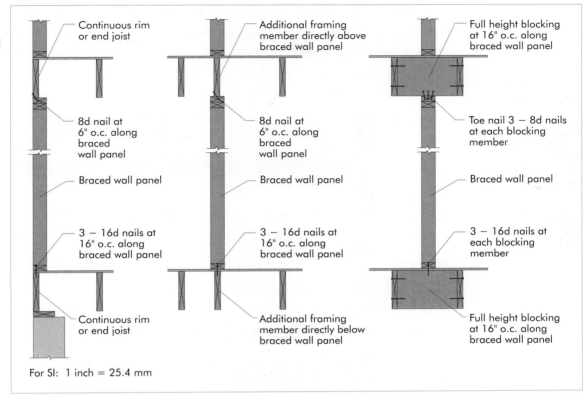

For SI: 1 inch = 25.4 mm

3. Connections of *braced wall panels* to concrete or masonry shall be in accordance with Section R403.1.6.

See **CHAPTER 2** of this guide for IRC Section R403.1.6.

R602.10.8.1 Braced wall panel connections for Seismic Design Categories D_0, D_1 and D_2.

Braced wall panels shall be fastened to required foundations in accordance with Section R602.11.1, and top plate lap splices shall be face-nailed with at least eight 16d nails on each side of the splice.

Structures in areas of high seismicity need to have the capacity to withstand greater loads; therefore, additional provisions are required to ensure that these loads are transferred through the braced wall panels to the foundation. The requirements of IRC Section R602.10.8.1 ensure the top plate lap splices and foundation connections have the needed higher load capacity.

The requirement for eight 16d nails on each side of the lap splice in SDC D_0, D_1 and D_2 is given in IRC Section R602.10.8.1. Note that IRC Table R602.3(1), Item 14 requires a 24-inch overlap to provide sufficient length to put in the eight 16d nails.

Note that Footnote c of IRC Table R602.10.3(4) (**TABLE 3.6**) requires the number of 16d nails used in the splice plate to be increased to twelve on either side of the splice when the braced wall line spacing is increased over 25 feet in SDC D_0, D_1 and D_2.

Recall, when the first bracing panel is displaced from the corner by more than the permitted 10 feet, the collector design information in **APPENDIX A** is appropriate for top plate/collector splices. See **FIGURE 3.56**.

FIGURE 3.56

Top plate splice for SDC D$_0$, D$_1$ and D$_2$

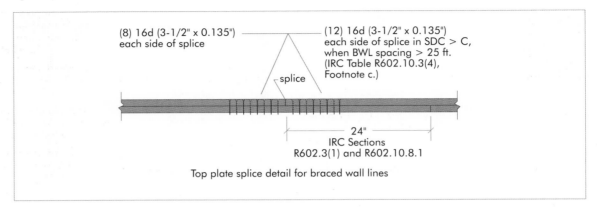

(8) 16d (3-1/2" x 0.135") each side of splice

(12) 16d (3-1/2" x 0.135") each side of splice in SDC > C, when BWL spacing > 25 ft. (IRC Table R602.10.3(4), Footnote c.)

splice

24"
IRC Sections
R602.3(1) and R602.10.8.1

Top plate splice detail for braced wall lines

R602.10.8.2 Connections to roof framing. Top plates of exterior *braced wall panels* shall be attached to rafters or roof trusses above in accordance with Table R602.3(1) and this section. Where required by this section, blocking between rafters or roof trusses shall be attached to top plates of *braced wall panels* and to rafters and roof trusses in accordance with Table R602.3(1). A continuous band, rim, or header joist or roof truss parallel to the *braced wall panels* shall be permitted to replace the blocking required by this section. Blocking shall not be required over openings in continuously sheathed *braced wall lines*. In addition to the requirements of this section, lateral support shall be provided for rafters and ceiling joists in accordance with Section R802.8 and for trusses in accordance with Section R802.10.3. Roof ventilation shall be provided in accordance with Section R806.1.

Although initially addressed in the 2009 IRC, complex roof shapes used in modern design have necessitated prescriptive connection details to ensure an effective load path exists.

These connection details represent a simple principle: braced wall panels extend from diaphragm to diaphragm and must be connected at both top and bottom. The roof and floor sheathing are the structural diaphragms of the building. IRC Figures R602.10.8.2(1)-(3) (**FIGURES 3.57-3.59**) illustrate the required connections and blocking between braced wall panels and roof framing/diaphragm, which are summarized in **TABLE 3.34**.

Note that it is only the exterior walls that are required to be attached in accordance with this section. From an engineering perspective, interior braced wall panels must also be tied into the roof diaphragm. The details shown in IRC Figures R602.10.8(1) and (2) (**FIGURES 3.57** and **3.58**) prescriptively provide for braced wall panel-to-ceiling connections for interior braced wall panels as well. If these details are used on an interior braced wall line, the connection from the framing of the braced wall panels to the roof framing above needs to accommodate vertical movement of the roof framing, in order to prevent "truss uplift" and gypsum ceiling cracking.

TABLE 3.34

Summary of bracing connection and blocking requirements between braced wall panels and roof framing

Seismic Design Category and Wind Speed	Distance (bottom of roof sheathing to top of top plate)	Blocking[a]
SDC A, B, C and wind speed less than 100 mph	9-1/4" or less	Not Required per IRC Section R602.10.8.2, Item 1. Roof framing attached per IRC Table R602.3(1)
	Greater than 9-1/4" to 15-1/4"	Required above braced wall panels per IRC Section R602.10.8.2, Item 1 and IRC Figure R602.10.8.2(1)
SDC D_0, D_1, D_2 or wind speed 100 mph or greater	15-1/4" or less	Required above braced wall panels per IRC Section R602.10.8.2, Item 2 and IRC Figure R602.10.8.2(1)
All SDCs and wind speeds	15-1/4" and greater	Required above braced wall panels per IRC Section R602.10.8.2, Item 3 and IRC Figures R602.10.8.2(2) or R602.10.8.2(3)

a. Rafter or truss connection to top plate per IRC Table R602.3(1).

1. For Seismic Design Categories A, B and C and wind speeds less than 100 mph (45 m/s) where the distance from the top of the *braced wall panel* to the top of the rafters or roof trusses above is 9-1/4 inches (235 mm) or less, blocking between rafters or roof trusses shall not be required. Where the distance from the top of the *braced wall panel* to the top of the rafters or roof trusses above is between 9-1/4 inches (235 mm) and 15-1/4 inches (387 mm), blocking between rafters or roof trusses shall be provided above the *braced wall panel* in accordance with Figure R602.10.8.2(1).

Note that the annotation in IRC Figure R602.10.8.2(1) (***FIGURE 3.57***) requires solid blocking only at the top of braced wall panels. If continuous sheathing bracing methods are used, blocking is required only at the top of each full-height wall segment counted as a braced wall panel in the wall line below.

FIGURE 3.57

Braced wall panel connection – low-heel trusses

IRC Figure R602.10.8.2(1)

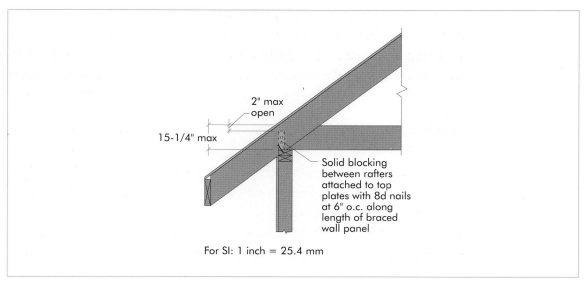

2" max open

15-1/4" max

Solid blocking between rafters attached to top plates with 8d nails at 6" o.c. along length of braced wall panel

For SI: 1 inch = 25.4 mm

FIGURE R602.10.8.2(1)
BRACED WALL PANEL CONNECTION TO PERPENDICULAR RAFTERS

2. For Seismic Design Categories D_0, D_1 and D_2 or wind speeds of 100 mph (45 m/s) or greater, where the distance from the top of the *braced wall panel* to the top of the rafters or roof trusses is 15-1/4 inches (387 mm) or less, blocking between rafters or roof trusses shall be provided above the *braced wall panel* in accordance with Figure R602.10.8.2(1).

IRC Section R602.10.8.2, Item 1 provides what is essentially an exemption from required blocking for SDC A, B and C and wind speeds less than 100 mph, where the distance from the top of the rafters or roof trusses to the perpendicular top plates is 9-1/4 inches or less, provided the rafters or roof trusses are connected to the top plates of braced wall panels in accordance with IRC Table R602.3(1).

IRC Figure R602.10.8.2(1) (**FIGURE 3.57**) illustrates the required detailing and connection for relatively low-heel trusses and rafters (less than or equal to 15-1/4 inches between the bottom of roof diaphragm sheathing and the top of double top plate). For such applications, the addition of solid lumber blocking is sufficient to prevent the trusses or conventional framing members from rolling over when subjected to wind and/or seismic loads. Attachment per IRC Table R602.3(1), Items 1, 2 and 5 – nailing at the bottom of the roof framing and blocking – is required to transfer the lateral forces (that push the roof framing along the top plate) from the roof sheathing (or diaphragm) into the braced wall line. The 2-inch gap at the top of the blocking permits required roof ventilation.

IRC Figure R602.10.8.2(2) (**FIGURE 3.58**) illustrates an alternate connection between a braced wall panel and roof sheathing (or diaphragm) that, while less direct, will provide adequate transfer of lateral forces from the roof diaphragm to the braced wall line. This detail does not provide lateral stability of the trusses at the bearing point (see truss installation diagrams) or the required roof venting. While the code permits various bracing methods for this application (IRC Figure R602.10.8.2 (2), Note a), the user must be careful to specify only those methods that have sufficient weather resistance or provide a covering with an approved exterior finish. Note that the edge nailing requirement for the bracing method used at the soffit is provided in IRC Table R602.3(1) and is not necessarily the same as the roof or wall sheathing edge nailing, unless the same material is used for both applications.

FIGURE 3.58

Braced wall panel connection - soffit blocking

IRC Figure R602.10.8.2(2)

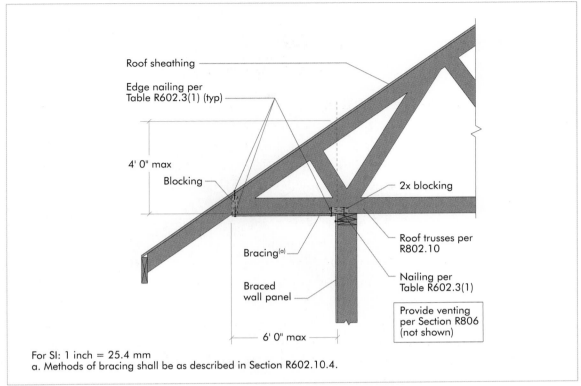

Roof sheathing

Edge nailing per Table R602.3(1) (typ)

4' 0" max

Blocking

2x blocking

Bracing⁽ᵃ⁾

Braced wall panel

Roof trusses per R802.10

Nailing per Table R602.3(1)

Provide venting per Section R806 (not shown)

6' 0" max

For SI: 1 inch = 25.4 mm
a. Methods of bracing shall be as described in Section R602.10.4.

FIGURE R602.10.8.2(2)
BRACED WALL PANEL CONNECTION OPTION TO PERPENDICULAR RAFTERS OR ROOF TRUSSES

3. Where the distance from the top of the *braced wall panel* to the top of rafters or roof trusses exceeds 15-1/4 inches (387 mm), the top plates of the *braced wall panel* shall be connected to perpendicular rafters or roof trusses above in accordance with one or more of the following methods:

    3.1. Soffit blocking panels constructed in accordance with Figure R602.10.8.2(2);

    3.2. Vertical blocking panels constructed in accordance with Figure R602.10.8.2(3);

FIGURE 3.59

Braced wall panel connection – maximum height 4 feet

IRC Figure R602.10.8.2(3)

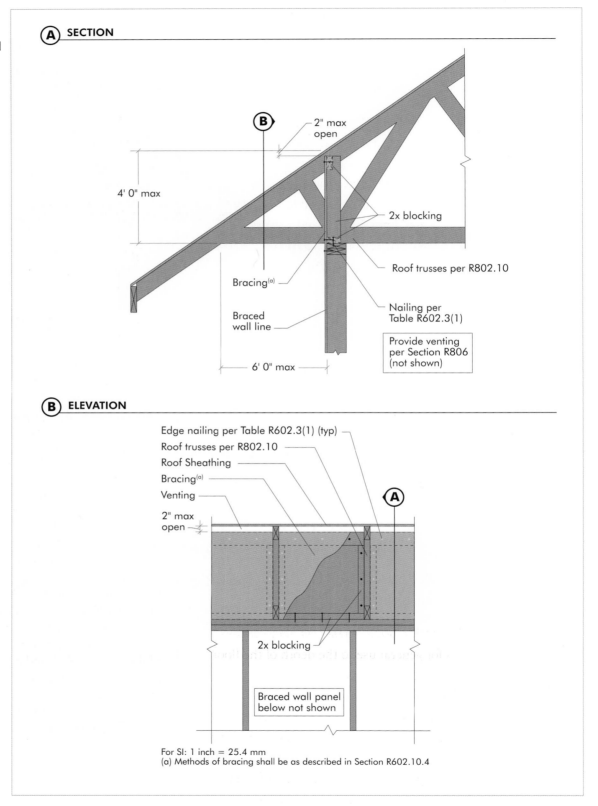

Ⓐ SECTION

B

2" max open

4' 0" max

2x blocking

Roof trusses per R802.10

Bracing⁽ᵃ⁾

Braced wall line

Nailing per Table R602.3(1)

Provide venting per Section R806 (not shown)

6' 0" max

Ⓑ ELEVATION

Edge nailing per Table R602.3(1) (typ)

Roof trusses per R802.10

Roof Sheathing

Bracing⁽ᵃ⁾

Venting

2" max open

Ⓐ

2x blocking

Braced wall panel below not shown

For SI: 1 inch = 25.4 mm
(a) Methods of bracing shall be as described in Section R602.10.4

FIGURE R602.10.8.2(3)
BRACED WALL PANEL CONNECTION OPTION TO PERPENDICULAR RAFTERS OR ROOF TRUSSES

3.3. Full-height engineered blocking panels designed in accordance with the AF&PA WFCM; or

3.4. Blocking, blocking panels, or other methods of lateral load transfer designed in accordance with accepted engineering practice.

IRC Figure R602.10.8.2(3) (**FIGURE 3.59**) illustrates a connection applicable for raised-heel trusses of up to 4 feet in height. In addition to transferring the lateral load from the roof sheathing (or diaphragm) to the braced wall line, this method also addresses lateral stability of the trusses at the bearing point. Ventilation is provided by a gap of up to 2 inches at the top of braced panels between trusses. While the code permits any bracing methods listed in IRC Section R602.10, the user must be careful to specify only those methods that have sufficient weather resistance or provide a covering with an approved exterior finish.

R602.10.9 Braced wall panel support

R602.10.9 Braced wall panel support.

Braced wall panel support shall be provided as follows:

1. Cantilevered floor joists complying with Section R502.3.3 shall be permitted to support *braced wall panels*.

IRC Section 502.3.3 restricts floor cantilevers for general use to the depth of the floor joist. Thus a 2x10 floor joist can cantilever out 9-1/4 inches for all cases covered by the IRC without other considerations. IRC Table R502.3.3(1) permits greater length cantilevers if the structure above the cantilever is limited to a single light-frame wall and roof. The length of these cantilevers can be as long as 48 inches under certain circumstances.

PARTIAL-HEIGHT BLOCKING

The continuous 2-inch gap at the top of the blocking or blocking panel shown in IRC Figures R602.10.8.2(1) and R602.10.8.2(3) was new in the 2009 IRC. In the past, lateral blocking required to resist racking or cross-grain bending of the roof framing was specified as full-height from top of top plate to bottom of sheathing. Where ventilation openings were required, an engineered solution was necessary.

A 2002 HUD-PATH investigation of conventional roof framing connections showed that lateral blocking for typical rafter/ceiling-joist assemblies and low-heel trusses was not required in low-wind, low-seismic conditions. This testing forms the basis for the requirements of IRC Section R602.10.8.2, Item 1 and Figures R602.10.8.2(1)-(3) (**FIGURES 3.57-3.59**).

For deeper assemblies and higher-load conditions, it is possible to engineer "partial-height" blocking that does not extend the full depth of the rafter or truss heel. Guidance for estimating cross-grain bending stresses in natural lumber is provided in the USDA FPL Wood Handbook. Using a conservative estimate of the cross-grain bending stress, it was determined that a continuous 2-inch gap at the top of solid blocking or a blocking panel would not compromise the structural performance of the roof framing for loads within the scope of the IRC.

Without the guidance for the use of cantilevers provided in the 2012 IRC Section R602.10.9, Item 1, the user would be left with the general provisions in IRC Section R502.3.3. Note also that IRC Section R502.2.1 requires a complete load path at the bottom and top of each braced wall panel. This leads the user back to IRC Figures R602.10.8(1) and (2) (**FIGURES 3.54** and **3.55**), as well as IRC Table R602.3(1), to glean the cantilever attachment details. See **FIGURE 3.60**.

FIGURE 3.60

Braced wall line connections over cantilever foors

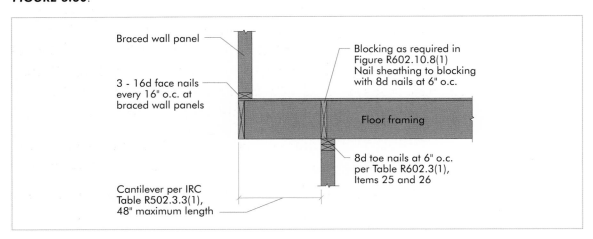

Note that in SDC C, D_0, D_1 and D_2, further limitations are provided for cantilevers at braced wall lines. These are listed in IRC Section 301.2.2.2.5, Item 1. See **CHAPTER 2**.

2. Raised wood floor or pier foundations supporting *braced wall panels* shall be designed in accordance with accepted engineering practice.

Elevated post and pier foundations generally provide little lateral support to the structure above. Lateral support instead typically comes from diagonal bracing or other elements of the foundation; however, there are ways of cantilevering the posts of the foundation by burying the ends deeply into the ground, so that they develop lateral-load resisting characteristics.

It is difficult to accurately and fully present all of the post and pier lateral support methods in one set of prescriptive provisions. For this reason, post and pier foundations supporting braced wall panels must be engineered in accordance with the IBC or referenced documents.

3. Masonry stem walls with a length of 48 inches (1219 mm) or less supporting *braced wall panels* shall be reinforced in accordance with Figure R602.10.9. Masonry stem walls with a length greater than 48 inches (1219 mm) supporting *braced wall panels* shall be constructed in accordance with Section R403.1 Methods ABW and PFH shall not be permitted to attach to masonry stem walls.

Past field problems have made it clear that free-standing unreinforced masonry foundations adjacent to garage doors (or similar openings) may not perform well with narrow bracing options. The ICC Ad Hoc Wall Bracing Committee and the National Concrete Masonry Association developed IRC Figure R602.10.9 (**FIGURE 3.61**), along with provisions for the reinforcement of masonry stem walls that support braced wall panels. The provisions are intended for masonry stem walls adjacent to garage doors or similar openings.

- The reinforcement details in IRC Figure R602.10.9 are appropriate for masonry stem walls that are up to 4 feet in length and not more than 4 feet in height.

- If the masonry stem walls are taller than 4 feet, an engineered design of the reinforcement is required.

- If the masonry stem walls are longer than 4 feet, this specific reinforcement is not necessary (standard construction in accordance with IRC Section R403.1 is sufficient).

- Masonry stem walls are not permitted to support Method ABW and PFH bracing unless specifically engineered for such applications.

TABLE 3.35 provides IRC reinforcing requirements for wall lines with and without braced wall panels.

TABLE 3.35

2012 IRC Reinforcement requirements

Code Provision	Code Section	Provision	Concrete Footings and Foundation Walls	
			Low to Moderate Seismic Regions SDC A–C	High Seismic Regions SDC D_0–D_2
Footing Requirements R403	R403.1.3	Construction Joint	No reinforcement requirements, unless required by other sections of code	1-#4 vertical at 48" o.c. with standard hook1 at bottom bars when a construction joint exists between the footing and stem wall
	R403.1.3	Masonry stem wall		1-#4 vertical at 48" o.c. with standard hook1 at bottom bar in footing when a masonry stem wall is placed on a concrete footing
	R403.1.3.1	Concrete stem wall		1-#4 horizontal within 12" of the top of wall
				1-#4 horizontal located 3" to 4" from bottom of footing
	R403.1.3.2	Slab with turned down footing		1-#4 horizontal at top and bottom[2]
				1-#3 vertical at 48" o.c. with standard hook to top and bottom bars when slab and footing cast separately
Concrete Foundation Walls (Basement Walls) R404	Table R404.1.2(1)	Horizontal Reinforcement	1-#4 required at top and mid-height (or third points)	1-#4 horizontal required within 12 inches of top and near mid-height
	Tables R404.1.2(2) thru R404.1.2(9)	Vertical Reinforcement	Rebar required according to appropriate table, read footnotes for additional requirements	Rebar required according to appropriate table, read footnotes for additional requirements
	R404.1.4.2	Concrete foundation walls in SDC D_0–D_2	No additional reinforcement requirements	Walls less than or equal to 7.5" thick require 1-#4 vertical bar at 48" o.c.
Wall Bracing R602.10	R602.10.6, Figures R602.10.6.1 and R602.10.6.2	Alternate wall bracing (ABW, PFH)	Methods ABW and PFH required 1-#4 horizontal top and bottom of footing	Methods ABW and PFH required 1-#4 horizontal at top and bottom of footing
	R602.10.9, Figure R602.10.9	Short concrete walls supporting braced wall panel	Rebar required complying with Figure R602.10.9 if wall length, height, and thickness are L ≤ 48" AND H > 12" AND T < 6"	Rebar required complying with Figure R602.10.9 if wall length, height, and thickness are L ≤ 48" AND H > 12" AND T < 6"

1. See Figure R611.5.4(3) for detail of standard hook.
2. For slabs-on-ground cast monolithically with the footing, locating 1-# 5 bar or 2-# 4 bars in the middle third of the footing depth shall be permitted as an alternative to placement at the footing top and bottom.

4. Concrete stem walls with a length of 48 inches (1219 mm) or less, greater than 12 inches (305 mm) tall and less than 6 inches (152 mm) thick shall have reinforcement sized and located in accordance with Figure R602.10.9.

New for 2012 is this provision that provides for the use of cast-in-place concrete stem walls for these narrow wall applications. The same reinforcement requirements are appropriate for such concrete stem walls, but the restriction against use with Methods ABW and PFH does not apply.

FIGURE 3.61

Reinforcement of masonry or concrete stem walls supporting bracing elements

IRC Figure R602.10.9

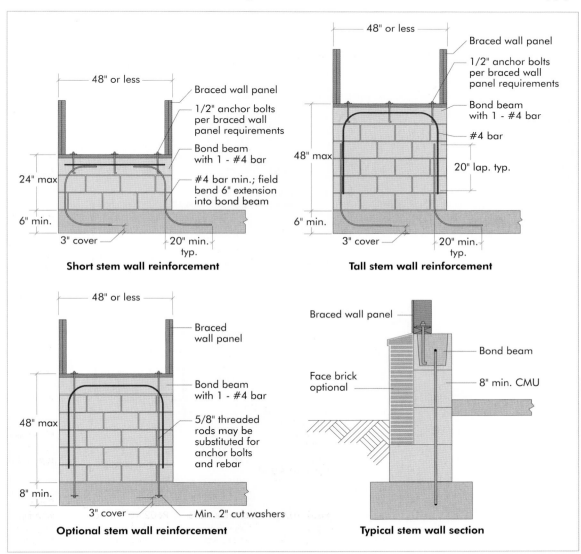

FIGURE R602.10.9
MASONRY STEM WALLS SUPPORTING BRACED WALL PANELS

R602.10.9.1 Braced wall panel support for Seismic Design Category D$_2$. In one-story buildings located in Seismic Design Category D$_2$, *braced wall panels* shall be supported on continuous foundations at intervals not exceeding 50 feet (15 240 mm). In two-story buildings located in Seismic Design Category D$_2$, all *braced wall panels* shall be supported on continuous foundations.

Special bracing support provisions apply to the highest Seismic Design Category covered in the IRC. IRC Section R602.10.9.1, unchanged from 2009, addresses braced wall panel support for SDC D$_2$. Although the section now applies to all braced wall lines, note that the exception applies only to interior braced wall panels/lines, **FIGURE 3.62** illustrates foundation support at a 50-foot interval for a one-story home in SDC D$_2$. **FIGURE 3.63** illustrates all interior braced wall panels/lines supported for a two-story home in SDC D$_2$.

FIGURE 3.62

Single-story foundation support in SDC D$_2$

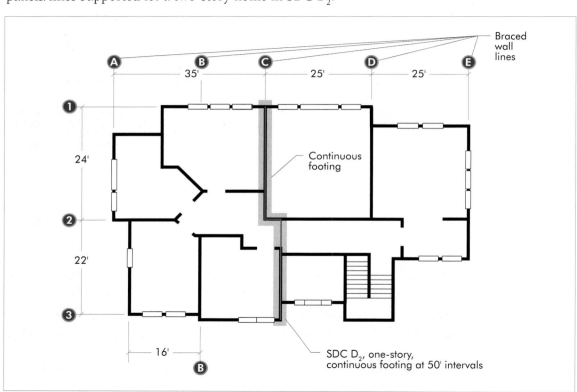

Note that in **FIGURE 3.62**, while wall lines B and D are interior braced wall lines, they do not have a continuous foundation. If the structure was two stories, then a continuous foundation would be required under all the braced wall lines.

FIGURE 3.63

**Two-story
foundation
support in SDC D$_2$**

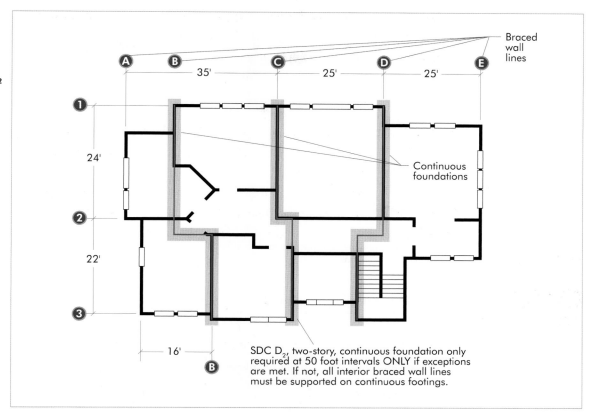

Braced wall lines

Continuous foundations

SDC D$_2$, two-story, continuous foundation only
required at 50 foot intervals ONLY if exceptions
are met. If not, all interior braced wall lines
must be supported on continuous footings.

Exception: Two-story buildings shall be permitted to have interior *braced wall panels*
supported on continuous foundations at intervals not exceeding 50 feet (15 240 mm)
provided that:

No longer must all interior braced wall panels be supported on continuous foundations: the
above exception to IRC Section R602.10.9.1 permits interior braced wall panels in two-story
buildings to be supported on continuous foundations at no more than 50-foot intervals. All
three of the following conditions must be met for the exception to be valid (see **FIGURE 3.63**).

1. The height of cripple walls does not exceed 4 feet (1219 mm).

2. First-floor *braced wall panels* are supported on doubled floor joists, continuous blocking
   or floor beams.

3. The distance between bracing lines does not exceed twice the building width measured
   parallel to the *braced wall line*. (See **FIGURE 3.64.**)

FIGURE 3.64

Braced wall spacing

IRC Section R602.10.9.1

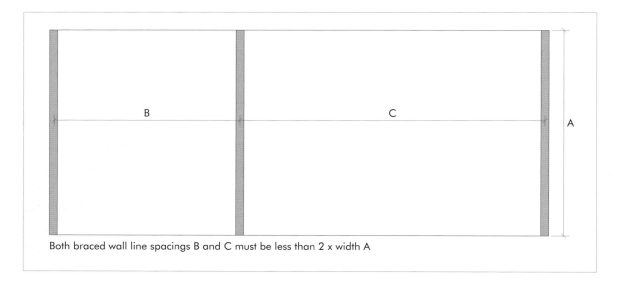

B | C | A

Both braced wall line spacings B and C must be less than 2 x width A

TABLE 3.36 provides continuous footing foundation requirements for interior braced wall panels in SDC D_2.

TABLE 3.36

SDC D_2 interior braced wall panel (BWP) – continuous footing foundation requirements

IRC Sections R403.1.2 and R602.10.9.1

Number of Stories	Continuous Foundation ≤ 50 ft	Continuous Foundation > 50 ft
Single Story	No requirement for continuous foundation/footing	Use R403.1.2 - most restrictive, requires continuous footing below all interior BWPs
Two Story	Use R602.10.9.1 – most restrictive, requires continuous foundation below all interior BWPs	Requires continuous foundation below all interior BWPs
Two Story Exception		Use R403.1.2 – most restrictive, requires continuous footing below all interior BWPs

1. IRC Section R403.1.2 refers to a continuous footing
2. IRC Section R602.10.9.1 refers to a continuous foundation
3. For SDC D_0 and D_1, IRC Section R403.1.2 gives foundation requirements

R602.10.10 Panel joints. All vertical joints of panel sheathing shall occur over, and be fastened to, common studs. Horizontal joints in *braced wall panels* shall occur over, and be fastened to, common blocking of a minimum 1-1/2 inch (38 mm) thickness.

IRC Section R602.10.10 (formerly 2009 IRC Section R602.10.8) requires that all vertical and horizontal joints in panel sheathing used for bracing occur over and be attached to common framing or blocking. This is to ensure that the bracing performs as intended when subjected to lateral loads. New for 2012 is an exception that permits vertical joints to be made by spiking together pairs of studs. The requirement for horizontal joint blocking also has some exceptions.

Exceptions:

1. Vertical joints of panel sheathing shall be permitted to occur over double studs, where adjoining panel edges are attached to separate studs with the required panel edge fastening schedule, and the adjacent studs are attached together with two rows of 10d box nails [3 inches by 0.128 inch (76.2 mm by 3.25 mm)] at 10 inches o.c. (254 mm).

While the original provision calls for adjacent panels to meet over common framing, this provision permits the use of double studs at the joint between adjacent panel edges, provided the studs are spiked together sufficiently to transfer shear stresses from one panel to the next. This provision is the result of concern over the difficulty of placing adjacent panel edges over a single 1-1/2-inch surface of the common wall stud. This exception also simplifies retrofit of braced wall panels and field repairs without the need for additional engineering and simplifies the use of prefabricated wall panels.

2. Blocking at horizontal joints shall not be required in wall segments that are not counted as *braced wall panels.*

This horizontal joint exception permits unblocked horizontal joints of sheathing panels <u>not used</u> as braced panels. However, panel manufacturers or panel associations may recommend blocking the horizontal joints of sheathing panels regardless of whether they are used as braced panels. For example, brittle finishes (such as synthetic stucco) over sheathing panels may require blocked horizontal panel edges to prevent cracking, even when the sheathing panels are not used for wall bracing.

3. Where the bracing length provided is at least twice the minimum length required by Table R602.10.3(1) and Table R602.10.3(3) blocking at horizontal joints shall not be required in *braced wall panels* constructed using Methods WSP, SFB, GB, PBS or HPS.

When horizontal joints of braced wall panels are not blocked, the effectiveness of the bracing is reduced and additional bracing is required. Consequently, for Methods WSP, SFB, GB, PBS and HPS, horizontal blocking of the braced wall panels may be eliminated, provided that twice the minimum required bracing length is used in the wall line. The purpose of this exception is to provide a construction alternative to installing horizontal blocking when circumstances permit. Note that this provision may be of particular value in narrow lots where adjacent structures sit very close together. Typically in such instances, few, relatively small openings are placed in the facing walls between structures. In such cases, it can often be relatively easy to double the amount of bracing in order to eliminate horizontal blocking, especially when continuous sheathing is used. Note that the type finish used over the bracing panels may dictate that joints be blocked, as is often the case for some brittle finishes (such as synthetic stucco).

4. When Method GB panels are installed horizontally, blocking of horizontal joints is not required.

The required bracing length for Method GB (gypsum board) is based on its vertical application with horizontal joints occurring over framing or blocking. Method GB bracing is considerably stronger when installed horizontally. The fourth exception permits Method GB bracing to be unblocked when it is installed horizontally.

R602.10.11 Cripple wall bracing. Cripple walls shall be constructed in accordance with Section R602.9 and braced in accordance with this section. Cripple walls shall be braced with the length and method of bracing used for the wall above in accordance with Tables R602.10.3(1) and R602.10.3(3), and the applicable adjustment factors in Table R602.10.3(2) or R602.10.3(4), respectively, except that the length of cripple wall bracing shall be multiplied by a factor of 1.15. The distance between adjacent edges of *braced wall panels* shall be reduced from 20 feet (6096 mm) to 14 feet (4267 mm).

Note that the reduction in spacing between braced wall panels from 20 feet to 14 feet is based on a submittal made for the 2012 IRC. The intent of the submittal was to only reduce the braced wall panel spacing for seismic applications, not wind. An error was made in the correlation of the Public Comment and this distinction was unfortunately lost.

A cripple wall is a less-than-full-height wall that is used to raise the elevation of a floor above the foundation, as shown in **FIGURE 3.65**. Cripple walls are also often used in conjunction with a stepped foundation to maintain a common plate elevation when the foundation drops away from the plate line, accommodating a sloped building site, as shown in **FIGURE 3.66**. In either case, a cripple wall has the same limitations as any other stud wall in that it has no lateral load capacity without the use of bracing panels.

FIGURE 3.65

Cripple wall used to raise floor elevation

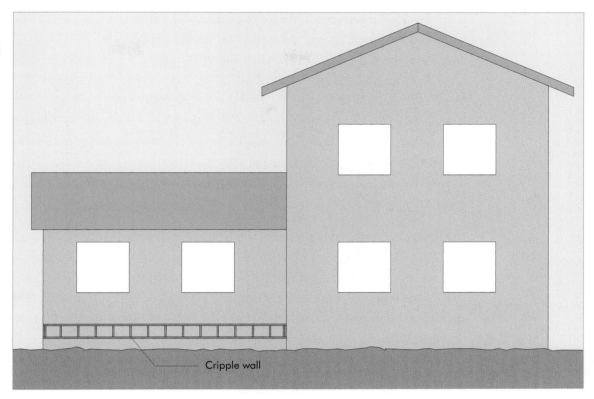

Cripple wall

FIGURE 3.66

Cripple wall used with a stepped foundation

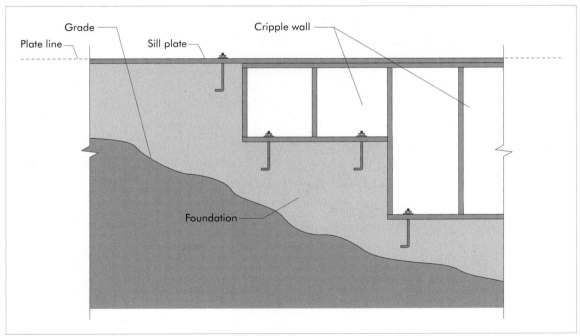

Grade

Plate line

Sill plate

Cripple wall

Foundation

Even though they are less than full height, cripple walls are still a part of the load path and are subject to the same vertical and horizontal loads as full-height walls. In fact, because gravity and lateral loads get larger as building height increases, cripple walls are subject to even greater loads than the walls in stories above them. Because of these larger loads, IRC Section R602.10.11 requires the length of bracing used for the cripple wall to be 15 percent greater (multiplied by a factor of 1.15) than the bracing in IRC Tables R602.10.3(1) and (3) (**TABLES 3.3** and **3.5**) and the maximum braced wall panel spacing in the cripple wall line is reduced from 20 to 14 feet, measured between braced wall panel adjacent edges. The cripple walls can be braced using any method in any SDC except D_2. Note that the adjustments of IRC Tables R602.10.3(2) and (4) still apply, in addition to the 15 percent increase for cripple walls.

EXAMPLE: A cripple wall supports the first story of a two-story residence. Per IRC Table R301.2(1) of the locally adopted IRC, the design wind speed is 90 mph and the SDC is A. The builder is planning on using Method SFB (structural fiberboard sheathing) bracing. After reviewing the requirements of IRC Tables R602.10.3(1) and (2) (**TABLE 3.3 AND 3.4**)), the builder determines that 9.5 feet of bracing is required for the first floor. How much bracing is required for the cripple wall supporting that floor?

ANSWER: IRC Section R602.10.11 requires an increase in the minimum amount of bracing by 15 percent; therefore, 9.5 feet x 1.15 = 10.9 feet of Method SFB bracing for the cripple wall. Note that this section of the code also decreases the maximum distance between braced wall panels in the cripple walls from 20 to 14 feet.

Bracing length requirements specifically for cripple walls in SDC D_2 are provided in IRC Table R602.10.3(3) (**TABLE 3.5**). While the 15 percent increase does not need to be applied to these values, the braced wall panel maximum spacing requirements do apply, per IRC Section R602.10.11.

> **R602.10.11.1 Cripple wall bracing for Seismic Design Categories D_0 and D_1 and townhouses in Seismic Design Category C.** In addition to the requirements in Section R602.10.11, the distance between adjacent edges of *braced wall panels* for cripple walls along a *braced wall line* shall be 14 feet (4267 mm) maximum.

This section has changed little since the 2006 IRC. It has become redundant, as IRC Section R602.10.11 also requires a braced wall panel spacing in cripple wall lines of 14 feet in all seismic design categories. Note that the distance between cripple wall braced wall panels reflects the new metric for braced wall panel spacing. Instead of center-to-center the numbers reflect distance between adjacent edges of the braced wall panels: 25 feet center-to-center, is now 20 feet between adjacent edges and 18 feet center-to-center for cripple braced wall panels is now 14 feet between adjacent edges.

Where *braced wall lines* at interior walls are not supported on a continuous foundation below, the adjacent parallel cripple walls, where provided, shall be braced with Method WSP or Method CS-WSP in accordance with Section R602.10.4. The length of bracing required in accordance with Table R602.10.3(3) for the cripple walls shall be multiplied by 1.5. Where the cripple walls do not have sufficient length to provide the required bracing, the spacing of panel edge fasteners shall be reduced to 4 inches (102 mm) on center and the required bracing length adjusted by 0.7. If the required length can still not be provided, the cripple wall shall be designed in accordance with accepted engineering practice.

As the seismic force on a structure increases, the lateral load acting on the cripple walls also increases. For SDC D_0 and D_1, IRC Section R602.10.11.1 requires increased *exterior* cripple wall bracing when *interior* braced walls are not supported by a continuous foundation. (Note that this requirement is in addition to the 15 percent increase requirement for braced wall panel support in IRC Section R602.10.11.) Without direct interior foundation support, these interior braced wall lines transfer the lateral forces into the floor diaphragm instead of the foundation. The floor diaphragm, in turn, transfers these lateral forces into the adjacent cripple walls. Therefore, the wall bracing at the adjacent cripple walls (specified in IRC Table R602.10.3(3) (**TABLE 3.5**) and adjusted in accordance with IRC Table R602.10.3(4) (**TABLE 3.6**)) must be increased to accommodate the increased load. This is done by multiplying the length of the required adjacent cripple wall bracing parallel to the unsupported interior braced wall by a factor of 1.5, as shown in **FIGURE 3.67**. Note also that only bracing Methods WSP and CS-WSP may be used for the cripple wall bracing.

FIGURE 3.67

Cripple wall bracing in SDC D₀ and D₁

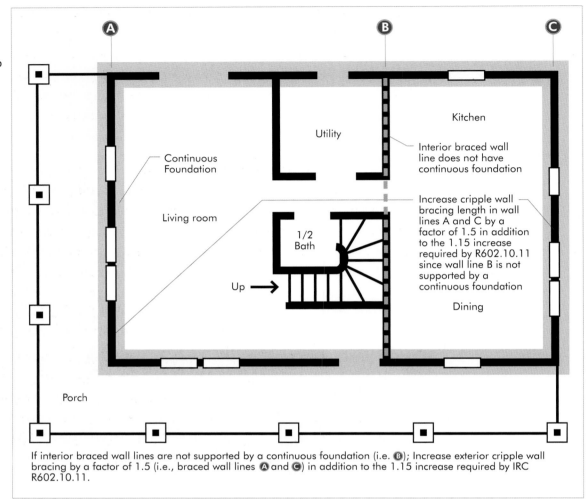

Utility

Kitchen

Continuous Foundation

Interior braced wall line does not have continuous foundation

Living room

Increase cripple wall bracing length in wall lines A and C by a factor of 1.5 in addition to the 1.15 increase required by R602.10.11 since wall line B is not supported by a continuous foundation

1/2 Bath

Up →

Dining

Porch

If interior braced wall lines are not supported by a continuous foundation (i.e. Ⓑ); Increase exterior cripple wall bracing by a factor of 1.5 (i.e., braced wall lines Ⓐ and Ⓒ) in addition to the 1.15 increase required by IRC R602.10.11.

R602.10.11.2 Cripple wall bracing for Seismic Design Category D₂. In Seismic Design Category D₂, cripple walls shall be braced in accordance with Tables R602.10.3(3) and R602.10.3(4).

At a glance, this section may appear to conflict with the provisions of IRC Section R602.10.11.1, as it could be misinterpreted as requiring fewer bracing requirements for SDC D₂ than for D₀ and D₁. This is not the case. As always, the intent of the code is that, when provisions are based on SDC or wind speed, all provisions that apply to lesser/preceding SDCs or wind speeds must be met in addition to the provisions that apply to the SDC or wind speed in question. In this case, the provisions for D₀ and D₁ are required in addition to the D₂ provisions. Note that the braced wall panel lengths required for SDC D₂ are based solely on the bracing length requirements of IRC Tables R602.10.3(3) and (4) (**TABLE 3.5** and **3.6**).

Note also that IRC Table R602.10.3(3) (**TABLE 3.5**) includes specific cripple wall bracing requirements for D₂ that do not apply to other SDCs.

R602.10.11.3 Redesignation of cripple walls. Where all cripple wall segments along a *braced wall line* do not exceed 48 inches (1219 mm) in height, the cripple walls shall be permitted to be redesignated as a first-*story* wall for purposes of determining wall bracing requirements. Where any cripple wall segment in a *braced wall line* exceeds 48 inches (1219 mm) in height, the entire cripple wall shall be counted as an additional *story*. If the cripple walls are redesignated, the stories above the redesignated *story* shall be counted as the second and third stories, respectively.

New to the 2012 IRC is the two-tiered approach to cripple wall re-designation. In the 2009 edition, any cripple wall could be redesignated ("…shall be permitted to be redesignated") at the discretion of the designer, allowing floors to be redesignated as second and third as appropriate. For 2012, only cripple walls that do not exceed 48 inches in height have the option of being redesignated. Walls with any cripple wall segment taller than 48 inches shall be redesignated, with stories above being counted as the second and third as appropriate.

When redesignation is used, the cripple walls are considered the first story, while the first full-height story becomes the second story, etc., as shown in **FIGURES 3.68a** and **3.68b**.

Note that in SDC D_2, IRC Table R602.10.3(3) (**TABLE 3.5**) only permits buildings of up to two stories, thus limiting the redesignation option to one-story buildings. With redesignation, a one-story becomes a two-story, which is the maximum number of stories permitted in SDC D_2. If a two-story structure is located above a redesignated cripple wall foundation, the second story would become the third story. A three-story structure in SDC D_2 is required to be designed in accordance with the IBC. See **FIGURE 3.68c**.

FIGURE 3.68a

Redesignating cripple walls

IRC Section R602.10.11.3

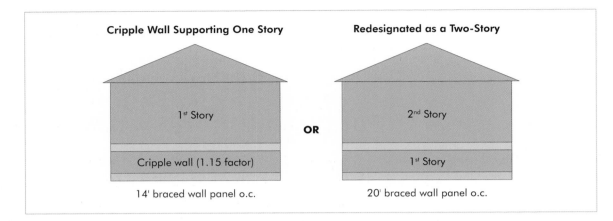

FIGURE 3.68b

Less than 110 mph wind and SDC A-D$_1$ example

IRC Section R602.10.11.3

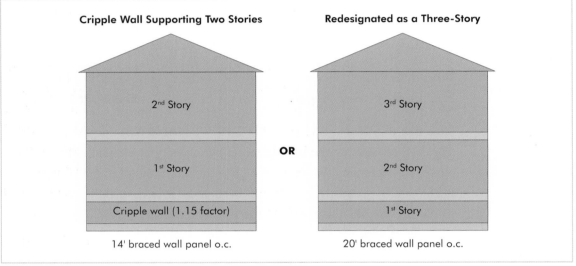

FIGURE 3.68c

Less than 110 mph and SDC D$_2$ example

IRC Section R602.10.11.3

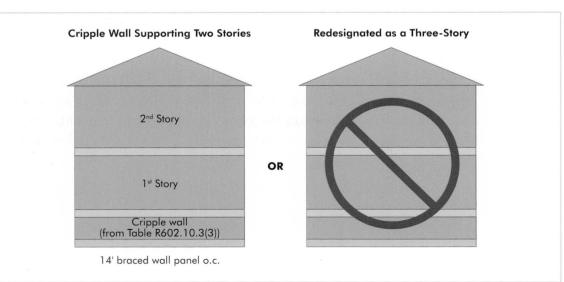

5. All exterior walls shall have gypsum board with a minimum thickness of 1/2 inch (12.7 mm) installed on the interior side fastened in accordance with Table R702.3.5.

This limitation is essentially the same as the "legacy" bracing provisions. Bracing lengths required are based on gypsum wall board placed on the inside of the braced wall lines. What is not permitted in the use of simplified wall bracing is the adjustment factor for those infrequent occasions when gypsum board in not placed on the inside wall surface.

6. The structure shall be located where the basic wind speed is less than or equal to 90 mph (40 m/s), and the Exposure Category is A or B.

In keeping with the goals of the ICC Ad Hoc Wall Bracing Committee to make bracing relatively simple for the modest one- and two- family dwelling, the scope of simplified wall bracing is limited to areas of 90 mph winds or less and areas of less severe exposure.

7. The structure shall be located in Seismic Design Category A, B or C for detached one- and two-family dwellings or Seismic Design Category A or B for townhouses.

This limits the scope of simplified wall bracing to regions of lower seismicity.

8. Cripple walls shall not be permitted in two-story buildings.

A further limitation to the scope and complexity of simplified wall bracing.

R602.12.1 Circumscribed rectangle. The bracing required for each building shall be determined by circumscribing a rectangle around the entire building on each floor as shown in Figure R602.12.1 (**FIGURE 3.79**). The rectangle shall surround all enclosed offsets and projections such as sunrooms and attached garages. Open structures, such as carports and decks, shall be permitted to be excluded. The rectangle shall have no side greater than 60 feet (18 288 mm), and the ratio between the long side and short side shall be a maximum of 3:1.

This limitation serves several purposes:

1. It limits the size of the building within the scope of simplified wall bracing.

2. The 3:1 ratio eliminates very long structures where unblocked wood structural panel roof and floor diaphragms lose their ability to transfer loads into the braced wall lines due to excessive deflection under wind or seismic loads.

3. It introduces a new and simpler way to distribute bracing along the exterior walls. For example, in a T- or L-shaped building, there may be multiple exterior braced wall lines along one side of the circumscribed rectangle. The number of bracing units is specified in IRC Table R602.12.4 (**TABLE 3.37**) for "each side" of the circumscribed rectangle; however, no guidance is provided as to which braced wall lines should receive these braced wall panels outside of the distribution rules provided in IRC Section R602.12.5. As long as the distribution rules are met, the bracing panels may be distributed however the designer prefers. See **FIGURE 3.80**.

FIGURE 3.79

Circumscribed rectangles

IRC Figure R602.12.1

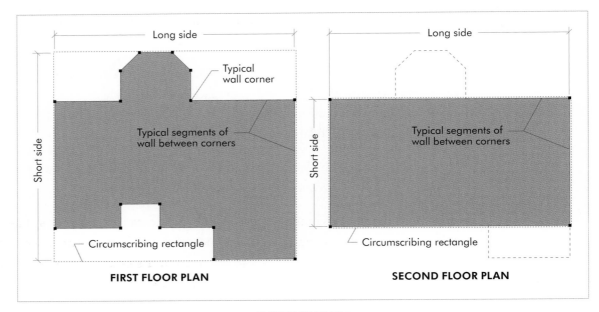

FIGURE R602.12.1
RECTANGLE CIRCUMSCRIBING AN ENCLOSED BUILDING

FIGURE 3.80

Simplifed wall bracing - distribute bracing units on exterior walls as suits designer

IRC Section R601.12.1

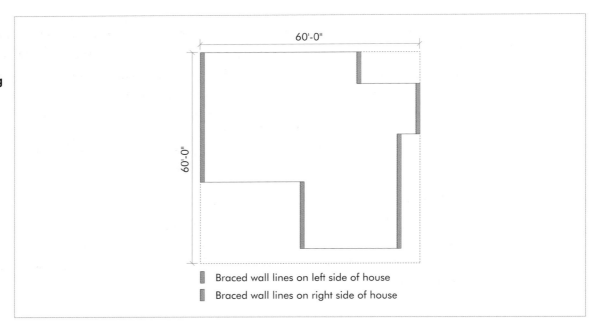

R602.12.2 Sheathing materials. The following sheathing materials installed on the exterior side of exterior walls shall be used to construct a bracing unit as defined in Section R602.12.3. Mixing materials is prohibited.

In an effort to keep the simplified wall bracing method simple, only two sheathing types are recognized: wood structural panels and structural fiberboard sheathing. The intermittent and continuous methods for both materials are included, as well as a number of portal frame methods described later.

1. Wood structural panels with a minimum thickness of 3/8 inch (9.5 mm) fastened in accordance with Table R602.3(3).

2. Structural fiberboard sheathing with a minimum thickness of 1/2 inch (12.7 mm) fastened in accordance with Table R602.3(1).

R602.12.3 Bracing unit. A bracing unit shall be a full-height sheathed segment of the exterior wall with no openings or vertical or horizontal offsets and a minimum length as specified herein. Interior walls shall not contribute toward the amount of required bracing. Mixing of Items 1 and 2 is prohibited on the same story.

Instead of dealing with a length of bracing, simplified wall bracing uses "bracing units." Per this section, the units must be full height with no offsets, on the exterior walls only (no interior braced walls) and no mixing of methods on the same story of the structure.

1. Where all framed portions of all exterior walls are sheathed in accordance with Section R602.12.2, including wall areas between bracing units, above and below openings and on gable end walls, the minimum length of a bracing unit shall be 3 feet (914 mm).

Users of the 2009 IRC will recognize the "including all wall areas between bracing units, above and below openings and on gable end walls…" as language used to define continuously sheathed bracing units (Methods CS-WSP and CS-SFB). For simplified wall bracing, these methods (used as bracing units) have a minimum length of 3 feet.

2. Where the exterior walls are braced with sheathing panels in accordance with Section R602.12.2 and areas between bracing units are covered with other materials, the minimum length of a bracing unit shall be 4 feet (1219 mm).

As above, users of the 2009 IRC will recognize this as the definition of intermittent bracing (Methods WSP and SFB). For simplified wall bracing, the minimum length of a bracing unit in this case is 4 feet. No partial credit adjustments for less than 48-inch-lengths are permitted when using simplified wall bracing. (IRC Table R602.10.5.2 (**TABLE 3.29**) is not permitted for use with simplified wall bracing.)

R602.12.3.1 Multiple bracing units. Segments of wall compliant with Section R602.12.3 and longer than the minimum bracing unit length shall be considered as multiple bracing units. The number of bracing units shall be determined by dividing the wall segment length by the minimum bracing unit length. Full-height sheathed segments of wall narrower than the minimum bracing unit length shall not contribute toward a bracing unit except as specified in Section R602.12.6.

This section permits the total length of all qualifying bracing segments to be used for determining the number of bracing units for a specific wall.

EXAMPLE: Compute the bracing units present in ***FIGURE 3.81***. The wall is continuously sheathed with wood structural panels. Only full-height segments with a length greater than that specified in IRC Section R602.12.3 are "qualified" bracing segments (36 inches for continuous methods) and can count for computing required length of bracing.

FIGURE 3.81

Computing number of bracing units in a wall line

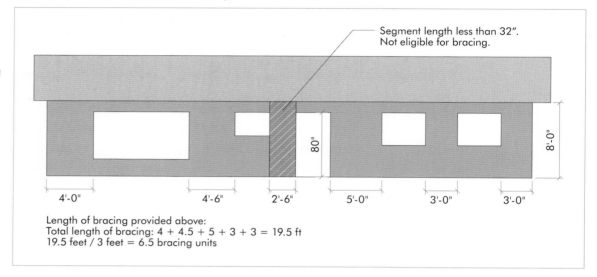

Segment length less than 32". Not eligible for bracing.

80"

8'-0"

4'-0"   4'-6"   2'-6"   5'-0"   3'-0"   3'-0"

Length of bracing provided above:
Total length of bracing: 4 + 4.5 + 5 + 3 + 3 = 19.5 ft
19.5 feet / 3 feet = 6.5 bracing units

R602.12.4 Number of bracing units. Each side of the circumscribed rectangle, as shown in Figure R602.12.1, shall have, at a minimum, the number of bracing units in accordance with Table R602.12.4 placed on the parallel exterior walls facing the side of the rectangle. Bracing units shall then be placed using the distribution requirements specified in Section R602.12.5.

See ***TABLE 3.37*** for determination of the number bracing units required at each side of the structure. Note that, per Footnote c, the sides of the rectangle must be rounded up to the neatest 10-foot increment and that, per Footnote a, interpolation shall not be permitted. Once again, it is clear that the emphasis was on simplicity in the development of these provisions.

This provision permits the distribution of the number of bracing units required on each side of the structure however the designer prefers. See ***FIGURE 3.80***.

Note that the bracing placement rules of IRC Section R602.12.5 must also be met and, in many cases, will require more bracing units than the minimum number required by IRC Table R602.12.4 (***TABLE 3.37***).

TABLE 3.37

Determination of number bracing units required at each side of the structure

IRC Table R602.12.4

TABLE R602.12.4
MINIMUM NUMBER OF BRACING UNITS ON EACH SIDE OF THE CIRCUMSCRIBED RECTANGLE

Story Level	Eave-To-Ridge Height (feet)	Minimum Number Of Bracing Units On Each Long Side[a, b]						Minimum Number Of Bracing Units On Each Short Side[a, b]					
		Length of short side (feet)[c]						Length of long side (feet)[c]					
		10	20	30	40	50	60	10	20	30	40	50	60
	10	1	2	2	2	3	3	1	2	2	2	3	3
		2	3	3	4	5	6	2	3	3	4	5	6
	15	1	2	3	3	4	4	1	2	3	3	4	4
		2	3	4	5	6	7	2	3	4	5	6	7

For SI: 1 inch = 25.4 mm, 1 foot = 304.8 mm.
a. Interpolation shall not be permitted.
b. Cripple walls or wood-framed basement walls in a walk-out condition of a one-story structure shall be designed as the first floor of a two-story house.
c. Actual lengths of the sides of the circumscribed rectangle shall be rounded to the next highest unit of 10 when using this table.

R602.12.5 Distribution of bracing units. The placement of bracing units on exterior walls shall meet all of the following requirements as shown in Figure R602.12.5.

As mentioned before, the distribution rules will be more stringent than the minimum number of bracing units required per IRC Table R602.12.4 (**TABLE 3.37**). A good strategy may be to insert the bracing units as required by the minimum placement rules first on the building plan, and then see if the requisite number of bracing units has been met. If the requisite number of bracing units has not been met, the designer can add additional bracing units as necessary.

The following distribution rules are self explanatory. A unit of bracing for a continuous method (Methods CS-WSP or CS-SFB) is 36 inches, and 48 inches for an intermittent method (Methods WSP or SFB). The length of a unit of bracing for each of the narrow panel methods is as specified in IRC Section R602.12.6. The distribution rules are illustrated in **FIGURE 3.82**.

1. A bracing unit shall begin no more than 12 feet (3658 mm) from any wall corner.

2. The distance between adjacent edges of bracing units shall be no greater than 20 feet (6096 mm).

3. Segments of wall greater than 8 feet (2438 mm) in length shall have a minimum of one bracing unit.

FIGURE 3.82

Simplified wall bracing distribution rules

IRC Figure R602.12.5

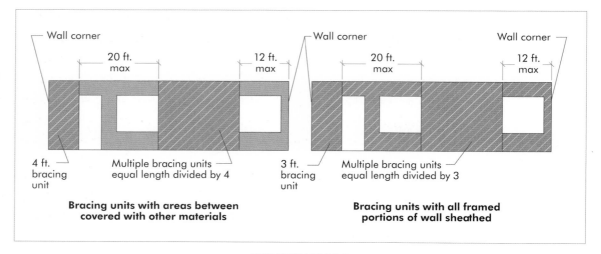

FIGURE R602.12.5
BRACING UNIT DISTRIBUTION

R602.12.6 Narrow panels. The bracing methods referenced in Section R602.10 and specified in Sections R602.12.6.1 through R602.12.6.3 shall be permitted when using simplified wall bracing.

Note that the reference to IRC Section R602.10 above is only for use of the descriptions and figures for Methods CS-G, CS-PF, PFH and PFG (*FIGURES 3.41, 3.42, 3.45* and *3.46*).

R602.12.6.1 Method CS-G. *Braced wall panels* constructed as Method CS-G in accordance with Tables R602.10.4 and R602.10.5 shall be permitted for one story garages when all framed portions of all exterior walls are sheathed with wood structural panels. Each CS-G panel shall be equivalent to 0.5 of a bracing unit. Segments of wall which include a Method CS-G panel shall meet the requirements of Section R602.10.4.2.

Method CS-G (continuously sheathed wood structural panel adjacent to garage openings), fabricated in accordance with IRC Table R602.10.4 (*TABLE 3.24*) and with a minimum length requirement per IRC Table R602.10.5 (*TABLE 3.28*), is permitted for use with simplified wall bracing. Also IRC Table R602.10.6.4 (*TABLE 3.31*) provides tension strap requirements for pony walls, although the 10-foot-story-height limitation for simplified wall bracing applies when the pony wall detail is used. These references are deemed to be appropriate for use with this section. Note that Method CS-G is a continuous sheathing method and can only be used in a continuously sheathed story, per IRC Section R602.10.4.2. See *FIGURE 3.41*.

R602.12.6.2 Method CS-PF. *Braced wall panels* constructed as Method CS-PF in accordance with Section R602.10.6.4 shall be permitted when all framed portions of all exterior walls are sheathed with wood structural panels. Each CS-PF panel shall equal 0.5 bracing units. A maximum of four CS-PF panels shall be permitted on all segments of walls parallel to each side of the circumscribed rectangle. Segments of wall which include a Method CS-PF panel shall meet the requirements of Section R602.10.4.2.

Like the Method CS-G above, the use of the Method CS-PF (continuously sheathed portal frame) (**FIGURE 3.42**) can only be used in a continuously sheathed story. Each side of an opening that uses one of these methods is equivalent to half of a bracing unit. Also like Method CS-G above, the description of Method CS-PF and tension strap provisions of IRC Figure R602.10.6.4 and IRC Table R602.10.6.4 (**TABLE 3.31**) were left out of IRC Section R602.12.6.2 but are both deemed appropriate and meet the intent of the provisions. The 10-foot-story-height limitation for the simplified wall bracing still applies when the pony wall detail is used.

R602.12.6.3 Methods PFH and PFG. *Braced wall panels* constructed as Method PFH and PFG shall be permitted when bracing units are constructed using wood structural panels. Each PFH panel shall equal one bracing unit and each PFG panel shall be equal to 0.75 bracing units.

These two portal frames are the narrow wall bracing elements appropriate for use as intermittent methods. They are to be fabricated using wood structural panel sheathing, as shown in IRC Figures R602.10.6.2 and R602.10.6.3 (**FIGURES 3.45** and **3.46**), even though the figures are not specified in IRC Section R602.12.6.3. As with the other narrow panel methods described above, the tension strap provisions of IRC Table R602.10.6.4 (**TABLE 3.31**) are also deemed appropriate, although the 10-foot-story-height limitation for simplified wall bracing still applies when the pony wall detail is used.

R602.12.7 Lateral support. For bracing units located along the eaves, the vertical distance from the outside edge of the top wall plate to the roof sheathing above shall not exceed 9.25 inches (235 mm) at the location of a bracing unit unless lateral support is provided in accordance with Section R602.10.8.2.

This section mirrors the connection to roof framing portion of the R602.10 bracing provisions and ensures the load path from the roof diaphragm to the braced wall panels.

R602.12.8 Stem walls. Masonry stem walls with a height and length of 48 inches (1219 mm) or less supporting a bracing unit or a Method CS-G, CS-PF or PFG *braced wall panel* shall be constructed in accordance with Figure R602.10.9. Concrete stem walls with a length of 48 inches (1219 mm) or less, greater than 12 inches (305 mm) tall and less than 6 inches (152 mm) thick shall be reinforced, sized and located in accordance with Figure R602.10.9.

These provisions ensure a solid foundation for the narrow panel methods permitted for use with simplified bracing method and are placed to ensure a full and complete load path.

4 WHOLE HOUSE CONSIDERATIONS

Putting it all together

Previous chapters in this guide have explained the bracing code provisions and provided bracing method examples limited to single braced wall lines. This chapter provides application examples of these methods used together on modern house plans. A summary list of the bracing methods is provided in **TABLE 4.1**, while detailed requirements for each method are provided in **CHAPTER 3**.

What is the intent?

When the plan layout of a home design is not specifically addressed by the provisions in the IRC, two questions to ask are:

1. What is the intent of the bracing provisions?

2. Is the intent being met by the bracing provided?

In these situations, it is necessary to communicate with the local building official to determine a proper interpretation. In many cases, the building official may have already encountered the same issue and have a solution.

Note that any concern regarding interpretation of the bracing provisions should be discussed with the building official before the plans are finalized in order to avoid an extensive redesign.

CHAPTER 4

Summary

Whole house examples

TABLE 4.1 provides a list of the bracing methods used in this chapter's examples. A more comprehensive table, including a summary of placement and application requirements for each method, is provided at the end of this guide (page 264) for quick reference. **TABLE 4.2** provides an index of this chapter's examples, including the parameters and bracing methods used in each example.

TABLE 4.1

Summary of bracing methods used in examples

See page 264 for a more comprehensive overview of the bracing methods

Bracing Method	Method Description
LIB	Let-in-bracing
DWB	Diagonal wood boards
WSP	Wood structural panel
BV-WSP	Wood structural panels with stone or masonry veneer
SFB	Structural fiberboard sheathing
GB	Gypsum board
PBS	Particleboard sheathing
PCP	Portland cement plaster
HPS	Hardboard panel siding
ABW	Alternate braced wall
PFH	Portal frame with hold downs
PFG	Portal frame at garage door openings in Seismic Design Categories A, B and C
CS-WSP	Continuously sheathed wood structural panel
CS-G	Continuously sheathed wood structural panel adjacent to garage openings
CS-PF	Continuously sheathed portal frame
CS-SFB	Continuously sheathed structural fiberboard

TABLE 4.2

Example index

Example	Wind Speed	Wind Exposure	Seismic Design Category (SDC)	Number of Stories	Bracing Method
4.1	90	B	C	2	SFB, GB
4.2	90	B	C	2	WSP
4.3	85	B	D_2	2	WSP, GB
4.4	95	C	A	1	WSP, ABW, PFG, GB
4.5	85	C	B	1	LIB, DWB, GB, PBS, HPS
4.6	105	B	B	2	WSP, ABW, SFB, GB
4.7	105	B	D_0	1	CS-WSP, CS-PF

Note that the intent of the following examples is to provide guidance on the use of the bracing provisions in the 2012 IRC. In developing these examples, every effort has been made to capture the letter as well as the intent of the provisions. While the ICC Ad Hoc Wall Bracing Committee, APA and ICC staff have endeavored to make the provisions as clear and unambiguous as possible, different interpretations are possible. It is also possible to select different wall lines as braced wall lines or employ different bracing methods and arrive at a different but still correct solution.

Example 4.1 demonstrates how a simple house can comply with the IRC wall bracing provisions. Later examples will demonstrate more complex designs.

Example 4.1: Two-story house in SDC C

The basic wind speed is 90 mph with Exposure Category B. The roof has an eave-to-ridge height of 10 feet. Intermittent Method SFB (structural fiberboard sheathing) will be used as the bracing material on the exterior braced wall lines. Method GB (gypsum board) will be used on the interior braced wall lines. All braced walls have a height of 9 feet.

Example 4.1 highlights:

- The amount of bracing required is based on the ≤ 90 mph wind speed category (IRC Table R602.10.3(1)).

- Braced wall panels are permitted to be located 10 feet from each end of braced wall lines (IRC Section R602.10.2.2).

- For a single-family dwelling located in SDC C, the seismic provisions of the IRC do not apply. Therefore, the provisions defining irregular buildings (IRC Section R301.2.2.2.5) and bracing lengths based on SDC (IRC Table R602.10.3(3)) do not apply.

FIGURES 4.1a and **4.1b** show the house and braced wall segments for each story. **TABLES 4.1a** and **4.1b** summarize the amount of bracing required and the amount of bracing provided for each braced wall line on each story.

FIGURE 4.1a

First-story plan with intermittent Method SFB (structural fiberboard sheathing) and GB (gypsum board) braced wall panels

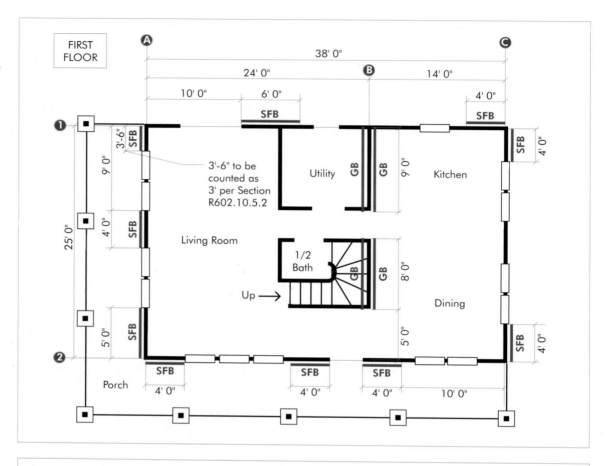

TABLE 4.1a

Calculations for the first of two stories to determine the required bracing length based on wind speed

IRC Table R602.10.3(2) Wind Adjustment Factors (*TABLE 3.4*)	Numbered Wall Lines	Lettered Wall Lines
Exposure Category	1.00	1.00
Roof Eave-to-Ridge Height	1.00	1.00
Wall Height	0.95	0.95
Number of Braced Wall Lines	1.00	1.30
Gypsum Board Fastening	1.00	0.70[a]
Wind Factor Total	**0.95**	**0.87**

Braced Wall Line	Bracing Method	Braced Wall Line Spacing (ft)	Required Bracing (ft)	Wind Factor Total	Total Required Bracing Length (ft)	Bracing Length Provided (ft)	Status
1	SFB	25	9.0	0.95	8.55	10	Okay
2	SFB	25	9.0	0.95	8.55	12	Okay
A	SFB	24	8.7	1.24	10.79	12	Okay
B	GB w/ 4" nailing	24	15.2	0.87	13.19	17	Okay
C	SFB	14	5.4	1.24	6.70	8	Okay

a. Braced Wall Line B only.

Note that for braced wall line B in Example 4.1, the reduction in required bracing provided for gypsum board fastening at 4" o.c. in accordance with IRC Table R602.10.3(2) was used as an alternative to increasing the required length of Method GB bracing.

In example 4.1, an interior braced wall line is not required in order to meet the braced wall line spacing limits (for wind ≤ 60') but was required to accommodate the wall bracing lengths required in IRC Table R602.10.3(1). If you remove the interior braced wall line and rely solely on Method SFB for the exterior walls, with 38 feet braced wall line spacing, the minimum required length = 0.95 x 13.3 = 12.64 feet, which is greater than the sheathable wall areas. Instead of using an interior braced wall line, the designer may choose to use Method CS-WSP (continuously sheathed wood structural panel) on braced wall lines A and C, which would meet the required bracing (11.4 x 0.95 = 10.83 feet).

FIGURE 4.1b

Second-story plan with intermittent Method SFB (structural fiberboard sheathing) braced wall panels

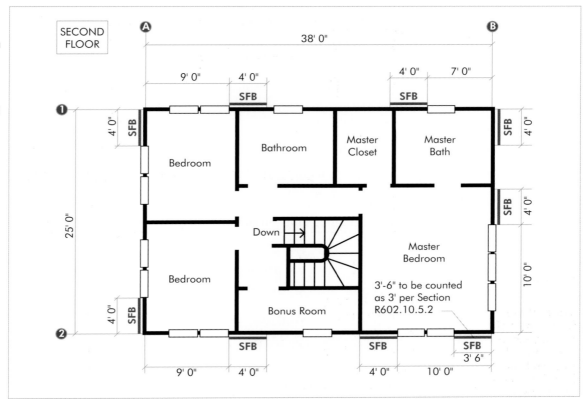

TABLE 4.1b

Calculations for the second of two stories to determine the required bracing length based on wind speed

IRC Table R602.10.3(2) Wind Adjustment Factors (*TABLE 3.4*)	Numbered Wall Lines	Lettered Wall Lines
Exposure Category	1.00	1.00
Roof Eave-to-Ridge Height	1.00	1.00
Wall Height	0.95	0.95
Number of Braced Wall Lines	1.00	1.00
Wind Factor Total	**0.95**	**0.95**

Braced Wall Line	Bracing Method	Braced Wall Line Spacing (ft)	Required Bracing (ft)	Wind Factor Total	Total Required Bracing Length (ft)	Bracing Length Provided (ft)	Status
1	SFB	25	4.75	0.95	4.51	8	Okay
2	SFB	25	4.75	0.95	4.51	11	Okay
A	SFB	38	7.10	0.95	6.75	8	Okay
B	SFB	38	7.10	0.95	6.75	8	Okay

Although Method SFB bracing was used, the solution would be identical if using Method DWB (diagonal wood boards), WSP (wood structural panel), PBS (particleboard sheathing), PCP (Portland cement plaster), HPS (hardboard panel siding) or CS-SFB (continuously sheathed structural fiberboard). Note that if using the continuous sheathing bracing Method WSP, the required length of bracing would be less than the required length for the other methods, per IRC Table R602.10.3(1). As discussed earlier in the example, the interior braced wall line on the first story could also be eliminated if Method CS-WSP were used on the exterior braced wall lines A and C.

Example 4.2: Two-story house in SDC C using Simplified Wall Bracing

The basic wind speed is 90 mph with Exposure Category B. The roof has an eave-to-ridge height of 10 feet. Method WSP (wood structural panel) will be used as the bracing material on all framed portions of all exterior walls. All braced walls have a height of 9 feet.

Example 4.2 highlights:

- Meets IRC Section R602.12 conditions for simplified wall bracing.

- Enclosed portion falls within 60-foot x 60-foot circumscribed rectangle, and ratio of long side/short side < 3/1 (IRC Section R602.12.1).

- The amount of bracing required is based on IRC Table R602.12.4 (*Minimum Number of Bracing Units…*).

- Braced wall panels are permitted to be located 12 feet from wall corners. Adjacent bracing units shall be spaced within 20 feet (IRC Section R602.12.5).

- Bracing is Method WSP (IRC Section R602.12.2).

- The minimum length of a bracing units shall be 3 feet when all framed portions of all exterior walls are sheathed with Method WSP bracing; otherwise, the minimum length shall be 4 feet. (IRC Section R602.12.3).

FIGURES 4.2a and **4.2b** show the house and bracing units for each story. **TABLES 4.2a-4.2c** summarize the amount of bracing required and the amount of bracing provided for each braced wall line on each story.

FIGURE 4.2a

First-story plan with continuous Method WSP (wood structural panel) braced units

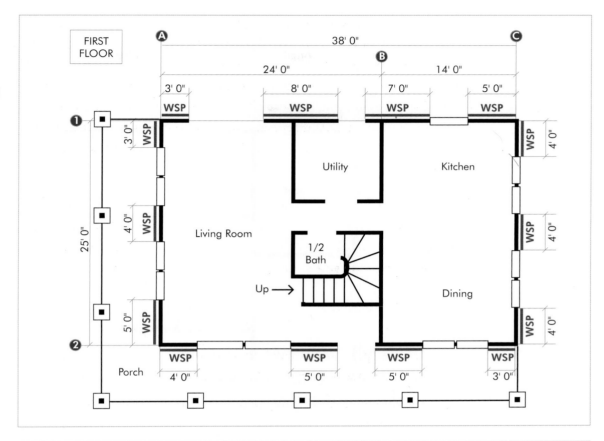

TABLE 4.2a

Number of bracing units required

Number of Required Bracing Units per IRC Table R602.12.4 (*TABLE 3.37*)	Numbered Wall Lines (Long Sides)[a]	Lettered Wall Lines (Short Sides)[b]
1st Story	3	4
2nd Story	2	2

a. The number of required bracing units on the long side is based on the Length of the short side = 25'. The table requires lengths to be rounded up to the next highest unit of 10 = 30'.

b. The number of required bracing units on the short side is based on the Length of the long side = 38'. The table requires lengths to be rounded up to the next highest unit of 10 = 40'.

TABLE 4.2b

Calculations for the required bracing units based on building dimensions for the first story

Braced Wall Line	Sheathing Material	Required Bracing Units (#)	Sheathing Continuous/ Intermittent	Required Bracing Unit Length (ft)	Provided Bracing[a]	Bracing Units Provided[b]	Status
1	WSP	3	C	3	23	7	Okay
2	WSP	3	C	3	17	5	Okay
A	WSP	4	C	3	12	4	Okay
C	WSP	4	C	3	12	4	Okay

a. The provided bracing = the sum of each wall segment that meets the minimum length required per R602.12.3 (3' for continuously applied sheathing).

b. The number of bracing units provided is = (the provided bracing)/(the minimum bracing unit length required). The number shall be rounded down to the nearest whole number. (R602.12.3.1)

FIGURE 4.2b

Second-story plan with intermittent Method WSP (wood structural panel) braced units

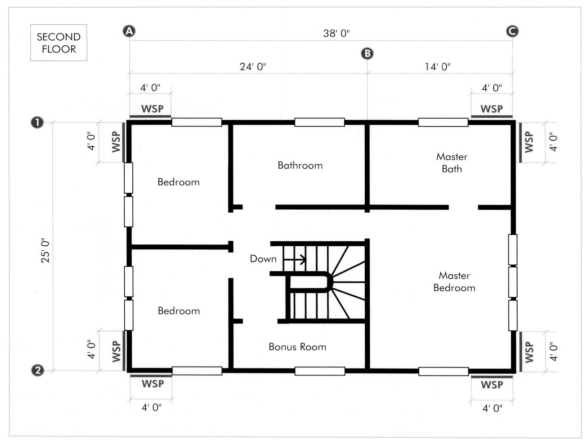

TABLE 4.2c

Calculations for the required bracing units based on building dimensions for the second story (for bracing units required, see *TABLE 4.2a*)

Braced Wall Line	Sheathing Material	Required Bracing Units (#)	Sheathing Continuous/ Intermittent	Required Bracing Unit Length (ft)	Provided Bracing[a]	Bracing Units Provided[b]	Status
1	WSP	2	Int	4	8	2	Okay
2	WSP	2	Int	4	8	2	Okay
A	WSP	2	Int	4	8	2	Okay
C	WSP	2	Int	4	8	2	Okay

a. The provided bracing = the sum of each wall segment that meets the minimum length required per R602.12.3 (4' for intermittently applied sheathing).

b. The number of bracing units provided is = the provided bracing/the minimum bracing unit length required. The number shall be rounded down to the whole number. (R602.12.3.1)

Example 4.3: Two-story house in SDC D$_2$

The basic wind speed is 85 mph with Exposure Category B. The roof has an eave-to-ridge height of 8 feet. Intermittent Method WSP (wood structural panel) will be used as the bracing material on the exterior braced wall lines. Intermittent Method GB (gypsum board) will be used on the interior braced wall lines. All braced walls have a height of 10 feet.

Example 4.3 highlights:

- The amount of bracing required based on the greater amount required by the ≤ 85 mph wind speed category and SDC D$_2$.

- For a single-family dwelling located in SDC D$_0$, D$_1$ and D$_2$, braced wall panels on the second floor cannot be placed over an opening on the first floor except in certain cases (IRC Section R301.2.2.2.5, Item 3, Exceptions).

- In SDC D$_0$, D$_1$ and D$_2$, braced wall panels are not permitted to be located away from the ends of braced wall lines except in certain cases and only with Method WSP (IRC Section R602.10.2.2.1, Exceptions).

- For structures in SDC D$_0$, D$_1$ and D$_2$, braced wall line spacing is limited to 25 feet (IRC Section R602.10.1.3 and Table R602.10.1.3).

FIGURES 4.3a and **4.3b** show the house and braced wall segments for each story. **TABLES 4.3a** and **4.3b** summarize the amount of bracing required and the amount of bracing provided for each braced wall line on each story, based on wind and seismic requirements respectively.

FIGURE 4.3a

First-story plan with intermittent Methods WSP (wood structural panel) and GB (gypsum board) braced wall panels

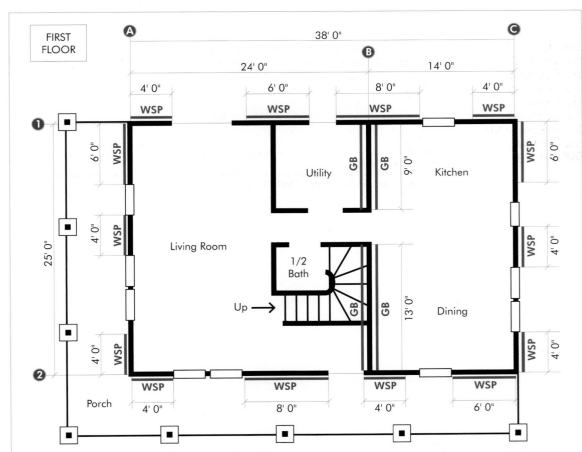

TABLE 4.3a

Calculations for the first of two stories to determine the required bracing length based on wind speed and Seismic Design Category

WIND CALCULATIONS

IRC Table R602.10.3(2) Wind Adjustment Factors (*TABLE 3.4*)	Numbered Wall Lines	Lettered Wall Lines
Exposure Category	1.00	1.00
Roof Eave-to-Ridge Height	0.94	0.94
Wall Height	1.00	1.00
Number of Braced Wall Lines	1.00	1.30
Wind Factor Total	**0.94**	**1.22**

Braced Wall Line	Bracing Method	Braced Wall Line Spacing (ft)	Required Bracing (ft)	Wind Factor Total	Total Required Bracing Length (ft)	Bracing Length Provided (ft)	Status
1	WSP	25	8.0	0.94	7.52	22	Okay
2	WSP	25	8.0	0.94	7.52	22	Okay
A	WSP	24	7.7	1.22	9.39	14	Okay
B	GB	24	13.5	1.22	16.47	22	Okay
C	WSP	14	4.7	1.22	5.73	14	Okay

SEISMIC CALCULATIONS

IRC Table R602.10.3(4) Seismic Adjustment Factors (*TABLE 3.6*)	Adjustments
Story Height	1.00
Wall Dead Load	1.00
Roof/Ceiling Dead Load	1.00
Stone/Masonry in SDC C-D$_2$	n/a
Cripple Wall	n/a
Seismic Factor Total	**1.00**

Braced Wall Line	Bracing Method	Braced Wall Line Length (ft)	Required Bracing (ft)	Braced Wall Line Spacing Factor	Seismic Factor Total	Total Required Bracing Length (ft)	Bracing Length Provided (ft)	Status
1	WSP	38	20.90	1.0	1.0	20.90	22	Okay
2	WSP	38	20.90	1.0	1.0	20.90	22	Okay
A	WSP	25	13.75	1.0	1.0	13.75	14	Okay
B	GB	25	18.75	1.0	1.0	18.75	22	Okay
C	WSP	25	13.75	1.0	1.0	13.75	14	Okay

FIGURE 4.3b

Second-story plan with intermittent Methods WSP (wood structural panel) and GB (gypsum board) braced wall panels

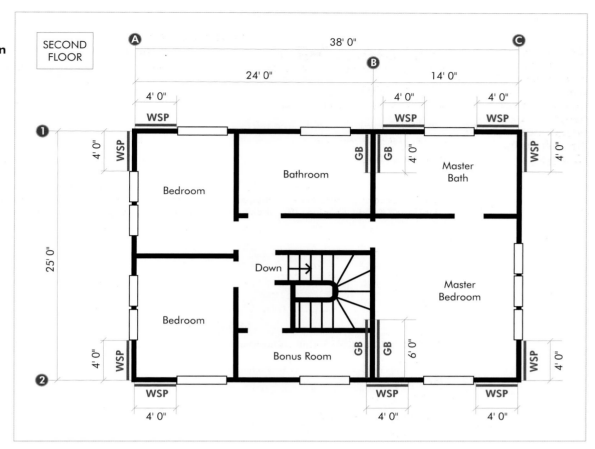

TABLE 4.3b

Calculations for the second of two stories to determine the required bracing length based on wind speed and Seismic Design Category

WIND CALCULATIONS

IRC Table R602.10.3(2) Wind Adjustment Factors (*TABLE* 3.4)	Numbered Wall Lines	Lettered Wall Lines
Exposure Category	1.00	1.00
Roof Eave-to-Ridge Height	0.88	0.88
Wall Height	1.00	1.00
Number of Braced Wall Lines	1.00	1.30
Wind Factor Total	**0.88**	**1.14**

Braced Wall Line	Bracing Method	Braced Wall Line Spacing (ft)	Required Bracing (ft)	Wind Factor Total	Total Required Bracing Length (ft)	Bracing Length Provided (ft)	Status
1	WSP	25	4.25	0.88	3.74	12	Okay
2	WSP	25	4.25	0.88	3.74	12	Okay
A	WSP	24	4.10	1.14	4.67	8	Okay
B	GB	24	7.00	1.14	7.98	10	Okay
C	WSP	14	2.60	1.14	2.96	8	Okay

SEISMIC CALCULATIONS

IRC Table R602.10.3(4) Seismic Adjustment Factors (*TABLE* 3.6)	Adjustments
Story Height	1.00
Wall Dead Load	1.00
Roof/Ceiling Dead Load	1.00
Stone/Masonry in SDC C-D_2	n/a
Cripple Wall	n/a
Seismic Factor Total	**1.00**

Braced Wall Line	Bracing Method	Braced Wall Line Length (ft)	Required Bracing (ft)	Braced Wall Line Spacing Factor	Seismic Factor Total	Total Required Bracing Length (ft)	Bracing Length Provided (ft)	Status
1	WSP	38	9.50	1.0	1.0	9.50	12	Okay
2	WSP	38	9.50	1.0	1.0	9.50	12	Okay
A	WSP	25	6.25	1.0	1.0	6.25	8	Okay
B	GB	25	10.00	1.0	1.0	10.00	10	Okay
C	WSP	25	6.25	1.0	1.0	6.25	8	Okay

Example 4.4: One-story house in SDC A

The basic wind speed is 95 mph with Exposure Category C. The roof has an eave-to-ridge height of 10 feet. Intermittent Methods WSP (wood structural panel), ABW (alternate braced wall), PFG (portal frame at garage door openings in Seismic Design Categories A, B and C) and GB (gypsum board) will be used as the bracing material on the braced wall lines. All braced walls have a height of 10 feet.

Example 4.4 highlights:

- The amount of bracing required is based on 95 mph wind speed, which is within the ≤ 100 mph wind speed category.

- Use of the 30-inch-wide minimum Method PFG panel (IRC Tables R602.10.4 and R602.10.5). The actual bracing length of Method PFG is equivalent to its measured length times a factor of 1.5 per IRC Table R602.10.5.

- Use of the 34-inch-wide Method ABW panel (IRC Tables R602.10.4 and R602.10.5).

- Use of different bracing methods in one wall line per IRC Section R602.10.4.1.

- Use of braced wall lines that end at the intersection of another braced wall line rather than the end of the house (IRC Section R602.10.1.1).

FIGURE 4.4 shows the house and braced wall segments. **TABLE 4.4** summarizes the amount of bracing required and the amount of bracing provided for each braced wall line.

234 | CHAPTER 4

FIGURE 4.4

One-story plan with intermittent Methods WSP (wood structural panel), GB (gypsum board), ABW (alternate braced wall) and PFG (portal frame at garage) braced wall panels

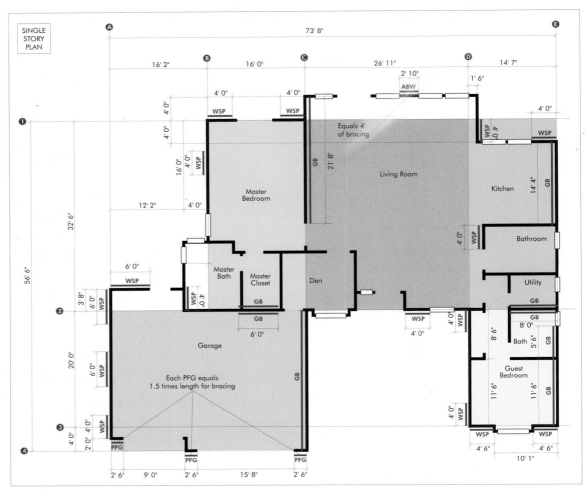

TABLE 4.4

Calculations to determine the required bracing length based on wind speed

IRC Table R602.10.3(2) Wind Adjustment Factors (*TABLE 3.4*)	Numbered Wall Lines	Lettered Wall Lines
Exposure Category	1.20	1.20
Roof Eave-to-Ridge Height	1.00	1.00
Wall Height	1.00	1.00
Number of Braced Wall Lines	1.45	1.60
Wind Factor Total	**1.74**	**1.92**

Braced Wall Line	Bracing Method	Braced Wall Line Spacing (ft)	Required Bracing (ft)	Wind Factor Total	Total Required Bracing Length (ft)	Bracing Length Provided (ft)	Status
1	WSP, ABW	32.50	7.50	1.74	13.05	16.00	Okay
2	WSP, GB	32.50	12.88	1.74	22.41	24.00	Okay
3	WSP	20.00	5.00	1.74	8.70	9.00	Okay
4	PFG	24.00	5.80	1.74	10.09	11.25	Okay
A	WSP	32.17	7.43	1.92	14.27	16.00	Okay
B	WSP	16.17	4.04	1.92	7.76	8.00	Okay
C	GB	26.92	10.92	1.92	20.97	22.83[a]	Okay
D	WSP	26.92	6.38	1.92	12.25	16.00	Okay
E	GB	14.58	6.33	1.92	12.15	15.67[a]	Okay

a. Bracing lengths for Method GB (gypsum board) are based on the application of gypsum board on both faces of a braced wall panel. When Method GB bracing is provided on only one side of the wall, the contributing length shall be halved... (IRC Table R602.10.5)

Note that in the above example, single-sided Method GB bracing was used to facilitate ease of construction. For exterior walls, the use of one-sided Method GB bracing on the interior of the wall gives the designer greater freedom in selecting exterior finishing materials. On interior braced wall lines with single-sided Method GB wall bracing, only the Method GB side of each wall requires the 7-inch on center fastener spacing as required by the bracing method. Where gypsum board is installed as an interior finish material and not as Method GB bracing, the fastener spacing requirements of IRC Tables R602.3(1) or R702.3.5 are appropriate. Where Method GB is used on both sides of the wall, 7-inch fastener spacing is required on both sides of the wall.

Braced wall lines C, D and E have more than the required bracing. The designer could choose to reduce the lengths of braced wall panels, but would need to verify the spacing requirements are still met: 10 feet spacing to end of each braced wall line and 20 feet spacing between adjacent edges of braced wall panels. In a similar manner, braced wall line 1 appears to have more than the required braced wall panel length; however, this length is required in order to meet the spacing rules.

Example 4.5: One-story house in SDC B

The basic wind speed is 85 mph with Exposure Category C. The roof has an eave-to-ridge height of 14 feet. Intermittent braced wall panels constructed from intermittent Methods LIB (let-in bracing), DWB (diagonal wood boards), GB (gypsum board), PBS (particleboard sheathing) and HPS (hardboard panel siding) will be used. All braced walls have a height of 10 feet.

Example 4.5 highlights:

- The amount of bracing required is based on 85 mph winds.

- Use of different bracing methods in one wall line and in different wall lines per IRC Section R602.10.4.1.

FIGURE 4.5 shows the house and braced wall segments. *TABLE 4.5* summarizes the amount of bracing required and the amount of bracing provided for each braced wall line.

FIGURE 4.5

One-story plan with intermittent Methods HPS (hardboard panel siding), GB (gypsum board), DWB (diagonal wood boards), PBS (particleboard sheathing) and LIB (let-in bracing)

TABLE 4.5

Calculations for the first story to determine the required bracing length based on wind speed

IRC Table R602.10.3(2) Wind Adjustment Factors (*TABLE* 3.4)	Numbered Wall Lines	Lettered Wall Lines
Exposure Category	1.20	1.20
Roof Eave-to-Ridge Height	1.24	1.24
Wall Height	1.00	1.00
Number of Braced Wall Lines	1.45	1.60
Wind Factor Total	**2.16**	**2.38**

Braced Wall Line	Bracing Method	Braced Wall Line Spacing (ft)	Required Bracing (ft)	Wind Factor Total	Total Required Bracing Length (ft)	Bracing Length Provided (ft)	Status
1	HPS	32.50	5.38	2.16	11.62	16.00	Okay
2	GB & PBS	32.50	9.25	2.16	19.98	20.00ª	Okay
3	DWB	20.00	3.50	2.16	7.56	9.00	Okay
4	PBS	24.00	4.10	2.16	8.86	12.00	Okay
A	LIB	32.17	9.15	2.38	21.78	24.00	Okay
B	LIB	16.17	5.04	2.38	12.00	12.00	Okay
C	GB & PBS	26.92	7.73	2.38	18.37	18.83ª	Okay
D	GB & PBS	26.92	7.73	2.38	18.37	20.00ª	Okay
E	GB	14.58	4.65	2.38	11.05	15.67ª	Okay

a. Bracing lengths for Method GB (gypsum board) are based on the application of gypsum board on both faces of a braced wall panel. When Method GB bracing is provided on only one side of the wall, the contributing length shall be halved... (IRC Table R602.10.5)

Note that braced wall line E has more than the required bracing. The designer could choose to reduce the lengths of braced wall panels, but would need to verify the spacing requirements are still met: 10 feet spacing to end of each braced wall line and 20 feet spacing between adjacent edges of braced wall panels. Braced wall lines 1 and 4 appear to have more than the required braced wall panel length; however, this length is required in order to meet the spacing rules. Lastly, Method LIB (let-in bracing) requires a minimum length of 69 inches for a 10-foot wall, per IRC Table R602.10.5.

Example 4.6: Two-story house in SDC B

The basic wind speed is 105 mph with Exposure Category B. The roof has an eave-to-ridge height of 12 feet. Intermittent Methods WSP (wood structural panel) and ABW (alternate braced wall) will be used as the bracing material on the first story exterior braced wall lines. Method SFB (structural fiberboard sheathing) will be used on the second story exterior braced wall lines. Intermittent Method GB (gypsum board) will be used on the interior braced wall lines for both the first and second stories. All braced walls have a height of 9 feet.

Example 4.6 highlights:

- The amount of bracing required is based on 105 mph winds, which is within the ≤ 110 mph wind speed category.

- Use of the 32-inch-wide Method ABW panel (IRC Tables R602.10.4 and R602.10.5).

- Use of braced wall lines at interior of structure.

- Use of walls greater than 10 feet tall.

- Use of bracing on a second story that does not have bracing on the first story aligned below it.

- Use of different bracing methods in different wall lines and stories per IRC Section R602.10.4.1.

The wall at the front entry exceeds the 100 mph wind speed limitations of the allowable stud length IRC Table R602.3.1. IRC Table R602.3(5) may be used to select the proper stud size, provided the limitations of the table are met. In this case, the entrance foyer wall must be a nonbearing wall. Stud heights that fall outside the scope of either of these tables must be sized based on engineering for the gravity and wind or seismic loads imposed.

The maximum allowed height of a braced wall panel is 12 feet. Walls taller than 12 feet are not permitted to contribute to the required bracing. The tall wall in this example may be considered an opening in the braced wall line, because the distance between the inside edges of the adjacent wall bracing panels is less than 20 feet.

FIGURES 4.6a and **4.6b** show the house and braced wall segments. **TABLES 4.6a** and **4.6b** summarize the amount of bracing required and the amount of bracing provided for each braced wall line.

FIGURE 4.6a

First-story plan with intermittent Methods WSP (wood structural panel) and ABW (alternate braced wall) braced wall panels

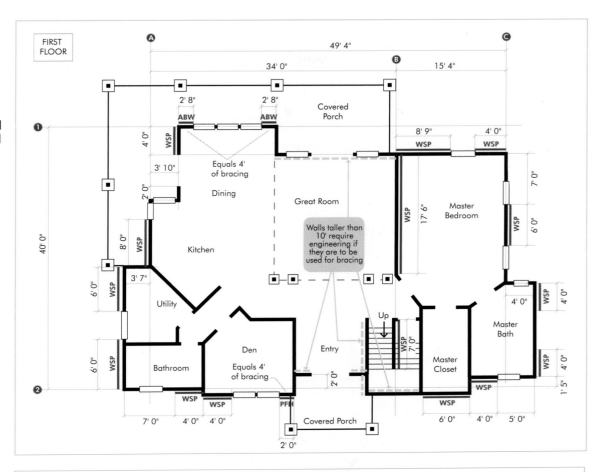

TABLE 4.6a

Calculations for the first of two stories to determine the required bracing length based on wind speed

IRC Table R602.10.3(2) Wind Adjustment Factors (*TABLE 3.4*)	Numbered Wall Lines	Lettered Wall Lines
Exposure Category	1.00	1.00
Roof Eave-to-Ridge Height	1.06	1.06
Wall Height	0.95	0.95
Number of Braced Wall Lines	1.00	1.30
Wind Factor Total	**1.01**	**1.31**

Braced Wall Line	Bracing Method	Braced Wall Line Spacing (ft)	Required Bracing (ft)	Wind Factor Total	Total Required Bracing Length (ft)	Bracing Length Provided (ft)	Status
1	WSP, ABW	40.00	20.50	1.01	20.71	20.75	Okay
2	WSP	40.00	20.50	1.01	20.71	22.00	Okay
A	WSP	34.00	17.80	1.31	23.32	24.00	Okay
B	WSP	34.00	17.80	1.31	23.32	24.50	Okay
C	WSP	15.33	8.67	1.31	11.36	14.00	Okay

FIGURE 4.6b

Second-story plan with intermittent Methods SFB (structural fiberboard sheathing) and GB (gypsum board) braced wall panels

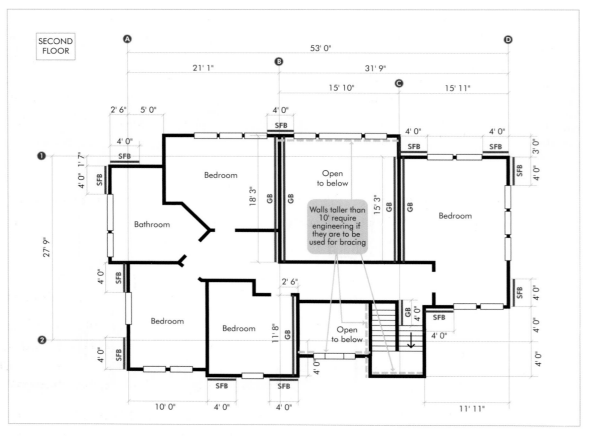

TABLE 4.6b

Calculations for the second of two stories to determine the required bracing length based on wind speed

IRC Table R602.10.3(2) Wind Adjustment Factors (*TABLE 3.4*)	Numbered Wall Lines	Lettered Wall Lines
Exposure Category	1.00	1.00
Roof Eave-to-Ridge Height	1.12	1.12
Wall Height	0.95	0.95
Number of Braced Wall Lines	1.00	1.45
Wind Factor Total	**1.06**	**1.54**

Braced Wall Line	Bracing Method	Braced Wall Line Spacing (ft)	Required Bracing (ft)	Wind Factor Total	Total Required Bracing Length (ft)	Bracing Length Provided (ft)	Status
1	SFB	27.75	7.94	1.06	8.41	16.00	Okay
2	SFB	27.75	7.94	1.06	8.41	12.00	Okay
A	SFB	21.08	6.27	1.54	9.66	12.00	Okay
B	GB	21.08	10.49	1.54	16.15	24.08ª	Okay
C	GB	15.92	8.16	1.54	12.57	17.25ª	Okay
D	SFB	15.92	4.78	1.54	7.36	8.00	Okay

a. Bracing lengths for Method GB (gypsum board) are based on the application of gypsum board on both faces of a braced wall panel. When Method GB bracing is provided on only one side of the wall, the contributing length shall be halved... (IRC Table R602.10.5)

Example 4.7: One-story house in SDC D$_0$

The basic wind speed is 105 mph with Exposure Category B. The roof has an eave-to-ridge height of 10 feet. Method CS-WSP (continuously sheathed wood structural panel) and CS-PF (continuously sheathed portal frame) will be used as the bracing material on the exterior braced wall lines. Method CS-WSP will be used on the interior braced wall lines. All braced walls have a height of 8 feet. All windows have clear openings of 64 inches and all doors have clear openings of 80 inches.

Example 4.7 highlights:

- The amount of bracing required is based on the greater amount required by the $\leq$ 110 mph wind speed category and SDC D$_0$.

- Use of continuous wood structural panel bracing.

- Use of braced wall line spacing adjustment factors to accommodate braced wall line spacing exceeding 25 feet per IRC Table R602.10.1.3 and IRC Table R602.10.3(4).

- Restriction of the use of different bracing methods in different wall lines per IRC Section R602.10.4.1, Item 2. (Mixing of continuous and intermittent bracing methods from braced wall line to braced wall line within a story is only allowed in SDC A-C; interior braced wall lines in SDC D$_0$ must be sheathed with Method CS-WSP.).

FIGURE 4.7 shows the house and braced wall segments. **TABLE 4.7** summarizes the the amount of bracing required and the amount of bracing provided for each braced wall line.

FIGURE 4.7

Single-story plan with Methods CS-WSP (continuously sheathed wood structural panel) and CS-PF (continuously sheathed portal frame) braced wall panels

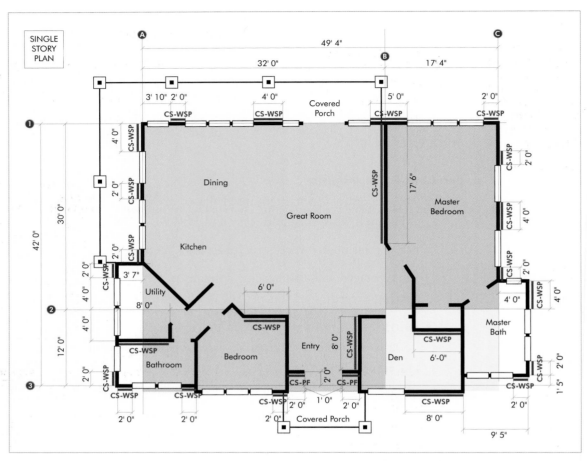

TABLE 4.7

Calculations for the first story to determine the required bracing length based on wind speed and Seismic Design Category

WIND CALCULATIONS

IRC Table R602.10.3(2) Wind Adjustment Factors (*TABLE 3.4*)	Numbered Wall Lines	Lettered Wall Lines
Exposure Category	1.00	1.00
Roof Eave-to-Ridge Height	1.00	1.00
Wall Height	0.90	0.90
Number of Braced Wall Lines	1.30	1.30
Wind Factor Total	**1.17**	**1.17**

Braced Wall Line	Bracing Method	Braced Wall Line Spacing (ft)	Required Bracing (ft)	Wind Factor Total	Total Required Bracing Length (ft)	Bracing Length Provided (ft)	Status
1	CS-WSP	30.00	7.00	1.17	8.19	13.0	Okay
2	CS-WSP	30.00	7.00	1.17	8.19	20.0	Okay
3	CS-WSP, CS-PF	12.00	3.40	1.17	3.98	20.0	Okay
A	CS-WSP	32.00	7.40	1.17	8.66	12.0	Okay
B	CS-WSP	32.00	7.40	1.17	8.66	25.5	Okay
C	CS-WSP	17.33	4.47	1.17	5.23	14.0	Okay

SEISMIC CALCULATIONS

IRC Table R602.10.3(4) Seismic Adjustment Factors (*TABLE 3.6*)	Adjustments
Story Height	1.00
Wall Dead Load	1.00
Roof/Ceiling Dead Load	1.00
Stone/Masonry in SDC C-D$_2$	n/a
Cripple Wall	n/a
Seismic Factor Total	**1.00**

Braced Wall Line	Bracing Method	Braced Wall Line Length (ft)	Required Bracing (ft)	Braced Wall Line Spacing Factor	Seismic Factor Total	Total Required Bracing Length (ft)	Bracing Length Provided (ft)	Status
1	CS-WSP	49.33	7.59	1.20	1.00	9.11	13.0	Okay
2	CS-WSP	56.92[a]	8.74	1.20	1.00	10.49	20.0	Okay
3	CS-WSP, CS-PF	56.92[a]	8.74	1.00	1.00	8.74	20.0	Okay
A	CS-WSP	42.00	6.42	1.28	1.00	8.22	12.0	Okay
B	CS-WSP	43.00	6.58	1.28	1.00	8.42	25.5	Okay
C	CS-WSP	40.58	6.19	1.00	1.00	6.19	14.0	Okay

a. The Total Required Bracing Length for a Braced Wall Line > 50' can be calculated using extrapolation of the values found in Table R602.10.3(3).

Notes:

- In SDC D_0, braced wall line spacing is limited to 25 feet, except for two conditions, per IRC Table R602.10.1.3. First, you are allowed to increase the braced wall line spacing to 35 feet to allow for a single room not to exceed 900 square feet. (In **EXAMPLE 4.7**, the great room exceeds 900 square feet.) Second, you are allowed to increase the braced wall line spacing to 35 feet provided that you increase the required length of bracing per IRC Table R602.10.3(4). The distance between wall lines A and B requires an adjustment factor of 1.28 to increase from 25 feet (between braced wall lines) to 32 feet, per IRC Table R602.10.3(4).

- The distance between wall lines 1 and 2 requires an adjustment factor of 1.20 to increase from 25 feet (between braced wall lines) to 30 feet, per IRC Table R602.10.3(4).

- In this example, all wall lines are controlled by the seismic calculation. Wall line 3 utilizes Method CS-PF, which allows for the use of 24-inch panels on either side the doorway. However, the designer could choose not to include these two walls and still have enough length (16 feet) and meet the 20-foot spacing requirement between adjacent braced wall panels.

- Braced wall lines 1 and B will require an 1,800 lb hold down at the first braced wall panel since they are not at the corner nor is there space for a 24-inch section of sheathing at the corner.

Bracing in high seismic regions (SDC D_0, D_1 and D_2)

Bracing in high seismic regions requires significantly greater bracing lengths. Additional requirements include:

- Braced wall line spacing must not exceed 25 feet, except that braced wall line spacing can be up to a maximum of 35 feet with the exceptions defined in IRC Table R602.10.1.3.

- Braced wall panels must be located at ends of braced wall lines, with exceptions for Method WSP (wood structural panel), CS-WSP (continuously sheathed wood structural panel), CS-G (continuously sheathed wood structural panel adjacent to garage openings), CS-PF (continuously sheathed portal frame) and BV-WSP (wood structural panels with stone or masonry veneer) bracing, as defined in IRC Section R602.10.2.2.1.

- Adhesive attachment of bracing panels is not permitted, as discussed in IRC Table R602.10.4, Footnote a.

- Minimum 3-inch x 3-inch x 0.229-inch (9-gage) steel plate washers are required on all anchor bolts for all braced wall line sill plates, as described in IRC Section R602.11.1.

- Additional attachment and foundation requirements apply, as discussed in IRC Sections R602.10.8.1 and R602.11.

- Houses cannot have irregularities without meeting additional requirements, as discussed in IRC Section R301.2.2.2.5.

- Additional limitations on connections to roof framing, as prescribed in IRC Section R602.10.8.2, Item 2.

These added requirements can restrict the application of prescriptive bracing in high seismic regions. Additionally, the lateral-force-resisting system may require engineering because many modern home designs have architectural features or irregularities which exceed the prescriptive IRC limits.

A good resource for wall bracing applications in high seismic regions is the *Homebuilders Guide to Earthquake Resistant Design and Construction* (FEMA 232).

APPENDIX

Appendix A: Collectors

When bracing is placed farther from the end of the braced wall line than specified (10 feet in SDC D_0, D_1 and D_2 – Methods WSP (wood structural panel) and CS-WSP (continuously sheathed wood structural panel) only – or 10 feet for all bracing methods in SDC A, B and C) the limits of the IRC are exceeded. In the 2012 IRC, references to collector design (previously included in R602.10.11.3 in the 2006 IRC) were omitted because they were considered to be redundant with Section R104.11, which permits approved designed solutions for any situation that falls outside of the scope of the IRC. A collector (sometimes called a "drag strut") is an engineered element used for such applications. Prescriptive information is presented on the following pages. (Engineering information is provided in the free APA publication, *Technical Topics: Collector Design for Bracing in Conventional Construction*, Form TT-102. Visit www.apawood.org.)

Note that collector design, like any alternate proposed in accordance with IRC Section R104.11, must be approved by the building official. It might prove prudent to contact your local building official during the drawing-development phase of the project.

APPENDIX

Summary

What is a collector and what does it do?

The collector is a part of the lateral load path. Just as a beam in the vertical load path accumulates (or "collects") gravity loads and carries them over an opening to the jack studs on each side, the collector has a similar function in the lateral load path. It collects the lateral loads from the roof or floor diaphragm (roof sheathing and floor sheathing, respectively) above an opening and distributes them into the braced wall panels on either side (or one side, as circumstances dictate) of this opening in the braced wall line below. Thus, a collector is needed to evenly distribute the load among the bracing panels in a given wall line.

What does a collector look like and how do I design one?

In the type of structures considered by the IRC, the collector is normally already in place in the form of the wall double top plate or top plate/header combination (see **FIGURE A.1**).

FIGURE A.1

First bracing panel shown 14 feet from corner

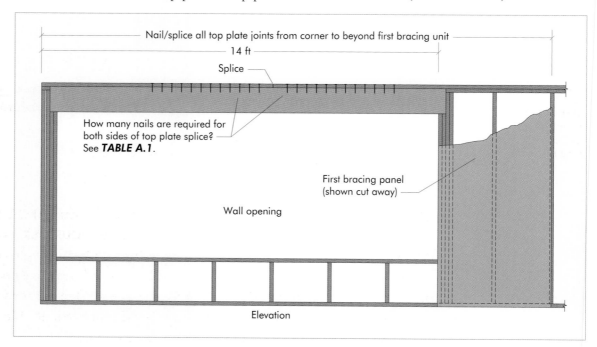

Nail/splice all top plate joints from corner to beyond first bracing unit

14 ft

Splice

How many nails are required for both sides of top plate splice? See **TABLE A.1**.

First bracing panel (shown cut away)

Wall opening

Elevation

In terms of load path, the roof or upper-floor framing is attached to the wall top plate. The top plate is also a part of the framing for the bracing panels immediately below. This connection between the roof or floor framing and the wall ensures that the horizontal lateral loads (from the floor or roof sheathing/diaphragm above) are distributed into the bracing panels (vertical lateral load resisting elements). The IRC Table R602.3(1), Item 14 attachment requirement for double top plate splices (minimum 24-inch offset with eight 16d nails on each side of the splice) ensures continuity along the 10-foot corner distance limit. Beyond these limits, the prescriptive top plate splice cannot be counted on to transfer loads. The IRC-required fastener schedule (IRC

Table R602.3(1), Item 16) for the wall bottom plate of the bracing panel (three 16d face nails into joist or blocking every 16 inches on center) completes the load path to the foundation or floor below.

Choosing a collector

The good historical performance of traditional framing methods in conventional construction has led to code provisions that permit the first bracing panel to be placed away from the corner up to a set distance without requiring the builder to be concerned with the collector design. For distances in excess of those permitted by the code, the material properties of a single 2x4 top plate are generally adequate to distribute the applied load for conventional construction. The difficulty lies in providing sufficient attachment between the upper and lower top plates (or the upper top plate and header below) to transfer the load at "splice locations" where joints in the double top plate occur (see *FIGURE A.2*).

FIGURE A.2

Splice at top panel required to transfer load across joint in lower plate to upper top plate and back down into the lower plate after the splice

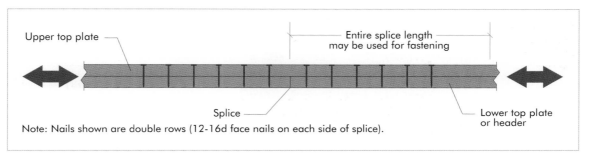

Note: Nails shown are double rows (12-16d face nails on each side of splice).

The IRC requires that a minimum splice nailing of eight 16d face nails (IRC Table R602.3(1), Item 14) – or in the case of SDC D_0, D_1 and D_2, as illustrated in *FIGURE A.2*, twelve 16d face nails (IRC Table R602.10.3(4), for braced wall line spacing > 25 feet) – be placed on both sides of the top plate joint. Note that each side of the joint is a "lapped area". The normal double top plate face nailing requirements (IRC Table R602.3(1), Item 13) may be counted toward the minimum number, but the minimum number must be met. Note that IRC Section R602.10.8.1 is more specific in its treatment of top plate lap splices, requiring:

"...at least eight 16d nails on each side of the splice."

What is the length of the top plate that must be spliced?

Since the purpose of the collector is to "collect" the load from the structure above and transfer it into the bracing panel a distance away from the corner, the spliced top plate must run from the building corner to at least the far side of the first bracing panel.

The top plate splice design parameters can be represented in tabular form, as shown in **TABLE A.1**.

TABLE A.1

Top plate splice design table[a]

L (Distance between corner and beginning of first bracing panel in ft)		10 ft[c]	12 ft[c]	14 ft[c]	16 ft[c]	18 ft[c]	20 ft[c]
N (Number of 16d box nails required on each side of top plate joint)	Basic Wind Speed < 110 mph SDCs A-C	8 nails					
	SDCs D_0, D_1, D_2	8 nails	18 nails	21 nails	24 nails	27 nails	30 nails
	SDCs D_0, D_1 and D_2 and Table R602.10.3(4) Footnote for braced wall spacing > 25 ft.	12 nails					
Minimum double top plate size, species and grade[b]	2x4		SPF Stud Grade			DF Stud Grade or SPF #2	DF #2 or SPF #2
	2x6		SPF Stud Grade				

a. If 16d common nails (0.162 x 3-1/2 in.) are used, the number of nails in the above table may be multiplied by 0.73.
b. Once a size, species and grade is selected from the table, other sizes, species and grades listed to the right of the selected grade, or of greater strength per the NDS, may be substituted.
c. Engineered collector not required under the 2012 IRC for wind or SDCs A-D_2 when bracing starts within 10 ft of end of wall.

Design example: A home designer wants to place a bracing panel 14 feet away from a corner. The wall framing is 2x4. Select the lumber species and grade, and detail the collector. See **FIGURE A.1**.

Solution: **TABLE A.1** shows that for a given length (distance between corner and beginning of first bracing panel in feet) of 14 feet, the top plate splice made of 2x4 SPF (spruce-pine-fir) stud grade requires 21-16d box nails on each side of the top plate splice. If common nails are used, 16-16d common nails are required on each side of the top plate splice, per Footnote a of **TABLE A.1** (21 nails x 0.73 = 16 nails).

Where the splice occurs over a lower top plate, a minimum 4-foot overlap would, for this example, provide enough room for the required fasteners without causing splitting of the plates. (Note that although a 4-foot splice overlap would theoretically provide enough room, staggering each row of nails, blunting the tips of the nails, and/or using three rows of fasteners is recommended if splitting appears to be a problem given the wood resource used.) Where the splice occurs over a header, a lower top plate is not necessary. Note that using longer plates (12-16 feet) minimizes the number of plate splices required.

Appendix B: Bracing T- and L-Shaped Buildings

A common problem faced by residential designers is determining the amount and placement of braced wall panels and wall lines in non-rectangular residential structures. Non-rectangular building configurations include T-, L- and U-shaped buildings. Whether the home is fully engineered using the International Building Code (IBC), or designed and constructed by a builder using the prescriptive provisions of the International Residential Code (IRC), it's much easier to apply code provisions to rectangular structures.

So how is the code applied when designing a non-rectangular structure? The answer is the same for both the engineer using the IBC and the designer/builder using the IRC: divide the structure into separate rectangles, determine the shear walls or bracing requirements for each rectangle, and then reconnect the separate rectangles into a unified structure. This method eases the design process while still providing a safe, code-compliant structure. An example is presented below for an L-shaped building. L-shaped buildings are the most common non-rectangular configuration, but the same principles apply to T- and U-shaped buildings, as well as any other shape that can be divided into rectangles. This method can also be used for a large rectangular structure that falls outside of the scope of the IRC, by dividing the structure into two or more elements that do fall within the scope of the code.

Note that in some cases, this method can be conservative. For example, in *FIGURE B.1*, Box 1 and Box 2 partially shelter each other from the North/South wind, decreasing the overall load on the structure. As a result, bracing along lines 1, 2 and 3 will be somewhat conservative. Exact solutions are often both difficult to arrive at and expensive to build via a fully engineered design, so often a little conservatism is economical.

STEP 1: Divide the structure into rectangular elements. There are often multiple ways to do this. Typically, the easiest solution is to divide the building in such a way that the "common side" (or shared side) of the two rectangles contains wall segments which can be used for bracing. See **FIGURE B.1**:

FIGURE B.1

Divide structure into rectangular elements

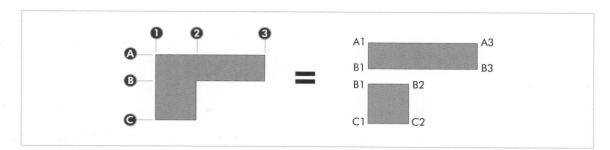

STEP 2: Determine bracing requirements for each individual rectangular element using the IRC bracing provisions. Each individual rectangle is treated and braced as if it were a completely independent, separate structure from the other rectangles. The braced wall line lengths and distance between braced wall lines are measured on each rectangle separately. See **FIGURE B.2**:

FIGURE B.2

Determine bracing requirements per the IRC prescriptive provisions for each rectangular element separately

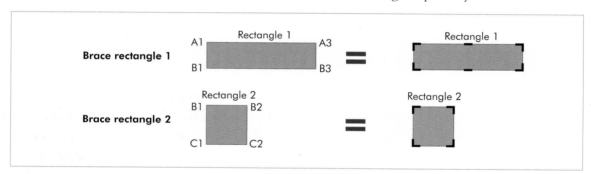

STEP 3: Rejoin the rectangles with bracing provided as shown in **FIGURE B.3**. The rules that must be applied to the common side when rejoining the rectangles are presented in the list below. Once rejoined, the increased common-side bracing will reflect the appropriate distribution of load. (Note that when this method is used in conjunction with the IRC Table R602.10.3(2) *Wind Adjustment Factors to the Required Length of Wall Bracing* (**TABLE 3.4**) the adjustment for number of braced wall lines (per plan direction) does not apply.)

FIGURE B.3

Rejoin rectangles with bracing provided

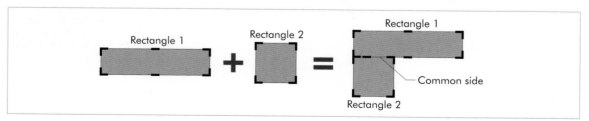

Rules for rejoining the rectangles at the common side:

1. The total bracing from both rectangles along the common side must be provided on the common side. In **FIGURE B.3**, one of the corner bracing elements of the two rectangles was moved to illustrate this point.

2. In the example shown above where the wall line for Rectangle 1 extends past the common side, the entire length of the common braced wall line of Rectangle 1 may be used to position the braced wall panels from both rectangles.

3. The wall bracing location provisions of IRC *Section R602.10.2.2* and *R602.10.2.2.1 (If applicable)* must be met along the common side, as well as along the extended wall line.

4. The 2012 IRC contains provisions permitting mixing of different bracing materials along a single wall line in SDC A, B and C. This would permit Method GB (gypsum board) bracing along the common side with other panel products used intermittently on the remaining exterior portions of the wall line. These provisions are found in IRC Section R602.10.4.1. Note that when bracing materials are mixed, the following provision applies:

    The length of required bracing for the *braced wall line* with mixed sheathing types shall have the higher bracing length requirement, in accordance with *Tables R602.10.3(1) and R602.10.3(3)*, of all types of bracing used.

5. If a physical wall is not available at the common wall location, then all of the bracing for both rectangles must be placed at the exterior extension of the common wall. If the non-existent common wall or an opening in that common wall exceeds 10 feet in length, an engineered collector/drag strut (*discussed in* **APPENDIX A**) must be used at the common wall location to transfer the bracing from both rectangles into the exterior extension of the common wall. See **FIGURE B.4**. As an alternative, in Step 1, divide the structure in such a way that there is a physical wall along the common wall. This will provide a location for braced wall panels.

FIGURE B.4
No wall at common wall line

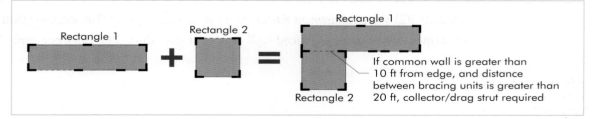

Appendix C: Interpolation

Interpolation is a mathematical tool that can be used to determine a value from a table that does not include the value you are seeking, but lies between values that are given in the table. For example, if you are looking for the amount of bracing required for a building sited where the basic wind speed is 110 mph with a braced wall line spacing of 23 feet, you will discover in IRC Table R602.10.1.2(1) that there are values given for braced wall line spacings of 20 and 30 feet, but not for 23 feet. In such cases, the user can assume the next larger braced wall line spacing (30 feet, in this example), but doing so may result in more bracing than is technically required, which may ultimately restrict the use of desired architectural features. A better solution is to use interpolation to find the value between 20 feet and 30 feet that corresponds to 23 feet.

Although the equation for interpolation (Equation 1) may appear daunting, the correct value is simple to compute with a standard calculator and, with a little practice, can actually be performed quite quickly. If interpolation is used, footnotes and adjustment factors are initially disregarded and then applied to the value after Equation 1 has been solved.

$$y = y_a + \frac{(x-x_a)(y_b-y_a)}{(x_b-x_a)}$$ Equation 1 (See Step 2 for an explanation of terms)

EXAMPLE: We are looking for the amount of wind bracing required for the first story of two stories in a 110 mph wind zone. We would like to use gypsum board double-sided bracing and our braced wall line spacing is 23 feet. Here are the steps to interpolate the correct value:

STEP 1. Find the proper table and look for a length of bracing required for a braced wall line spacing of 23 feet.

Exposure Category B
30 ft mean roof height
10 ft eave to ridge height
10 ft wall height
2 braced wall lines

Minimum total length (feet) of braced wall panels required along each braced wall line

Basic Wind Speed	Story Location	Braced Wall Line Spacing (ft)	Method LIB[f,h]	Method GB (Double-Sided)[g]	Methods DWB, WSP, SFB, PBS, PCP, HPS[f,i]	Cont. Sheathing
< 110 Mph		10	10.5	10.5	6.0	5.0
		20	19.0	19.0	11.0	9.5
		30	27.5	27.5	16.0	13.5
		40	36.0	36.0	20.5	17.5
		50	44.0	44.0	25.5	21.5
		60	52.5	52.5	30.0	25.5

The highlighted cells from this excerpt of IRC Table R602.10.3(1) reveal that a value for 23 feet is not offered; however, values are given for 20 and 30 feet. These are the values we need to interpolate.

STEP 2. Create a table with the values that we do know and the value that we want to know, as shown below:

Braced Wall Line Spacing (ft)	Method GB (Double- Sided)[g]
20	19
23	?
30	27.5

The values of this table are represented as:

$x_a = 20$	$y_a = 19$
$x = 23$	$y = ?$
$x_b = 30$	$y_b = 27.5$

STEP 3. Substitute the values into the interpolation equation:

$$y = y_a + \frac{(x - x_a)(y_b - y_a)}{(x_b - x_a)} \qquad \text{Equation 1}$$

$$y = 19 + \frac{(23-20)(27.5-19)}{(30-20)}$$

$$y = 21.6 \text{ feet of bracing required}$$

As stated previously, the alternative is to use the next larger braced wall line spacing: 30 feet, in this example, which would require 27.5 feet of bracing. Using interpolation, we reduce the amount of bracing required (27.5 feet – 21.6 feet = 5.9 feet) by nearly 6 feet! 6 feet of reduced bracing may be well worth the few minutes it takes to interpolate.

The above example is for wind bracing. The same principles apply to seismic bracing, but interpolation is applied to the braced wall line length instead of braced wall line spacing.

Appendix D: Comparison of the Location of Wall Bracing Information in the Three Editions of the IRC

TABLE D.1

Wall bracing information in the 2012, 2009 and 2006 editions of the IRC

Topic	2012	2009	2006
Corner Nailing	Table R602.3(1)	Figure R602.10.4.4(1)	Figure R602.10.5
BWP Uplift	R602.3.5	R602.10.1.2.1	NEP
Length of a BWL	R602.10.1.1	R602.10.1	R602.10.1
BWL Offsets	R602.10.1.2	R602.10.1.4	R602.10.1
Spacing of BWL	R602.10.1.3, Table R602.10.1.3	R602.10.1, R602.10.1.4, & R602.10.1.5, Tables R602.10.1.2(1) & (3), Figures 602.10.1.4(1), (3) & (4)	R602.10.1.1, R602.10.11.1
Angled Walls	R602.10.1.4, Figure R602.10.1.4	R602.10.1.3, Figure R602.10.1.3	NEP
BWP Uplift Load Path	R602.10.2.1 – details moved to R602.3.5	R602.10.1.2.1	NEP
Location BWPs	R602.10.2.2, Figure R602.10.2.2	R602.10.1.4, Figure R602.10.1.4(2)	R602.10.1
Location BWPs in SDC D_0, D_1 and D_2	R602.10.2.2.1	R602.10.1.4.1, Figure R602.10.1.4.1	R602.10.11.2
Min Number of BWPs	R602.10.2.3	NEP	NEP
Required Bracing Length, Wind & Seismic Application	R602.10.3	R602.10.1.2	R602.10.4, R602.10.6, & Table R602.10.1
Wind	Table R602.10.3(1)	Table R602.10.1.2(1)	Table R602.10.1
Wind Adjustment Factors	Table R602.10.3(2)	Table R602.10.1.2(1) footnotes	NEP
Seismic	Table R602.10.3(3)	Table R602.10.1.2(2)	Table R602.10.1
Seismic Adjustment Factors	Table R602.10.3(4)	Table R602.10.1.2(3)	Table R602.10.1 footnotes
Bracing Methods	Table R602.10.4	Tables R602.10.2, R602.10.4.1, & R602.10.5	R602.10.3, R602.10.5
Mixing Methods	R602.10.4.1	R602.10.1.1	NEP
Continuous Sheathing Methods	R602.10.4.2	R602.10.4, R602.10.5	R602.10.5
Interior Finish	R602.10.4.3	R602.10.2.1	NEP
Min Length BWP	Table R602.10.5	R602.10.1.2, R602.10.3, R602.10.4.2, R602.10.5.2, Tables R602.10.3, R602.10.3.1, R602.10.4.2 & R602.10.5.2	R602.10.4, R602.10.6.2, Tables R602.10.5 & R6012.10.6
ABW	Table R602.10.5	Table R602.10.3.2	Table R602.10.6
	Figure R602.10.6.1	Figure R602.10.3.2	R602.10.6 text
PFH	Table R602.10.5, Figure R602.10.6.2	Figure R602.10.3.3	R602.10.6.2 and Figure R602.10.6.2
PFG	Table R602.10.5, Figure R602.10.6.3	Figure R602.10.3.4	NEP
CS-PF	R602.10.6.4, Table R602.10.5 & Figure R602.10.6.4	R602.10.4.1.1, Figure R602.10.4.1.1	NEP
Tension Strap	Table R602.10.6.4	Table R602.10.4.1.1	NEP

NEP = No equivalent provision
BWL = Braced Wall Line
BWP = Braced Wall Panel

TABLE D.1
(Continued)

Wall bracing information in the 2012, 2009 and 2006 editions of the IRC

Topic	2012	2009	2006
Wall Bracing for Masonry Veneer in SDC D_0, D_1 and D_2	R602.10.6.5	R602.12	R703.7
End of Wall Line	R602.10.2.2, Figure R602.10.7	R602.10.1.4, R602.10.4.4	R602.10.1, R602.10.11.2
BWP to Roof Connections	R602.10.8, R602.10.8.2	R602.10.6, R602.10.6.2	R602.10.8
BWP Support	R602.10.8, R602.10.8.1, & R602.10.9	R602.10.6, R602.10.6.1 & R602.10.7	R602.10.8, R602.10.9
Panel Joints	R602.10.10	R602.10.8	R602.10.7
Cripple Walls	R602.9, R602.10.11, & R602.11.2	R602.9, R602.10. 9, & R602.11.2	R602.10.2, R602.10.11.4, & R602.11.3
Simplified Wall Bracing	R602.12	NEP	

NEP = No equivalent provision
BWL = Braced Wall Line
BWP = Braced Wall Panel

Appendix E: Mixing Bracing Methods

Mixing bracing methods, addressed in IRC Section R602.10.4.1, is one of the more confusing aspects of the 2012 IRC bracing provisions. This table is intended to help the user visualize the applicable provisions and where they apply.

TABLE E.1

Mixing bracing methods per IRC Section R602.10.4.1

		Section R602.10.4.1, Item	SDC A	SDC B	SDC C	SDC D$_0$	SDC D$_1$	SDC D$_2$
One- and two-family dwellings	1	Mixing intermittent and continuous methods story-to-story	•	•	•	•	•	•
	2a	Mixing intermittent methods only BWL-to-BWL within a story	•	•	•	•	•	•
	4	Mixing Methods CS-WSP, CS-G, CS-PF in a BWL	•	•	•	•	•	•
	2b	Mixing intermittent and continuous methods BWL-to-BWL within a story	•	•	•			
	3	Mixing intermittent methods along a BWL (using greatest length required of methods used)	•	•	•			
	5	Mixing intermittent methods on interior portions and continuous methods (CS-WSP, CS-G, CS-PF) on exterior portions of a BWL (using greatest length required of methods used)	•	•	•			
Townhouse	1	Mixing intermittent and continuous methods story-to-story	•	•	•	•	•	•
	2a	Mixing intermittent methods only BWL-to-BWL within a story	•	•	•	•	•	•
	4	Mixing Methods CS-WSP, CS-G, CS-PF in a BWL	•	•	•	•	•	•
	2b	Mixing intermittent and continuous methods BWL-to-BWL within a story	•	•	•			
	3	Mixing intermittent methods along a BWL (using greatest length required of methods used)	•	•				
	5	Mixing intermittent methods on interior portions and continuous methods (CS-WSP, CS-G, CS-PF) on exterior portions of a BWL (using greatest length required of methods used)	•	•				

BWL = Braced Wall Line
SDC = Seismic Design Category

Bibliography

- AWC WFCM. 2012. *Wood Frame Construction Manual for One- and Two- Family Dwellings.*
  American Wood Council, Washington, DC.

- APA – The Engineered Wood Association. 2010.
  Collector Design for Bracing in Conventional Construction.
  Form TT-102B. Tacoma, WA. www.apawood.org

- ASCE/SEI. 2010. *Minimum Design Loads for Buildings and Other Structures.*
  ASCE-7-10. American Society of Civil Engineers, Reston, VA.

- HUD. 2002. *Framing Connections in Conventional Residential Construction.*
  U.S. Department of Housing and Urban Development, Washington, DC.

- IBC. 2012. *International Building Code.* International Code Council, Washington, D.C.

- ICC-400. 2012. *Standard on the Design and Construction of Log Structures.*
  International Code Council, Washington, D.C.

- ICC-600. 2008. *Standard for Residential Construction in High-Wind Regions.*
  International Code Council, Washington, D.C.

- IRC. 2000. *International Residential Building Code.* International Code Council, Washington, D.C.

- IRC. 2006. *International Residential Building Code.* International Code Council, Washington, D.C.

- IRC. 2009. *International Residential Building Code.* International Code Council, Washington, D.C.

- IRC. 2012. *International Residential Building Code.* International Code Council, Washington, D.C.

- USDA Forest Service. 2010. *Wood Handbook: Wood as an Engineering Material.*
  Form FPL-GTR-190. USDA Forest Service, Forest Products Laboratory, Madison, WI.

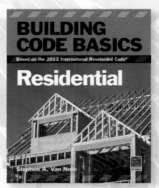

APA Delivers Confidence...

When you see fully sheathed wood walls with APA's stamp, you can be confident the home is built with the materials required to meet the most stringent bracing methods. Since the early fifties, APA has collaborated with code bodies to improve wall performance. This collaboration has included a significant evolution in the use of prescriptive wall bracing techniques specifying plywood and OSB. In high wind and seismic events, APA's expertise is on display with products that meet the industry's highest performance standards and wall bracing applications aimed at reducing the risk of catastrophic home failure. For our latest recommendations for building strong, safe and durable structures, visit www.apawood.org or www.performancewalls.org.

...and Information

APA offers a comprehensive set of services and tools for building design and construction professionals. If you're looking for detailed product information, training material or technical assistance, APA can help:

www.apawood.org – APA's flagship website is your link to in-depth technical and design information, featuring free instant downloads of more than 400 publications and over 200 CAD details for wood-frame construction.

www.performancewalls.org – Your leading resource for designing and building better walls, including energy-efficient, cost-effective advanced framing details and the new APA Simplified Wall Bracing Method.

Product Support – Need an immediate solution? Contact the APA Product Support Help Desk for answers to your questions about lateral bracing and engineered wood products. Call (253) 620-7400 or email help@apawood.org.

Training Support – APA offers free training and consultation services on the proper specification and application of APA products.

2012 IRC Bracing Methods Overview

Bracing Method	Description	Braced Wall Panel Lengths IRC Table R602.10.5		Max. Height	Max. Distance of First Braced Wall Panel From End of Braced Wall Line[a]	
		Wall Height	Min. Length		SDC A, B & C	SDC D_0, D_1 & D_2
LIB	Let-in bracing[b] IRC Table R602.10.4	8' 9' 10' 11' 12'	4' 7" to 8' 5' 2" to 9' 5' 9" to 10' Not permitted Not permitted	10'	10'	Not permitted
DWB	Diagonal wood boards IRC Table R602.10.4	8' 9' 10' 11' 12'	36"[c] to 4' 0" 42"[c] to 4' 0" 4' 0" 4' 5" 4' 10"	12'	10'	0'
WSP	Wood structural panel IRC Table R602.10.4	8' 9' 10' 11' 12'	36"[c] to 4' 0" 42"[c] to 4' 0" 4' 0" 4' 5" 4' 10"	12'	10'	10' with 1800 lb hold down, or a minimum 24" WSP panel each side of corner required
SFB	Structural fiberboard sheathing IRC Table R602.10.4	8' 9' 10' 11' 12'	36"[c] to 4' 0" 42"[c] to 4' 0" 4' 0" 4' 5" 4' 10"	12'	10'	0'
GB	Gypsum board – Single-sided IRC Table R602.10.4	8' 9' 10' 11' 12'	4' 0" 4' 0" 4' 0" 4' 5" 4' 10"	12'	10'	0'
	Gypsum board – Double-sided IRC Table R602.10.4	8' 9' 10' 11' 12'	4' 0" 4' 0" 4' 0" 4' 5" 4' 10"			
PBS	Particleboard sheathing IRC Table R602.10.4	8' 9' 10' 11' 12'	36"[c] to 4' 0" 42"[c] to 4' 0" 4' 0" 4' 5" 4' 10"	12'	10'	0'
PCP	Portland cement plaster IRC Table R602.10.4					
HPS	Hardboard panel siding IRC Table R602.10.4					
ABW	Alternate braced wall (SDC A, B & C) and wind speeds <110 mph IRC Table R602.10.4	8' 9' 10' 11' 12'	28" 32" 34" 38" 42"	12'	10'	N/A
	Alternate braced wall (SDC D_0, D_1 & D_2) and wind speeds <110 mph IRC Table R602.10.4	8' 9' 10' 11' 12'	32" 32" 34" Not permitted Not permitted	10'	N/A	0'
PFH	Portal frame with hold downs IRC Table R602.10.4	8'-10' 11' 12'	16" for one story. 24" for first of two stories. 18" for one story. 27" for first of two stories.[d] 20" for one story. 29" for first of two stories.[d]	10'[d]	10'	0'

Bracing Method	Description	Braced Wall Panel Widths		Max. Height	Max. Distance of First Braced Wall Panel From End of Braced Wall Line[a]	
		Wall Height	Min. Width		SDC A, B & C	SDC D₀, D₁ & D₂
PFG	Portal frame at garage door openings in SDC A, B & C IRC Table R602.10.4	8' 9' 10' 11' 12'	24" 27" 30" 33"[d] 36"[d]	10'[d]	10'	Not permitted
CS-WSP	Continuously sheathed wood structural panel IRC Table R602.10.4	See IRC Table R602.10.5.[e] Braced wall panel length varies with wall height and adjacent opening height.		12'	10' 24" min. corner detail or 800 lb hold down required	10' 24" corner detail or 1800 lb hold down required
CS-G	Continuously sheathed wood structural panel adjacent to garage door opening with header and supporting roof loads only IRC Table R602.10.4	8' 9' 10' 11' 12'	24" 27" 30" 33" 36"	12'	10' 24" min. corner detail or 800 lb hold down required	10' 24" corner detail or 1800 lb hold down required
CS-PF	Continuously sheathed portal frame IRC Table R602.10.4	8' 9' 10' 11' 12'	16" 18" 20" 22"[d] 24"[d]	10'[d]	10' 24" min. corner detail or 800 lb hold down required	10' 24" corner detail or hold down required
CS-SFB	Continuously sheathed structural fiberboard IRC Table R602.10.4	See IRC Table R602.10.5.[f] Braced wall panel length varies with wall height and adjacent opening height.		12'	10' 32" min. corner detail or 800 lb hold down required	Not permitted[g]

Bracing Method	Description	Condition	Bldg Type	Braced Wall Panel Lengths[h]		Max. Height	Max. Distance of First Braced Wall Panel from End of Braced Wall Line	
				Wall Height	Min. Width		SDC A, B & C	SDC D₀, D₁ & D₂
BV-WSP	Wood structural panels with stone or masonry veneer IRC Table R602.10.4[i]	Stone or masonry veneer greater than first story height	Detached one- and two-family dwellings	8' 9' 10' 11' 12'	48" 48" 48" 53" 58"	12'	N/A	10'
			Townhouses				N/A	Engineered design only

N/A = Not applicable

a. Braced wall panels shall be located not more than 20 ft measured between inside edges of adjacent bracing panels.

b. Not permitted on the first of three stories for wind. Only permitted for a one-story structure in SDC C. Not permitted in SDC D₀, D₁ or D₂. See IRC Tables R602.10.3(1) and R602.10.1.3(3) (**TABLE 3.3** and **3.5** of this publication).

c. See IRC Section R602.10.5.2 and Table R602.10.5.2 (**TABLE 3.29** of this publication) for effective bracing length.

d. Clear opening height = 10 ft minus depth of header. Wall height can be increased to 12 ft with pony wall.

e. For expanded table, see **TABLE 3.23** of this publication.

f. For expanded table, see **TABLE 3.26** of this publication.

g. When continuous structural fiberboard sheathing (Method CS-SFB) is used where the basic wind speed is in excess of 100 mph or in SDC D₀, D₁ or D₂, the CS-SFB braced wall line is required to be designed in accordance with accepted engineering practice and the provisions of the International Building Code (IBC). See IRC Table R602.10.4, Footnote d.

h. Refer to IRC Table R602.10.5 (**TABLE 3.28** of this publication).

i. Method applies to detached one- and two-family dwellings in SDC D₀, D₁ or D₂, only.